P9-CLX-549

the dynamics of change

by **DON FABUN**
Publications Editor
Kaiser Aluminum & Chemical Corporation

Assisted by
Niels Sundermeyer

Art Director
Bob Conover

Prentice-Hall, Inc.
Englewood Cliffs, N. J.

Sixth printing......March, 1970

©1967 by Kaiser Aluminum & Chemical Corporation
Copyright under International and Pan American
Copyright Conventions. All rights reserved.

Library of Congress Catalog Card Number: 67-25569
Printed in the United States of America

No part of this book may be reproduced in any form or by any
means, except for the inclusion of brief quotations in a review,
without permission in writing from the publisher.

Published by Prentice-Hall, Inc., Englewood Cliffs, N.J.
Prentice-Hall International, Inc., London
Prentice-Hall of Australia, Pty. Ltd., Sydney
Prentice-Hall of Canada, Ltd., Toronto
Prentice-Hall of India Private Ltd., New Delhi
Prentice-Hall of Japan, Inc., Tokyo

the dynamics of change 1-32

A review of the significant worldwide change that began shortly after World War II; the psychological basis for individual innovation leading to cultural change; the subculture of youth and other forces causing change in our times.

the promised land 1-38

Concepts of land use in a world where population is growing faster than our present ability to feed and shelter it. We begin to think of our relationship to space and time in different ways and to see ourselves as organisms that must find a way to live in harmony with our environment.

telemobility 1-30

For nearly all his time on earth, man has worked to find ways to transport his body to the scene he wants to experience. Now, we appear to be in a transitional phase in which, increasingly, the scene is brought electronically to the man. The result is that communication may replace transportation as far as the human body is concerned.

automation 1-30

An examination of some aspects of the world in which human beings may become themselves the environment in which an advanced generation of electronic brains will be able to hear, see, speak, reason, learn, repair themselves and reproduce their own kind.

the leisure masses 1-30

We discuss the time that may come when work will be a privilege and not a necessity and when many people may spend their entire lives without ever "working for a living." Nearly all of our institutions, our political and economic systems and our personal value judgments have developed in an economy of scarcity. In an economy of abundance, what new institutions will have to be devised?

foreseeing the unforeseeable 1-30

What if some of the things that *could* happen actually do happen? What kind of a world would we have if the "low probability" future actually comes to pass?

The material in this volume was originated in commemoration of the Twentieth Anniversary of Kaiser Aluminum & Chemical Corporation. It first appeared in a special series of six issues of Kaiser Aluminum NEWS.

At exactly 5:13 a.m., the 18th of April, 1906, a cow was standing somewhere between the main barn and the milking shed on the old Shafter Ranch in California, minding her own business. Suddenly, the earth shook, the skies trembled, and when it was all over, there was nothing showing of the cow above ground but a bit of her tail sticking up. □ For the student of change, the Shafter cow is a sort of symbol of our times. She stood quietly enough, thinking such gentle thoughts as cows are likely to have, while huge forces outside her ken built up all around her and—within a minute—discharged it all at once in a great movement that changed the configuration of the earth, and destroyed a city, and swallowed her up. And that's what we are going to talk about now; how, if we do not learn to understand and guide the great forces of change at work on our world today, we may find ourselves like the Shafter cow, swallowed up by vast upheavals in our way of life— quite early some morning.

THE WORLD ALTERS AS WE WALK IN IT

END OF AN ERA

"We, in the Twentieth Century, are concluding an era of mankind five thousand years in length....We open our eyes like prehistoric men; we see a world totally new."

KURT MAREK
Archeologist

A GREAT UPHEAVAL

"This world of ours is a new world, in which the unity of knowledge, the nature of human communities, the order of society, the order of ideas, the very notions of society and culture have changed, and will not return to what they have been in the past.

"What is new is new not because it has never been there before, but because it has changed in quality...

"One thing that is new is the prevalence of newness, the changing scale and scope of change itself, so that the world alters as we walk in it, so that the years of a man's life measure not some small growth or rearrangement or moderation of what he learned in childhood, but a great upheaval."

ROBERT OPPENHEIMER
Physicist

☐ One foot inextricably trapped in the clockwork mechanism of 19th Century science, and the other planted fearfully in the newly radiant soil of the 20th Century, Henry Adams, then 60 years old—and a student of change for forty of those—stood in the Gallery of Machines at the Great Paris Exposition of 1900 and saw—more clearly than most men of his time, or of now—one of the great fracture points in human history.

It was to be another sixty years and two World Wars later before the dimensions of the change he saw had become the common currency of popular journalism and awareness of change an accepted tool for survival.

For most of his life, Adams had been trying to make some sense out of history. It had not been an easy quest, for history appears to be what we want to make of it, and Adams found he could not make much of it.

In his *Education*, Adams said, "Satisfied that the sequence of men led to nothing and that the sequence of society could lead no further, while the mere sequence of time was artificial and the sequence of thought was chaos, he turned at last to the sequence of force, and thus it happened, after ten years pursuit, he found himself lying in the Gallery of Machines . . . his historical neck broken by the irruption of forces totally new."

What Adams had seen was that change is observed motion, and motion is the product of applied force. Man had begun by acquiring fire —and that was a force—and then sometime later the use of wind and water, and then he put water and fire together and turned the steam engine loose on the world. The period of time between each new acquisition and application of power was successively shorter. It was only a little after steam that he began applying electrical force and even more shortly after that discovered and put to work nuclear force.

By 1900, the power of the electrical age was best symbolized in the dynamo, a force that Adams found parallel to the force of the Christian Cross in the affairs of men. And, in the discoveries of Roentgen and Curie, in the hidden rays of the suprasensual, the dimensions of a vast new world powered in its course by the dance of electrons, were—at the turn of the century—already visible to those few pairs of eyes curious enough to see them.

It was possible to plot the progress of these new forces in graphs, and when this was done, and the different graphs compared, it was seen that —in almost any application of force you wanted to measure—there was a constant acceleration; the changes became larger and they occurred more frequently as we moved forward in time.

Several years ago, *Scientific American* plotted Adams' "Law of Acceleration." Graphs were made up of such processes as the discovery of natural forces, and the time lag between each successive discovery; tables were made that plotted the isolation of natural elements, the accumulation of human experience, the speed that transportation has achieved from the pace of a man walking to space satellites, and the number of electronic circuits that could be put into a cubic foot of space. In every case, the rising curves on the graphs showed almost identical shapes, starting their rise slowly, then sharper and sharper until, in our times, nearly every trend line of force is embarked on a vertical course.

Some of the idea of the dimensions of change in our times, and the acceleration of it, can be found in the fact that, "Half of all the energy consumed by man in the past two thousand years has been consumed within the last one hundred." Kenneth Boulding, the economist and writer, finds that, "For many statistical series of quantities of metal or other materials extracted, the dividing line is about 1910. That is, man took about as much out of mines before 1910 as he did after 1910."

The picture of our world that emerges is as if all the rockets at Cape Kennedy were to go off at once, in some grand Fourth of July, and their skyward-soaring trails were the trend lines of our exploding technology.

Writing on "The Era of Radical Change," in *Fortune* magazine, Max Ways has said, "Within a decade or two it will be generally understood that the main challenge to U.S. society will turn not around the production of goods but around the difficulties and opportunities involved in a world of accelerating change and ever-widening choices. Change has always been a part of the human condition. What is different now is the pace of change, and the prospect that it will come faster and faster, affecting every part of life, including personal values, morality, and religions, which seem most remote from technology.

"So swift is the acceleration that trying to 'make sense' of change will come to be our basic industry. Aesthetic and ethical values will be evolving along with the choices to which they will be applied. The question about progress will be 'how good?' rather than 'how much?' "

He goes on to point out that, "The break between the period of rapid change and that of radical change is not sharp; 1950 is an arbitrary starting date. More aspects of life change faster until it is no longer appropriate to think of society as mainly fixed, or changing slowly, while the tide flows around it. So many patterns of life are being modified that it is no longer useful to organize discussion or debate mainly around the relation of the new to the old.

"The movement is so swift, so wide and the prospect of acceleration so great that an imaginative leap into the future cannot find a point of rest, a still picture of social order."

We are told that 25 per cent of all the people who ever lived are

AD INFINITUM

"...exponential curves grow to infinity only in mathematics. In the physical world they either turn round and saturate, or they break down catastrophically. It is our duty as thinking men to do our best toward a gentle saturation, instead of sustaining the exponential growth though this faces us with very unfamiliar and distasteful problems."

Prof. DENNIS GABOR
Imperial College of
Science and Technology,
London

MILLENNIUM

"We are now living through the second great divide in human history, comparable in magnitude only with that first break in historic continuity—the shift from barbarism to civilization...
"The mood, the pace, the very 'feel' of existence, as well as one's underlying notions of time, beauty, space and social relations will be shaken...
"Given these changes, it becomes quite impossible to sustain the argument that what is happening now is anything like 'normal' progress, even for the kind of industrial society we have known for the past century. It is not merely a 'second industrial revolution.' Viewed as a violent break with historic continuity, our age takes on a significance that few ages in the past have had."

ALVIN TOFFLER
"Horizon"

PHOTO BY WILLIAM JACKSON © 1966

TOMORROW'S DAWN

*"The past is but the beginning of the
beginning, and all that is and has been
is but the twilight of the dawn. A day
will come when beings who are now
latent in our thoughts and hidden in our
loins . . . shall laugh and reach out
their hands amid the stars."*

H. G. WELLS
"The Discovery of the
Future."

alive today; that 90 per cent of all the scientists who ever lived are living now; the amount of technical information available doubles every ten years; throughout the world, about 100,000 journals are published in more than 60 languages, and the number doubles every 15 years.

We are told these things, but we do not always act as if we believed them. "The fact is," says Alvin Toffler in *Horizon* in the summer of 1965, "—and simple observation of one's own friends and associates will confirm it—that even the most educated people today operate on the assumption that society is relatively static. At best they attempt to plan by making simple straight-line projections of present trends. The result is unreadiness to meet the future when it arrives. In short, 'future shock'.

"Society has many built-in time spanners that help link the present generation with the past. Our sense of the past is developed by contact with the older generation, by our knowledge of history, by the accumulated heritage of art, music, literature and science passed down to us through the years. It is enhanced by immediate contact with the objects that surround us, each of which has a point of origin with the past, each of which provides us with a trace of identification with the past.

"No such time spanners enhance our sense of the future. We have no objects, no friends, no relatives, no works of art, no music or literature that originate in the future. We have, as it were, no heritage of the future."

And so, not having one, and needing it, we will have to develop one. This can be done, perhaps, by examining the forces of change around us and by trying to understand how they originated, where they are likely to be going, and how we can to some extent, by guiding them, cushion ourselves against "future shock."

We might begin by seeing ourselves in a somewhat different relationship to time than we are accustomed to. We can agree that there is not much we can do to affect the past, and that the present is so fleeting, as we experience it, that it is transformed into the past as we touch it. It is only the future that is amenable to our plans and actions. Knowing this, we can draw a broad general outline of the kind of future world we feel we would be most happy in. And because we have now arrived at a stage in our development, or shortly will arrive there, where our most pressing problems are not technological, but political and social—we can achieve the world that we want by working together to get it.

The forces of change, which we will shortly begin to discuss, *are* amenable to our guidance. If we seem to be hurried into the future by a runaway engine, it may be that the main reason it is running away is that we have not bothered yet to learn how it works, nor to steer it in the direction we want it to go. □

HOLD ON, NOW

"*The world is undergoing a transformation to which no change that has yet occurred can be compared, either in scope or rapidity.*"

CHARLES DE GAULLE

OF TIME AND THE RIVER

"*We are at one of the decisive turning points in the history of humanity, comparable to the domestication of animals, the invention of the earliest tools, the foundation of the first cities, and the conception of the heliocentric universe. At this turning point, we can look back and take stock of man's past achievements and failures. But we can also perceive the great perspectives in which future generations must make their contributions.*

"*No transformation produces a static and lasting result. Hence our environment is at any moment of human history the product of perennial revolution, of a continuous process of change. Man's adjustments to his environment are not a series of unrelated stages of development, . . . but an organic and integrated chain of events. Thus permanency exists only in the uninterrupted continuity of change and in the dynamic relations among all aspects of human activities. In other words, permanency without synthesis is a delusion.*"

E. A. GUTKIND
"Our World from the Air"

SiQNS of OUR CHANGiNG TiMES

MOSAIC

"British and American journalism has always tended to exploit the mosaic form of the newspaper format in order to present the discontinuous variety and incongruity of ordinary life."

MARSHALL McLUHAN
"Understanding Media"

© 1946 BY THE NEW YORK TIMES COMPANY. REPRINTED BY PERMISSION.

☐ Newspapers—shards of colored glass falling along the never-never paths of time—can indeed be said to form mosaics (though often not pretty ones) of the day-to-day life they describe. But in another sense, they can be viewed as signposts imbedded in their moment of history, which, when facing each other across a span of time, may indicate the displacement that our way of life undergoes—in much the same way that two posts placed on opposite sides of a known fault line in the earth will, in time, show a relative motion which can be measured.

Since we've quoted Max Ways as saying that 1950 might be considered as a starting date for the current era of radical change, a comparison between a newspaper just preceding that year and the one we read today might provide some startling measurements of change.

In 1946, for instance, those who remembered the economic hardship that immediately followed World War I and, most especially, the terrible years of depression prior to World War II, had every reason to feel uneasy—even fearful—about the future. To be sure, there was much to rejoice about—the end of a long, bloody war, the reuniting of families, the easing of wartime controls. But no one wanted to return to the deprivation he had known before the war. Industry, in high gear during the war years, now faced a shuddering change—retooling for a civilian rather than military demand. Science and technology now had to direct their efforts toward peacetime needs. Wartime plants were closed, transportation was slow, employment became suddenly unpredictable. In short, life was anything but comfortable with the war over—even such basic commodities as milk, gasoline and automobile tires were scarce. Such expressions as "television," "jet," "nuclear power" and "United Nations" were barely known — and their significance hardly realized.

But something happened along the way to today, a thunderous upheaval that sundered the path of time and cut yesterday adrift.

And today's newspaper portrays a way of life that is of quite a different grain and texture. It is a mosaic of bright colors and sound, in the rush of which can be glimpsed the unimaginable feats of a generation — the silvery dot of a space capsule carrying men around the globe, the awesome array of nuclear needles pointing at each other across continents, the tiny trickling fluids that are synthesizing life in a glass tube, the piercing white beam of a laser cutting through the hardest metals, the clamorous march of people demanding their equal rights, the quick flicker of a multi-colored television picture, the liquid swish of a huge jet transport.

We don't seem to talk about the same things today, or experience the same things, or even think the same way as we did then. Our lives are on this side of yesterday—and the earth is still rumbling under our feet. ☐

THE ANATOMY
of CHANGE

☐ Someone has suggested that the times we live in should be marked, "Subject to change without notice." At first, the suggestion seems not only witty, but apt. Peered at more nearly, it reveals an interesting contradiction, for the essence of change is that it *is* noticed.

Change may be described as a measurable difference that an organism experiences in relation to its environment. It is an individual reaction inside a nervous system. It is not, for the most part, the world that changes; it is our experience of it.

Consider our idea of the world in which we live. Historically most people believed that the world was the center of the universe and that the sun and stars revolved around it. Then it was suggested—just an idea in someone's mind—that a better way to view things was to consider that the earth revolved around the sun. Our world has never been the same since. But it was not the world that changed; it was our way of looking at it.

As we speak of it here, there are at least two orders of change. There is the change that Adams was trying to measure. It has to do with motion—motion as the result of the application of force. The force displaces things in time and space as we experience them. It is the kind of change we experience as the result of great natural forces: hurricanes and tornados, tidal waves and earthquakes, rain and wind and frost. What we experience as change is the *measure* of the way things have been displaced in time and space after a force has worked on our environment.

A part of this same order of change is the application of human forces; the introduction of the steam engine was like the explosion of a volcano to the slowly moving agrarian society of its time. So was the introduction of the electrical generator and its ability to apply force at a distance. It roared down on the cities built on steam and coal and destroyed them as utterly as some great natural cataclysm.

Such changes are quantitative and they can be measured—in terms of coal consumption, of steam pressure, of kilowatts per hour, of productivity and availability. In our society, we tend to think of change in terms of the numbers of things and to value their importance by the size of the numbers we apply to them.

But there is another order of change; it has to do with observable differences in our experience of the configuration of things. They do not, as we experience them, stand in the same relationship—left to right, top to bottom, front to back, color on color—as they did before. For the most part, this is what we mean by cultural and social change— a difference in the observed patterns of things. Here again, change is measurement, but what we measure is quality and not quantity.

VAGUE PROGENY

"When innovation takes place, there is an intimate linkage or fusion of two or more elements that have not been previously joined in just this fashion, so that the result is a qualitatively distinct whole . . . If we may use a biological analogy, an innovation is like a genetic cross or hybrid; it is totally different from either of its parents, but it resembles both of them in some respects."

H. G. BARNETT
from "Innovation: The
Basis of Cultural Change."

IS ANYONE DIZZY?

"Your plane is not in from Seattle yet, sir," she said. "There will be a slight delay."
"I happen to have information on that flight," I said. "The plane is actually at this moment still circling Moose Jaw while the pilots study a 1938 Texaco road map. They've been lost for an hour and are running dangerously low on sugar coated gum tablets and little dry sandwiches."
"But in a larger sense," said Nancy, "aren't we all still circling Moose Jaw?"

from "Still Circling Moose Jaw"
by RICHARD BISSELL
©1965, McGraw-Hill Book Co.

Different people respond differently to the same situation and, to this extent, innovation may be said to be "built into" the human nervous system. Thus we are all innovators. The drawings below show the degree to which we are unable to copy exactly a simple original. Sixteen people were asked to copy a picture, each one copying the one done by the preceding person. The drawings below are selected from the succession of drawings. The difference between the first one, on this page, and the last one, on the facing page, shows the amount of transformation that occurs in even a simple linear series of responses.

We do not consider the value of the Mona Lisa as a function of the size of the canvas on which it was painted, nor should we measure society solely on the number of artifacts it is able to manufacture.

At the basis of cultural change lies innovation. Innovation appears to be the process by which we put together existing things differently than we did before—words on a page, colors on a canvas, the ingredients of a chemical formula, the mixture of metals in an alloy, the order of symbols in a mathematical equation.

The basis of innovation appears to be the natural result of the interaction between the stimuli in our environment and the way that our nervous systems interpret the message they receive. The stimuli are constantly changing, the messages we receive from them are constantly changing, and our interpretation of the messages is constantly changing.

It is something like a game of cards (games are models of real life). Although the markings on them are always the same, Nature never deals us the same hands twice; we have to play each new hand as it falls. The essential difference is that in a game of cards, we are all agreed upon the rules; in Nature's game, we are not at all sure what the rules may be.

Thus we cannot *help* but innovate; we cannot of ourselves ever do exactly the same thing twice—we had to invent machines to do that. Some people seem to innovate more significantly than others; and certain societies, cultures and times appear to create an environment that is more conducive to individual innovations than others. The cumulative effect of some of the individual innovations becomes social change.

Most of us react to major changes with considerable reluctance and usually find the experience painful. Psychologically, there seems to be some neurological basis for this. We have, as Kenneth Boulding brilliantly explains in *The Image*, formed an image of the way things "should be." We have been taught, for instance, that effect *follows* cause, or that clocks "keep" time, or that because people disagree with us they are our enemies. These relationships of things to each other and to us are encoded in our nervous systems and we feel quite strongly that they are not to be bent, spindled or mutilated.

Then we are exposed to some new experience that breaks up the cherished pattern. Our equilibrium is disturbed and it may take considerable psychic energy (and some little pain) to construct a new relationship that will take into account the new evidence.

This may be one reason why the "established order" so vehemently resists change in our times. "Their entire stake of security and status," says Marshall McLuhan, "is in a single form of acquired knowledge, so that innovation for them is not novelty, but annihilation."

As Dostoevsky said, "taking a new step, uttering a new word, is what people fear most."

Or Eric Hoffer: "We can never be really prepared for that which is wholly new. We have to adjust ourselves, and every radical adjustment is a crisis in self-esteem . . . It needs inordinate self confidence to face drastic change without inner trembling."

Since we cannot control change itself, we seek to control the rate at which it affects our lives. We create institutions which serve as instruments to preserve some change we feel is good and to slow down that rate at which it is changed by still other innovations. Our system of law is an instrument for preserving certain acceptable changes in the conduct of an individual in a social environment; our formalized religions are institutions for preserving what were at one time great changes in the ethical and moral valuations of men; governments are devices for preserving past changes in the relationship between an individual and the society in which he lives.

In a rather fanciful way, one might consider that our institutions — and this would include business organizations as well as the other kinds—are the "chromosomes" of our society, and that they preserve in them the successful "gene" mutations of previous social, cultural and technological innovations. To protect themselves against further change, institutions harden their resistance by formalizing rituals, customs and "traditions." In a rapidly changing technology, the social organism thus preserved becomes unable to cope with its new environment and either must give way to the innovators, or fail to survive.

It is only quite recently that we have developed formal institutions as instruments for promoting change rather than preserving it—our research and development organizations. It is conceivable that other wholly new types of institutions — instruments — for controlling the acceleration of change may have to be developed, for there is serious doubt that our traditional institutions can long withstand the tidal wave of innovation that now threatens to engulf them.

For the first time in recorded history, we have arrived at a point where two great orders of change—like two enormous tuning forks—are vibrating together, forming a new resonance that is the tune and temper of our world. What we can hope to achieve is to transform resonance into a grand harmonic, and to do this we must try to understand the nature of the forces that are working on our times. □

"How come nothing's like it was until it's gone?"

WILL MASTIN
in "Yes, I Can!" by Sammy Davis, Jr.

she had so many children...

☐ For the student of change who trudged around the grounds of the New York World's Fair of 1964-65—avidly looking for vectors whose convergence might form an understandable picture of the world of 1986—the experience was singularly uninstructive.

Vectors—considered as lines of force that could shape our future —there were aplenty. But squinting along the lines of sight, trying to figure where they were going, revealed not only that they were not going to converge, they were not even parallel. There was a fracture here, a discontinuity that one could span with his feet within a few minutes but the mind could scarcely traverse.

One sat on his plastic seat and glided past the under-water, jungle-chopping, immaculately citied world of the future that General Motors feels we all may live in; and one could go to the General Electric rotunda and be hurtled down a spiral pathway by ushers with torches, to where in a split second and a flash of light and sonic boom there was unleashed before your very senses a discharge of the power of the future; and one could go to the U.S. Pavilion and take a wonderful, wild ride through American history, trying to count the dead passenger pigeons and buffalo and Indians enroute.

And then one could walk over to where a giant computer flashed out the number of people there were in the United States at that very moment. One stood mesmerized before the computer's grinning teeth, feeling that here was a force that the other exhibits had not reckoned with. In much less time than it took to eat a hot dog, the numbers had changed significantly and the world had changed, and it simply didn't seem to have been realized by the exhibits across the way. The wonders they promised did not, somehow, seem to take into account the numbers on the big tote board of the human race. In those numbers, one could see a wave of future force humping higher and higher toward the beach of the present. When it topples, one felt, it would rattle the picture windows of condominiums twenty years away.

At the present time, starting someplace about 1946, the average annual rate of increase in the world's population is about two per cent. Using the 1962 population as a base, and applying this rate of growth to it, shows that in 650 years—somewhat less than the time backward to the Renaissance—there would be, in our world, one person standing on each square foot of land. At this rate, the perimeter of the coating of human flesh on the globe would, in 6,200 years, be expanding at the speed of light—186,000 miles per second.

Of course, one knows this will not really happen; mathematics are one thing and human beings are another, but somewhere this side of the ultimate in geometrical progression, the rate of acceleration in

PHOTO BY BOB FRASER
FIGURES BY JOHN LARRECQ

the numbers of people in the world will be the real force behind the change of our future. Just in the time span we are considering here—between 1966 and 1986—there will be five people standing where three stand today; and that will be plenty to cope with.

What appears to have happened here is that we have discovered "death control" before we have discovered—or implemented—birth control. We got the technological cart before the horse, as it were, and what we see as a population explosion today is not the result of increased fertility on the part of the human species, but largely the biological fall-out from the application of DDT, penicillin and soap.

According to "The Poverty of Abundance," published by the Planned Parenthood Federation, "In Ceylon, the introduction of DDT was largely responsible in less than a decade for a 57 per cent decline in the death rate, a population increase of 83 per cent, and a resultant decline in per capita income." It goes on to say that, "There are nearly 300,000 babies born every day, two-thirds of them into families that are poor, hungry, ignorant, ill."

We have trouble thinking in global terms. When the population explosion is brought down to the statistics of a single country, one gets the sort of picture presented by Shri Asoka Mehta, of the India Planning Commission, in the *Hindalco Journal*, June of 1965:

In India, population increased 12 million between 1891 and 1921 27 million between 1921 and 1931 • 37 million between 1931 and 1941 44 million between 1941 and 1951 • 78 million between 1951 and 1961

Nothing one saw at the New York World's Fair seemed to have fed those figures into its design of the future.

As a force for change, the increase in the numbers of people living at one time exerts itself in a number of highly divergent ways. If one thinks of human beings as sort of ambulatory energy transfer systems, then the increase in numbers means the multiplication of scanning processes whose input is wavelengths and whose output is symbols. The more people there are, the more eyes scan and ears hear the world, and the more rapidly our information about it will increase.

But when it comes to cultural change, the mere increase in numbers will not in itself accelerate it. As H. G. Barnett says, in *Innovation: The Basis of Cultural Change*, "A large population wherein individual members remain intellectually isolated or antipathetic is not more productive of innovation than is a small group."

What a large increase in the numbers of people *does*, as a force for change, is to make us consider new ways of doing things because the old ones will not work any more. The Commission that was established in Tokyo a few years ago to plan for the needs of a Tokyo of

IT TOOK FROM	FOR EARTH'S POPULATION TO REACH
the beginning of man to the Neolithic age	7,990,000 years to reach 10 million
Neolithic to the Birth of Christ	10,000 years to reach 300 million
Birth of Christ to the days of Columbus	1,500 years to reach 500 million
Columbus to 1850 A.D.	350 years to reach 1 BILLION
1850 to 1925 A.D.	75 years to reach 2 BILLION
1925 to 1962 A.D.	37 years to reach 3 BILLION
and will take to 1975	13 years to reach 4 BILLION
and from there to 1982	7 years to reach 5 BILLION

TICK TOCK

"Assuming that you have a normal pulse beat, it will not quite keep up with the increase in world population...Every time your pulse throbs, the population of the world will have added more than one human being."

WILLIAM VOGT
"People!"

more than 20 million citizens in 1980, quickly found that nothing in human experience, no technique adopted in the past, is applicable to the kind of new problems that arise when one considers the population densities of the future.

When one considers that some cities in India may have populations of upwards of 36 million by 1986; that, according to the Chamber of Commerce of the United States *(Economics of Change: No. 1, 1965)*, "Our country may add as many people by 1985 as now live in all states West of the Mississippi River;" and that 35 years from now, if current trends continue, there will be more than six billion Africans, Asians and Latin Americans, constituting 85 per cent of the world's population, it becomes obvious, if it were not already, that population growth, as a force for change in the world's society, is transformed from a *quantitative* force to a *qualitative* one.

The increase in the numbers of people will not only force us to a new technology, but it will raise new questions as to the quality and purpose of life upon this planet. In these questions—and our attempts to find answers for them—lies the real significance of population as one of the key forces of future change. The numbers game becomes transformed into a search for new ethics, new philosophies, new moralities and new religions.

"By 1985," says John G. Welles, head of the University of Denver Research Institute, "we shall be asking some new questions. Among them; How many people should there be in the U.S.? In my state? In my community? And some old ones; questions which were raised and discussed openly over 2,000 years ago by the Greek philosophers. Who should be allowed to breed, with whom and how fast? The educated classes? The physically healthy? And should it be discovered that the poorer classes and the unhealthy are breeding faster than the rest of the nation—is the quality of the human race being downgraded?"

Here we are not talking about whether one genetic strain is "better" or "worse" than another, but whether any genetic strain can create the environment in which the individual can develop his fullest potential in a world that has not learned yet how to feed, clothe, shelter and educate two thirds of the people it now has.

Historian Arnold Toynbee gets to the heart of the meaning of the population explosion when he says, "The issue is, indeed, a religious one in the sense that it raises the question, 'What is the true end of Man? Is it to populate the Earth with the maximum number of human beings . . . or is it to enable human beings to lead the best kind of life that the spiritual limitations of human nature allow?'"

Trying to find answers to *that* question will shape all our futures. □

NON-CONFORMISTS

"Essentially then, the population problem (if we define it as such) is usually attributed to those individuals or groups who adhere only in a minor way to the value system of the middle class and who can only slightly, if at all, participate in its expectations, privileges and rewards."

DR. EDITH SHERMAN
Sociologist
University of Denver

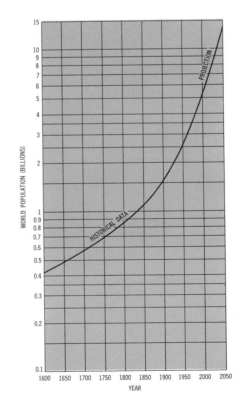

METROPOLIS

*"The city is a special receptacle for storing
and transmitting messages . . .*

*"The development of symbolic methods of storage
immensely increased the capacity of the city as a
container: it not merely held together a larger body
of people and institutions than any other kind of
community, but it maintained and transmitted a
larger portion of their lives than individual human
memories could transmit by word of mouth. This
condensation and storage, for the purpose of enlarging
the boundaries of the community in time and space,
is one of the singular functions performed by the city...
The city, as Emerson well observed, 'lives by
remembering'."*

LEWIS MUMFORD
"The City in History"

THE dimENSIONS of CHANGE

☐ The mere increase in the number of people on our planet, if they were evenly distributed over the land areas, would not in itself produce a powerful force for change. But when people are concentrated in a small space, the force for cultural, social and technological change increases, in much the same way that, if gases are pumped into a container, the number of collisions between the atoms or molecules in the gas will tend to rise.

Seen this way, the city is an instrument for accelerating change. It creates an environment in which dense concentrations of people of varying backgrounds can come into contact every day. The product of these contacts is accelerated cultural and social change.

For several thousand years the people of the world have been moving toward urban areas. This trek has become greatly accelerated in recent years. It was not until about 200 years ago that a city of a million people existed on earth. Today a city of a million may be considered relatively small. Within the easily foreseeable future, "At present rates of increase, city populations would multiply perhaps 40 times within the next 100 years," says Dr. Roger Revelle, director of the Center of Population Studies at Harvard University.

Within the next twenty years, if present trends continue, about three-fourths of all the world's people will live in urban areas. "When you talk about cities nowadays," says, *U.S. News & World Report* (November 15, 1965) "you have to include their fast-growing suburbs. The important population figure has become not that for the inner city but for the entire metropolitan area. . . Half of all Americans will live in three metropolitan areas by 1985."

People move to the city from the country to change their way of life. They may, if successful, eventually move to the suburbs, hoping to *preserve* their new way of life. The suburb is thus an instrument designed to slow the rate of cultural change, by grouping people of the same economic status, race, educational background and nationality together. To some extent they are successful, but the suburbs are still within the field of force emanating from the city and the product of that force is change.

It is possible that today's suburbs are the prototypes of the cities of tomorrow, for—with television—physical density and biological confrontation are no longer needed to bring about the interaction of different minds that is the accelerator of social change. The form of the city of the future—our immediate future—may be an electronic system rather than an architectural facade. ☐

ELBOW ROOM

In Colonial America, the average density of persons was one per square mile. In a circle 20 miles in diameter (figured on the basis that ten miles was the greatest distance a person could walk to work and back and still do a full day's work) this yields 314 persons inside the circle with the rather obvious chance of human contact of 313 to 1.

The opportunities for interpersonal communication—the exchange of ideas and information—were rather limited.

Today, Chicago has a population density of 10,000 persons per square mile, inside a 20 mile-diameter circle. Opportunities for human-to-human contact are more than 3 million to 1.

As people congregate in areas of higher population density, the opportunities for interchanges of information increase, and this can help to create the environment in which change takes place at an accelerated rate.

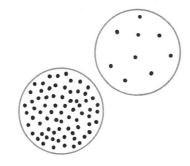

ACTION AT THE INTERFACE

A CLOSER LOOK

"Those who are concerned with structure on the superatomic scale find that there is more significance and interest in the imperfections in crystals than in the monotonous perfection of the crystal lattice itself. Like the biologist, the metallurgist is concerned with aggregates and assemblies in which repeated or extended irregularities in the arrangement of atoms become the basis of major structural features on a larger scale, eventually bridging the gap between the atom and things perceptible to the human senses."

CYRIL STANLEY SMITH
"Structure in Art and Science."

☐ Metallurgists tell us that it is at the boundary layers—the interfaces between crystals in metals—that action takes place under force; it is these imperfections that allow us to deform and shape metals mechanically. Geologists say that the great changes in the earth take place at boundary lines where forces meet—the surf at the shore, the rift between fault blocks moving in different directions, the edge where forest meets meadow. Sculptors direct their chisels along the fault lines of blocks of stone and diamond cutters cut along flaws.

Accelerated change, in both the human and the physical world, is more likely to take place along those interfaces where culture meets culture or different kinds of neighborhoods rub shoulders along a common street. Seen from above, a city is like a mosaic, or the pattern created by etching a polished cross section of metal. The edges where patterns touch each other are the channels along which change accelerates. In cities, the "dead" areas are those where borderlines do not exist; change moves there very slowly. We call them blighted areas.

"In any medium or structure," says Kenneth Boulding, "there is a break boundary at which the system suddenly changes into another or passes some point of no return in its dynamic process." Thus the break boundary in a city may not only be horizontal, as between different neighborhoods, but vertical, as in the process of economic and social mobility—layers upon layers, with the penthouse on the top. The horror of life in the city slum is an impelling force that motivates the less patient, or the more innovative, outward and upward, with the new boundary layers in between each successive stage they attain.

But it is also true in the technological and intellectual worlds that action is most likely to accelerate along the interface between different techniques or disciplines. The historian, Teggart, suggests that "the great advances of mankind have been due, not to the mere aggregation, assemblage or acquisition of disparate ideas, but to the emergence of a certain type of mental activity which is set up by the opposition of different idea systems."

We can look, then, for the future acceleration of change to come in part from the interfaces of the human world. With the advent of global visual communications, the interface leaps neighborhood lines and national borders, and the great discontinuity that will yield accelerated change in the next two decades will be between the "haves" and the "have nots," of the world, wherever they are.

In the "high noon" of tomorrow, it will be this confrontation—between the "haves" and the "have nots" on the main street of human awareness—that will shape our future. ☐

PHOTOGRAPH BY SUNDERLAND AERIAL PHOTOS

FRACTURE

In urban environments, social and cultural change are most apt to begin along the boundary layers—those discontinuities where different races, economic classes, religions or ideologies abrade each other—in somewhat the same way that it is at the interfaces formed by impurities or the edges of crystals in metal that slippage and, ultimately, complete fracture of the metal, take place under pressure.

COURTESY OF DUAINE MIZER—MET. LAB—THE DOW CHEMICAL CO.

THE subculture of youth

☐ We sometimes tend to think that the more important ideas and inventions were produced by mature minds as the result of deliberate thought and hard work. We may tend to think so, but there is little in the history of inventions to back us up.

According to Eric Hoffer, Hero's steam engine was used to work tricks in temples and to divert guests at banquets. In China, the compass was used to find a desirable orientation for graves, gunpowder to frighten away evil spirits, and printing to multiply amulets, playing cards and paper money. Buddhists used the water wheel to grind out prayers, not grain. He suggests that the domestication of animals may have come from children playing with the young of other species, long before they were used to pull plows or herd sheep.

It is leisure, not work, that produces most important innovations. Barnett says, "If a compendium of the thoughts of men conceived in leisure were available for reference it would be far more efficient to refer to it for solutions of practical problems than to set the best minds of the day to work on them. Leisured speculation is of high value, and it may be that in one way or another, it always plays a part in innovation."

One is reminded of Newton sitting beneath the apple tree, Archimedes in the bathtub, and Watts waiting for the kettle to boil. In such moments of nonconcentration, the "lens of the mind" may be said to open, and relationships between larger configurations can be observed. It may take a great deal of hard work to formulate an idea or to win acceptance for it, but it is likely it originated during a moment of relaxation. Edison is said to have observed that "genius is one per cent inspiration, ninety-nine per cent perspiration." He failed to add that they did not take place at the same time.

Another major source of innovation, as Hoffer points out, and an examination of patent rights would confirm, is the "newcomer." The newcomer may be an immigrant, newly arrived in an environment strange to him; an adolescent moving to puberty or from the latter to young maturity; an emigrant moving from the farm to the city, or from the city to wild territory; or a whole nation moving from agriculture to industrialization.

The feature common to them all, and the force that makes them innovate, is that they find themselves organisms in a strange environment. The old ways won't work any more, so they have to find new ones.

In a sense it might be said that the reason World War II marked a major turning point in the acceleration of cultural, social and technological change is that it did, indeed, make newcomers of us all. The impact of the war was to change our environment radically, and as

PHOTOGRAPHY BY STEPHEN FRISCH

"*My feeling is that the tendency to carry youthful characteristics into adult life, which renders man perpetually immature and unfinished, is at the root of his uniqueness in the universe, and is particularly pronounced in the creative individual. Youth has been called a perishable talent, but perhaps talent and originality are always aspects of youth, and the creative individual is an imperishable juvenile . . .*

"*We are more ready to try the untried when what we do is inconsequential. Hence the remarkable fact that many inventions had their birth as toys. In the Occident the first machines were mechanical toys, and such crucial instruments as the telescope and microscope were first conceived as playthings.*"

ERIC HOFFER in "The Ordeal of Change."

NO WIPE OUT

The face of change is a young one—and it comes in many colors. All previous revolutions had, as their goal, the attainment of some new state of equilibrium. What we are seeing in our time is a new order of revolution, whose goal is not a new equilibrium, but social disorder itself. It is the first social recognition that continuous change itself is a form of equilibrium—and that it is only in disorder that we find order. These kids are "surfing" and it is the essence of surfing that one should ride the turbulence without succumbing to it. You cannot have fun surfing on a slow wave—and you cannot surf at all on a frozen one.

A MATTER OF BREEDING

Where communications are free and open, one technological change begets another, setting up a chain of innovations. When one chain—such as the invention of interchangeable, movable typefaces—is joined to another—such as the idea of assembly line processes in manufacturing—then a technological explosion may take place that affects entire economic systems.

organisms seeking to find a new equilibrium, we were forced to innovate—or be lost in the maelstrom of a strange new world. It was the same everywhere—for Americans, Germans, Russians, English, French, Chinese, Africans, Japanese—they were suddenly trapped in a vast historical rift. Whether in foxhole or bomb shelter, waiting in a gun turret or sitting in a pilot's seat, we became, for that moment, separated from the group and dependent on our own actions—not society's—for individual survival. The wave of innovation from *that* global experience is still moving forward through the world.

Speaking of the United States, where the wave of war-born innovation is most apparent to us, Barnett says, "During the Second World War, there was a tremendous shifting and churning of the American population while the conflict lasted, and the stirring has not been quieted yet. Millions of men served in the armed forces, there to meet and be compelled to get along with others whose ways were diverse beyond their previous realization. Thousands of civilians changed their residences, their routine habits, and their ideas about other people, cities and customs. Families were disrupted, women worked as they had never worked before, new friendships and entirely new communities of strangers were formed. All these developments were new in themselves, but in addition the individuals who were involved had to make adjustments to meet the new conditions."

We have, since that time, added a new type of "newcomer" to the environment—whole nations of people who are making the transition from non-technological society to one more closely matching the machine societies of the Western world. They will be powerful sources of accelerated change.

Youth and the play instinct, leisure and change of environment are three powerful forces in the acceleration of change.

Consider then that by 1986, 35 per cent of all the people alive will be less than 15 years old; that even today, China has more children under ten than the total all-age population of Russia:

Consider that within less than a generation in the United States two per cent of the population may be able to produce all the food and manufactured goods required by the other 98 per cent; that the use of leisure time will be our greatest problem:

Consider that the world's migration—from rural areas to cities, from densely populated countries to sparsely settled ones; from basically under-developed societies (technologically) to industrial ones—is vastly increasing the number of newcomers in our future society:

Then ask yourself how *these* forces will accelerate the rate of change in the next twenty years! □

It was Benjamin Disraeli who once said:
"Almost everything that is great has been done by youth."
Here are a very few of the young people who have
made important contributions to society:

❅ CHARLES DARWIN
(1809-1882)
at age 27 began his observations
concerning the transmutation
of species that led to formulation
of his theory of evolution.

❅ ELI WHITNEY
(1765-1825)
invented the cotton gin at
age 28.

❅ SAMUEL COLT
(1814-1862)
made first wooden model
of revolver at age 16,
a metal model the next year,
and patented the first
revolver at age 21.

❅ SIGMUND FREUD
(1856-1939)
at 29 began studies which led to his
investigation of hysteria from a
psychological viewpoint and later to his
development of psychoanalysis.

❅ ALEXANDER
THE GREAT
(363-323 B.C.)
ruled as king of Mace-
donia at age 20, had con-
quered the civilized world
by the age of 27.

❅ MICHELANGELO
(1475-1564)
sculptured his Battle
of the Centaurs
at 17 and had completed
his famous Pieta and
Bacchus sculptures by the
age of 26.

❅ BLAISE PASCAL
(1623-1662)
had written a book on geometry
by the age of 16,
invented the adding machine at 19.

❅ CHARLES MARTIN
HALL
(1863-1914)
at age 23 was the first
man to produce
aluminum by electrolysis.

❅ THOMAS A. EDISON
(1847-1931)
patented the first
of his many inventions,
an electrical vote
recorder, at 21.

❅ ALBERT EINSTEIN
(1879-1955)
had mastered the works of Euclid,
Newton and Spinoza by the age of 15,
began work on his theory of
space-time relativity at age 26.

❅ JAMES WATT
(1736-1819)
began work on his idea for
a condensing steam engine
at 25, patented the first
practical steam engine
at 33.

❅ MICHAEL FARADAY
(1791-1867),
inventor of the electric motor,
at 21 began work in
electro-magnetics that led
to his invention.

❅ THE WRIGHT BROTHERS
WILBUR (1867-1912) and
ORVILLE (1871-1948)
began experimenting with aircraft
in their twenties, successfully
flew the world's first powered airplane
when Wilbur was 36 and Orville 32.

❅ PETR
TCHAIKOVSKY
(1840-1893)
wrote his first opera libret-
to at 28, his first complete
opera (Undine) at 29.

❅ ALEXANDER
GRAHAM BELL
(1847-1922)
worked on his idea
for a wireless telephone in his
twenties and patented the
first telephone at 29.

❅ WOLFGANG MOZART
(1756-1791)
began writing musical compositions
at 4, made his first tour as an
accomplished musician at 6, wrote
his first sonatas at 7 and
completed his first symphony at age 8.

❅ REMBRANDT
VAN RIJN
(1606-1669)
began serious painting in
oils at age 21, within a few
years had become a prom-
inent portrait painter.

❅ LUDWIG VAN
BEETHOVEN
(1770-1827)
wrote his first musical
composition at 13, pianoforte
quartets at 15, had written
and published his Opus I
by age 23.

тhouqhтs of a qlobal brain

□ For the most part, innovations have spread but slowly. Generations passed before the magnetic compass, gunpowder, metalworking, agriculture, the water wheel, papermaking, printing, arithmetic, geometry, chemistry and astronomy moved from the East to the West. Somewhat fewer generations were required for the feedback—power machinery, electricity, constitutional government, electronics and nuclear physics —to return from West to East. The skeletons of lost caravans and the hulks of burnt out bombers mark the trail between.

But in today's radiant dawn this good morning's Morning Star is a communications satellite, through which new ideas can move from one part of the world to the other with the speed of light. And it comes bearing the gift of universal language—the picture that moves needs no translation. The clear understandability of this "voice" makes a mockery of natural and political borders, and will in time remove from the news of the world the filters set there by those who know what is good for us to know. When people can see and judge events directly for themselves, it will be a very different world, indeed.

(It is true that there will be those who will not want us to hear the beat of this electronic mind nor see the visions it presents, but it has been our long-time experience that ultimately if there is a voice, the people will hear it; if there is a vision, the people will see it).

Now couple to this magic lantern an electronic nervous system of global dimensions that knits together electronic brains into a single, pulsating network of information, computation and projection. The planet will wear its neural system like a mantle, shuttling the world's changing pictures from pole to pole at the speed of light. Mankind's experience will be its input; vision and guidance can be its output.

Not since Alamogordo has man sent a beast of such magnitude rampaging through the world—but where the first one set out to annihilate man, this new power may seek him out to save him.

Of all the forces accelerating the change of our future, none seems so powerful as this world-wide voice coupled to an electronic brain— with it the vision of one world moves momentously closer to reality.

As Marshall McLuhan says, "If the work of the city is the remaking or translation of man into a more suitable form than his nomadic ancestors achieved, then might not our current translation of our entire lives into the spiritual form of information seem to make of the entire globe and of the human family, a single consciousness?"

And he asks further, "Can we possibly have a global consciousness without also developing a global conscience?" □

IMPLOSION

"After three thousand years of explosion, by means of fragmentary and mechanical technologies, the Western world is imploding. During the mechanical ages we had extended our bodies in space. Today, after more than a century of electric technology, we have extended our central nervous system itself in a global embrace, abolishing both time and space as far as our planet is concerned.

"Rapidly, we approach the final phase of the extensions of man—the technological stimulation of consciousness, when the creative process of knowing will be collectively and corporatively extended to the whole of human society, much as we have already extended our senses and nerves by the various media."

MARSHALL McLUHAN
University of Toronto

INFORMATION INFILTRATION

"It would be difficult to overstate the magnitude of change that will take place in the lives of all of us, in human history, as a result of the information revolution that has so unobtrusively taken place in our day.

"Information, its communication and use, is the web of society; the basis for all human understanding, organization and effort...."

JOHN DIEBOLD
from "Beyond Automation"

driftwood from the conceptual beach

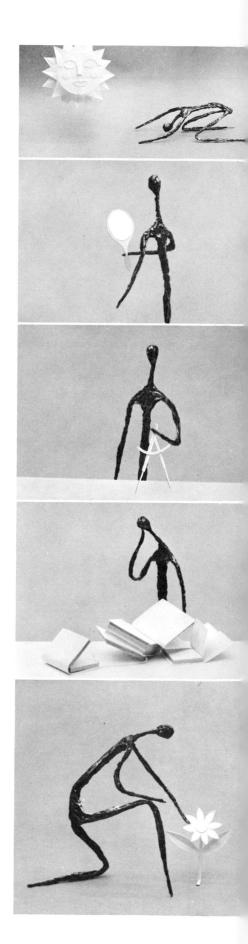

□ The student of change, searching barefoot such flotsam and jetsam as may be found on the shoals of our time, will take note that it is believed, perhaps not everywhere, that the hard radiation generated by our sun, the stars, and forces in our universe whose howls are not yet fully understood, will, from time to time, strike and thus change—through obliteration or rearrangement—certain symbols in our genetic codes. If it be viable, the new code will speak louder and louder in succeding generations, and thus we may have a salamander, where once there was a fish; or a man, where once there was a lemur.

In somewhat the same way, there are from time to time introduced into the human vernacular certain new ideas; the effects of hard radiation from minds that glow like suns or shine like stars, or cry in voices not yet fully understood. Since we began keeping score, there have been several of these mutations in the world-view. Once they were introduced, the world that followed, as we experience it, was never quite the same again. Each new mutation, broadening in ripples throughout the world of human thought, has had the effect of both diminishing man—and of enlarging him—as if a telescope were to be turned end for end.

On these pages we have attempted to recreate some of these mutations in thought, much as a disciple of each might have described the way he felt, and the way he thought, and what the texture of the universe he fingered with his mind seemed like to him. The student of change, sifting these artifacts from the sand, can assign no hierarchy to them, except to say that, as he found them, some were earlier, and some later, than others. They are like the strata that tell us of ancient, unknown seas; we cannot say that this one was better than another, but only that they seem—as we look at layer upon layer—to have succeeded one another in time. They are like the old suits hanging in our closet. We were happy and fashionable in them once; but we do not wear them very often anymore. Something has happened to them—or us.

What may they mean to us; what may they do to us? Listen to John Wilkinson, who, in *"The Quantitative Society"* says, "...one of the most persuasive schemata of writing history runs in terms of man's progressive abandonment of one favored position after another.

"Not long since he was a unique, rational being, beloved of God and occupying the center of the Cosmos. Through the eyes of Copernicus, Darwin, Freud and their successors, we have learned to view ourselves as spontaneously-generated bits of protoplasm, riddled with irrational fears and anxieties, and relegated to a rapidly shrinking rock in an absurdly out-of-the-way corner of the universe."

We can but watch and wonder, "What rough beast, its hour come 'round at last, slouches toward Bethlehem to be born?" □

HOW A MAN OF THAT AGE MIGHT DESCRIBE HIS VIEW OF THE WORLD

I *THE AGE OF PRIMITIVE REALISM* *From ? B.C. to 650 B.C.*	"We are two, the world and me. The world is just as I sense it (see it, touch it, taste it, smell it, hear it). The world is like me. In me there is a spirit; in the world as a whole, and in each part of the world that I deal with, there are spirits who rule. I have come to terms with these spirits. I do so by rituals, by magic. *The superior man*	*is the magician or witch doctor who knows the spirits and how to deal with them."* (In many parts of the world today, in all cultures and societies, there are still people who believe that there are "spirits" whose help can be invoked, or whose wrath avoided, through incantation of magic words and the performance of rituals.)	*"The world is what I feel it to be."*
II *THE AGE OF REASON* *From 650 B.C. to 350 B.C.*	FROM THALES THROUGH ARISTOTLE ✿ "We are now three: the world, I, facing the world, and I, observing myself looking at the world. To put order into the world, I classify things, qualities and actions in the world and in me. I take this classification into account when I want to guide my behavior. My ideal is to be as 'objective' as possible. My thinking must be orderly, as the world is orderly. My brain mirrors the world; to each thought corresponds a fact; to each word corresponds a	thing, a person, an action or a quality. If my thinking goes from one thought to another according to logic, it directs me through the world from one fact to the next. *Within my brain there is a miniature of the universe."* (Even after 2,000 years, there are still many people who think this way today. They are the 'practical' people; they accumulate 'facts' and pin labels on them, and base their conduct—and their appraisal of others—on 'facts' and labels.)	*"The world is what I say it is."*
III *THE AGE OF SCIENCE* *From 1500 A.D. to 1900 A.D.*	FROM COPERNICUS TO PLANCK ✿ "I do not confer with the spirits as did the primitive. Nor do I deceive myself as did the Metaphysician (II) who mistook his own voice for that of Nature. I ask Nature definite questions and Nature gives me clear-cut answers. I translate these answers into mathematical formulas that project my conclusions into the unknown, where I discover other facts that Nature has kept hidden since the beginning. *The superior man is the experimenter-mathematician, the man who expresses relations in formu-*	*las that reveal how the properties and the actions of men and things follow measurable sequences."* (The man of affairs today; the one who runs business and industry, serves in high governmental posts; writes and edits our journals and newspapers, is the product of colleges and universities whose curriculum is largely based on the experimenter-mathematician concept; he speaks in charts and graphs and figures, and bases his conduct upon them and his appraisal of others on the extent that they do so.)	*"The world is an immense machine and I can discover how it works."*
IV *THE AGE OF RELATIVISM* *From 1900 A.D. through 1966 A.D.*	FROM ROENTGEN THROUGH RUSSEL ✿ "I find that the further I ask questions, the less and less the world seems like a giant machine. I have trouble even asking the 'right' questions and the answers frequently baffle me. Even when I ask the 'right' questions and get the 'right' answers, I find that the answers are in terms of my frame of reference to the world I have *myself* created through centuries of observations. The structure of my world is built of *my own* postulates, which must be re-examined relentlessly. They	appear to be relative to my own space-time relationship with the cosmos, and with every unique event that I single out for study. What the primitivists thought of as spirits in nature, and the philosophers considered the 'facts' of nature, and the rationalists considered the 'laws' of nature, I find now to be but gross irregularities in the world as I see it through my inadequate senses and instruments. The only 'laws of nature' I can discover are statistical averages that provide rough indications of probabilities."	*"The world consists of probabilities that I create by my way of looking at them."*
V *THE AGE OF UNITY* *From 1966 A.D. to ? A.D.*	FROM PEIRCE THROUGH EINSTEIN AND REISER TO? "Having discovered that I cannot separate what I observe from my own act of observation, I begin to study my own way of observing. When I do this, I find that my observation does not consist solely of what goes on in my brain, but that my total organism, with all of its history, is also engaged. "I discover that my most clever formulations take their origin and their significance from an immediacy of felt contact, of fusion and oneness with what is going on, beyond the dimensional limits of symbols, and without the distinction between the self and the non-self. Out of this knowledge comes an awareness of my inter-relatedness with everything, from blind cosmic	energy to fellow human beings; the old, verbal distinctions between art and science and religion disappear—becoming an overall oneness of experience." (This concept, which after 2,000 years offers the promise that the powerful ethical systems of Christ, Buddha and Mohammed may fuse with the relativistic world of Einstein, the cyclic, recreative universe of Hoyle, the "participative iconology" of McLuhan and Ellul, is a still, small voice in our world of today. It can be heard in the enclaves of a handful of universities; in the words of a bearded poet somewhere east of midnight; and in the voiceless contemplation of a Zen disciple beside the dripping water and stone pools somewhere west of a Shoji screen. But it *can* be heard.)	*"My world has a structure that no formulation can encompass; I conceive of the world as my own total experience with it, and I play with my own symbolic constructs in a spirit of easy detachment."*

ITALICIZED MATERIAL BETWEEN QUOTATION MARKS IS FROM "EXPLORATIONS IN AWARENESS" BY J. SAMUEL BOIS. © 1957 BY HARPER & ROW, PUBLISHERS, INCORPORATED

TOMORROW AND TOMORROW AND TOMORROW...

COMMONWEALTH

"Because the time lag between invention and application now diminishes so swiftly, it becomes possible—and necessary—to forecast the ethical, social and economic implications of this development. Today, in our country and in certain other industrial nations, men are compelled to recognize and give assent to profound transformations in human values.

"Technological change has already largely eliminated people from production; it has sundered the hitherto socially essential connection of work to consumption. The citizens and the institutions of these nations must accommodate themselves to the law of material abundance; each individual can secure increase in his own well-being only through action that secures increase in the well-being of others."

GERARD PIEL
from "The Computer as
Sorcerer's Apprentice"

OUT TO LUNCH

"It is possible, if the human being falters even momentarily in accommodating himself to the technological imperative, that he will be excluded from it completely even in his mechanical functions, much as he finds himself excluded from any participation in an automated factory."

JACQUES ELLUL
"La Tecnique"

☐ We have talked here a little bit about some of the more powerful forces that change the lives of human beings. These forces have, of course, been at work in human societies since the beginnings of recorded history. Thus, what we have had to say so far has concerned the past and something of the immediate present.

Of the present we have said that there appears to have been recently a great quickening of the rate of change. This rapid acceleration seems to have begun around 1900 and to have taken a "quantum leap" shortly after World War II.

Now we are going to talk a little about some of the social, economic, political and moral problems this new era confronts us with. In discussing them, we are not suggesting solutions; we don't know, except in a general way, what they might be. In describing these problems, we necessarily run the risk of "advocacy." As Ellul pointed out in *Propoganda: The Formation of Men's Attitudes,* "because of the high place we accord sheer fact in our world, it is assumed that anyone who states a fact (even without passing judgment on it) is, therefore, in favor of it."

We believe we no more "advocate" a social fact by discussing it than we "advocate" thunder and lightning by discussing *them.* Still, there are a number of what appear to be social and economic facts in our times that are "not discussed among gentlemen." We might pause to see what might be the mechanism that makes discussion of drastic change dangerous.

One recent theory, suggested by the Canadian philosopher, Marshall McLuhan, is that the effect of a major technological change upon a society is to cause it to become "numb." It is something like the effect that an automobile accident, the death of a loved one, or the loss of one's job has on the individual. To protect the established image the individual has of himself and his relationship to the society he lives in, a numbness sets in. This temporary anesthesia, which in medicine might be diagnosed as "shock" for the individual, allows a period of time for the shattered image to rearrange itself and adjust to the change.

In societies suffering a sudden major technological change, this numbness takes the form of rejection, refusal to admit the existence of the change, ridicule and sometimes outright opposition. "I don't want to think about it" and "I don't want to discuss it" are often verbal clues that a person has undergone shock. The advent of the steam engine, electricity, telephone, radio, television, motor car, and airplane have all had somewhat the same initial reception in society.

Today, we are going through a period where the introduction of electronic communications, computers, automation and nuclear power, has created the same numbing shock as the earlier innovations. We have accustomed ourselves to a life in a world that was fragmented into little pieces; now we suddenly find ourselves considering a world that is all of a piece because any part of it can be experienced by us instantaneously. We find nothing in our history with which to form a comfortable image of ourselves in relation to our electronic environment. Nearly all of our hard-earned past has, in truth, become a "bucket of ashes."

"Human institutions in their earlier historical stages," says John Wilkinson in *The Quantitative Society,* "changed so slowly that human action was usually able to cope with their evolution . . . But after a certain point in an exponential curve has been reached in time, the curve's acceleration is so great that the explosive phase may be said to have set in, and the process is irreversible.

"It is the way of all human institutions to proceed, with the passage of time, from sense to nonsense and from use to abuse; but the characteristic of the exploding technological society is that changes sooner or later *must* take place in a fraction of the time necessary even to assess the situation."

One of the massive social changes that is the direct result of our newly exploited electronic technology—and one not yet fully appreciated (culture shock?)—is that since World War II our Western society has passed the point where the technical problem of making and selling things is of fundamental importance.

We now know pretty well how to produce metals, petroleum, power, food and so on, and we also know pretty well how they can be applied to man's benefit. We know we can increase production to any level we desire by the application of investment in the means of production, and we can increase the utility of products through research and development.

What we do not yet know is how to create a social, political and economic environment in which *all* the people have the power to purchase our products at a price that repays us for having produced and distributed them in the first place.

Thus the business of business would appear no longer merely to be productive—but to improve the very nature of the market itself. So, within the last few years, the over-all objectives of industry and politics have become one. A new role of business is to create a kind of society that can participate in and enjoy the new technological world which science and industry helped create.

This is going to be particularly difficult because all of our institu-

INTERCEPT

"Massive human institutions, like physical bodies, possess an 'inertia' that keeps them more or less in the motion and trajectory of the present . . . correspondingly massive forces are needed to bring about either a change of direction or a sensible deceleration and . . . such revolutionary forces, when applied, often bring about a state of affairs neither predicted nor predictable."

JOHN WILKINSON
from "The Quantitative Society"

RISING TIDE

"Great economic and social forces flow with a tidal sweep over communities that are only half conscious of what is befalling them. Wise are those who foresee what time is thus bringing and endeavor to shape institutions and mold men's thought and purpose in accordance with the change that is silently surrounding them."

JOHN, VISCOUNT MORLEY

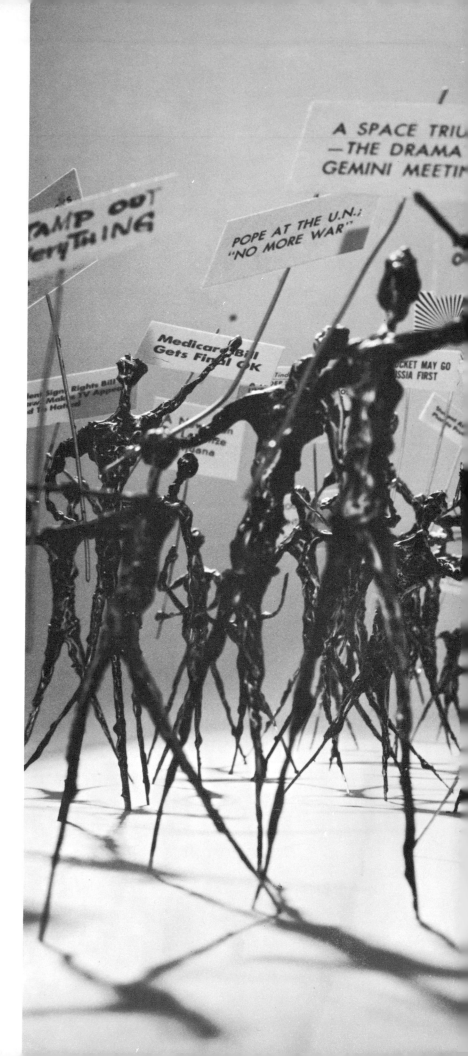

CONFRONTATION

"The mass movements, upheavals, and wars which are a by-product of change indicate that the process involves the deeper layers of man's soul. After all, change such as the world has seen during the last hundred years is something wholly unprecedented in human experience.

"It would be legitimate, therefore, to assume that there is in man's nature a built-in resistance to change. We are not only afraid of the new, but convinced that we cannot really change, that we can adapt ourselves to the new only by getting out of our skin and assuming a new identity. In other words, drastic change generates a need for a new birth and a new identity. And it perhaps depends on the way this need is satisfied whether the process of change runs smoothly or is attended with convulsions and explosions."

ERIC HOFFER

New Health Concept For City's Poor
NON-VIOLENT ACTION TAUGHT AT NEW SCHOOL
LSD Sparks Love Rally
TAXES ON RISE AGAIN
ANTI-WAR PROTEST HELD
FACULTY SUPPORTS STUDENT MOVEMENT
IT'S A MOD, MOD WORLD
Stage Protest

THE LONG WAIT

"The truth, the central stupendous truth, about developed countries today is that they can have—in anything but the shortest run—the kind and scale of resources they decide to have...It is no longer resources that limit decisions. It is the decision that makes the resources. This is the fundamental revolutionary change—perhaps the most revolutionary mankind has ever known."

U THANT, Secretary General
The United Nations

ZOO STORY

"Insects and birds and fish and animals live in an environment which is normal to them. Even in our city zoos we have created artificially a normal ecology for the animals. But we refuse to do it for our human brothers. For mountain goats, we make them some rocks to climb on; we give antelopes a park-like place with a moat around it; even the snakes enjoy air-conditioning! But we won't provide proper housing for human beings and a good community environment for our children."

TED F. SILVEY
AFL-CIO

NEW ETHIC

"In a sense, when work is reduced, as it almost certainly will be, there is a very real crisis of values for people generally. Great groups of people have been trained by nothing in their whole culture, background, religion and philosophic conceptions, for anything other than work as a meaningful activity."

LEO CHERNE
"Nation's Business"

tions have been created to deal with the problems of a world in which there was never enough of anything to go around. The business of industry was to produce as much as possible, and the function of government was to oversee the distribution of what was produced, for the greatest social and economic benefit commensurate with giving industry enough incentive to produce at all.

In addition to having reached the beginning of an "economy of abundance," the electronic advances have created the basis for a "participative society." In such a society, there is the opportunity for participation on the part of everyone, unlike most societies of the past which (because of the limitations of communications and the inability to produce enough goods for everyone) were run by a relatively small number of people at the "top." Social and political participation can be direct and universal in the electronic society.

But, Robert Hutchins points out, "With an educational system that does not educate and a system of mass communication that does not communicate, we have become incapable of the discussion by which political issues are determined." It is a grave question that has not yet been fully faced. "How shall a man be morally responsible for that to which he is not able to respond?" asks Wilkinson. "The contention that persons ignorant of technology can function in a democracy to any effect when the society is a technological one is dubious. Understanding is not a prerequisite of control, it *is* control."

Leo Cherne, in *Nation's Business,* has said, "If the businessman is not well informed, he will not even have a chance to exist as a businessman. It will not be possible for the businessman to remain indifferent to the world of science."

If the relationship which today's man of business has toward technology may require rapid readjustment in the future, then the problem of the often less well-informed employee and his family is still more acute. For the most part, an individual's personal and social identity has been and is now, what he *does*—how he makes his living. "In our society at the moment," comments Prof. Leroy Augenstein, Michigan State University, "we reward and thus challenge a man on the basis of whether he produces hard goods, or capital, or services. If we literally get to the situation of abundance, this will no longer work. How do you determine the value of a human being then?"

This loss of the identity historically conferred by the work-and-reward system raises the question of what people will do with the leisure that an economy of abundance will make available to them. "We must face the fact," says A. R. Martin, chairman of the American Psychiatric Association Committee on Leisure Time and Its Use, "that

PHOTO BY WILLIAM JACKSON © 1966

THE FLEDGLING

"What a monstrous spectre is this man, the disease of the agglutinated dust, lifting alternate feet or lying drugged with slumber; killing, feeding, growing, bringing forth small copies of himself; grown upon with hair like grass, fitted with eyes that move and glitter in his face; a thing to set children screaming.

—and yet, looked at nearlier, known as his fellows know him, how surprising are his attributes! Poor soul, here for so little, cast among so many hardships, filled with so many desires so incommensurate and so inconsistent, savagely surrounded, savagely descended, irremediably condemned to prey upon his fellow lives; who would have blamed him had he been a piece with his destiny and a being merely barbarous?

And we look and behold him instead filled with imperfect virtues; infinitely childish, often admirably valiant, often touchingly kind; sitting down, amidst his momentary life, to debate of right and wrong and the attributes of the deity; rising up to do battle for an egg or die for an idea; singling out his friends and his mate with cordial affection; bringing forth in pain, rearing with long-suffering solicitude, his young.

To touch the heart of his mystery, we find in him one thought, strange to the point of lunacy; the thought of duty; the thought of something owing to himself, to his neighbor, to his God; an ideal of decency, to which he would rise if it were possible; a limit of shame below which, if it be possible, he will not stoop . . .

. . . Of all earth's meteors, here at least is the most strange and consoling; that this ennobled lemur, this hair crowned bubble of the dust, this inheritor of a few years and sorrow, should yet deny himself his rare delights, and add to his frequent pains and live for an ideal, however misconceived . . ."

ROBERT LOUIS STEVENSON
"Pulvis et Umbra," from
Scribner's Magazine,
April, 1888.

a great majority of our people are not emotionally and psychologically ready for free time . . . This results in unhealthy adaptations which find expression in a wide range of sociopathologic and psychopathologic states. Among the social symptoms of this maladaption to free time are: low morale, civilian unrest, subversiveness and rebellion." Much of the unrest of our times comes from segments of the population whom the new technology already has "set free."

One rather promising line toward solution would certainly seem to be education for life in an electronic society. And yet, it would appear that our present system is still largely educating people for the kind of world that existed prior to 1950. "One information-processing device," says Wilkinson, "that cannot easily accommodate itself to the universal acceleration (of change) is the human brain. Generals are always fighting the last war; and educators . . . are always instructing the last generation . . . The average college student is a very badly programmed computer."

Perhaps, as H. G. Wells said some years ago, "Human history more and more becomes a race between education and catastrophe."

If this be so, then perhaps in its new role of enlarged social and moral responsibility in an era of abundance inhabited by a participative society, business must look into what can be done about education.

"One thing at fault," says Prof. Neil W. Chamberlain, Yale, "lies in our persistent notion that a person can acquire in the first 20 years or so of his life all the formal education he will need to keep him on an ascending career through the remaining 40 years or so of his working life."

It does now seem apparent that a system of universal and life-long education will have to be devised, and there is some question whether the traditional university or college is the place to do it. It may be that among other of its new responsibilities, business will also have to put its enormous talents and resources to work educating minds, with the same enthusiasm with which it has produced goods.

But to some, the question may arise, "Are we really equal to the challenge of the suddenly confronted new world?"

It seems to us that the answer to that was given, back in 1835, by Alexis de Tocqueville, who said in his *Democracy in America:*

"They (the Americans) have all a lively faith in the perfect ability of man, they judge that the diffusion of knowledge must necessarily be advantageous, and the consequences of ignorance fatal; they all consider society as a body in a state of improvement, humanity as a changing scene, in which nothing is, or ought to be, permanent; and they admit that what appears to them today to be good, may be superseded by something better tomorrow." □

VALEDICTORY

"It is my belief that, orienting ourselves in terms of time and events, we are but at the beginning of mighty changes in our way of working and living which will make it possible for us as a people to scale undreamed of heights.

"As people we are in a period of tremendous, dynamic advances forward —greater population, vaster markets, more opportunities, more challenges to men and women who will rise to meet them.

". . . count me among those who look upon our future as a great opportunity which can fill men's souls with hope."

HENRY J. KAISER
Ravenswood, W. Va., 1955

the promised land

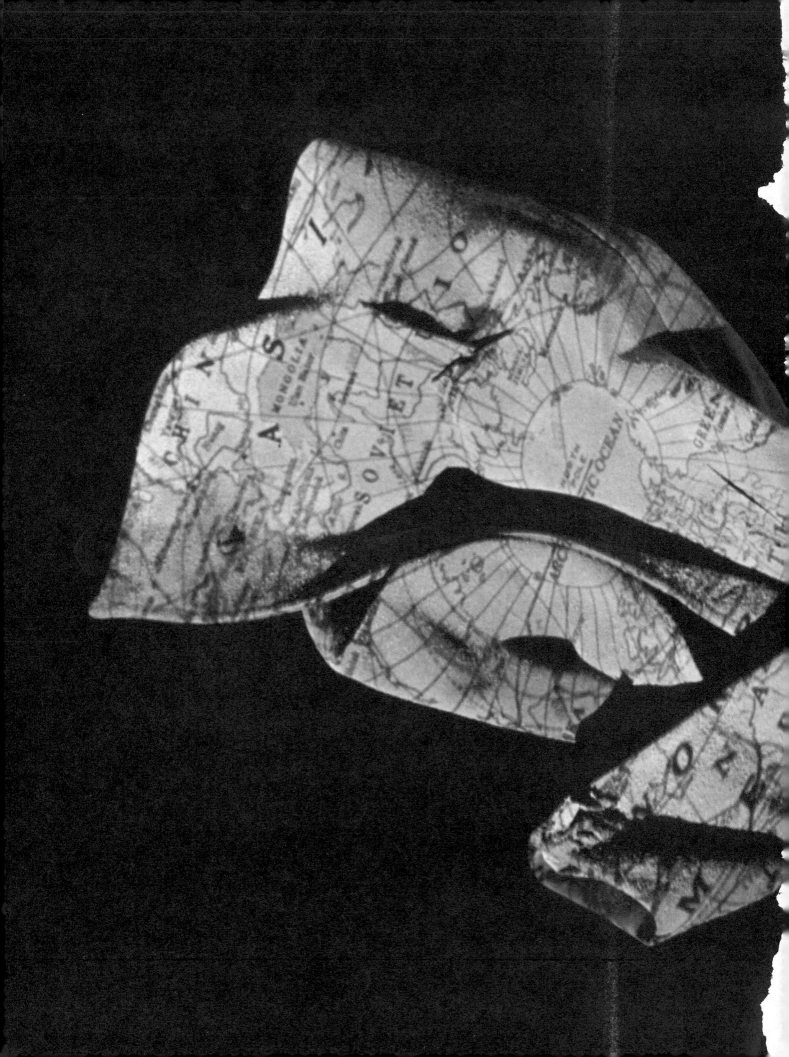

☐ "Our environment today is an eccentrically tailored cloak which enfolds all—but fits few. It binds here and chafes there, impairing the circulation and causing widespread irritation. The seams are frayed. Threadbare patches need reweaving, stains need removing. But the fabric of this universal cloak still has plenty of wear in it, which is a good thing because it is the only one we have. It won't last forever in a conscionable state, however, unless it stops being torn, trampled and cast into the corner. ☐ Our environment urgently needs restyling, mending, sprucing up. This we know because our senses and sensibilities tell us so. But how do we go about evaluating the work to be done? To achieve what ends? To preserve which values? To create which new ones? ☐ These are questions for anyone and everyone to ponder, for each man is his own expert in conceiving of the kind of world he wishes to experience." ☐

"31 MINDS EXPLORE OUR ENVIRONMENT"
National Association of Home
Builders - 1965

WHERE IS THE SWITCH THAT TURNS US ON?

HEADED WRONG WAY?

"The engineers have done a magnificent job in learning how to analyze, to build, to alter and control the physical environment. And today, with the computer, we can go even further. But I just have a sneaky notion—and I think I know a great many engineers who share it—that we are solving the wrong problems. We are building tremendous highways. We are slashing right through cities with elevated systems, subways, high speed transit systems, and maybe this is just what we should not be doing."

DR. ALBERT G. H. DIETZ
Prof. of Building Engineering, M.I.T.

THE UNCREATED

"For the last century, not merely have we been able to think of the world as a whole, in time and space, but we have been able through manifold inventions to act in the same fashion. Yet both our thinking and acting have been crude, not to say primitive, because we have not yet created the sort of self, freed from nationalistic and ideological obsessions, capable of acting within this global theater."

LEWIS MUMFORD

☐ There is a kind of globe you can buy for your home or office. With the light inside it turned off, you see the crazy-quilt pattern of the world's political areas. Turn the light on, and there appears a glowing map of the natural earth—the bottoms of oceans and seas; the tops of mountains and plains, deserts and jungles, glaciers and volcanoes; savannah and bushland and veldt. This is "the little room in God's house, where man spends all the day."

Someone searching for a symbol of the dominant theme of the next twenty years would be hard put to find one more fitting than this magic little globe, for much of our next two decades may well be spent resolving the conflict between the world revealed by scientific advances and existing political and economic systems.

Viewed this way, the globe showing the "old" world of political entities is a mosaic formed by the stains of ancient errors and their latest, uncertain compromises.

And, viewed this way, the "new" world reveals a continuum of interrelated and interacting forces; the up-thrust of mountain chains, the canyons that mark the downward slip of fault blocks, the lines ceaselessly spoken in the eternal dialogue between land and sea. And, over all, in loops and swirls of green, is a thin film of desire that takes the radiant energy of the sun, the invisible gasses of air, mixes a few trace chemicals from the earth with water, and combines them into the only truly valuable commodity on the planet—life itself.

This map shows no city limits, no county or state lines, no national borders; with today's technology, they have lost all meaning. Aircraft and satellites ignore them; electrical power and telephone lines, railroads and highways pass over them; radio and television and microwave and radar flow through them. The only thing that seems to be stopped by a border any more is human understanding.

What makes the little globe different from the one we live on is that we still haven't found the way to turn on the light that will transform the real one into a place where men and their world work in harmony, instead of against each other. Finding that way may be the hardest problem we have to face between now and 1986; meaningless lines on a political map have become the cage in which our minds are trapped.

For the man engaged in the daily business of "making a living" twenty years may seem like a long time off, and the conflict between institutions and scientific advances remote from his daily concern. But, with longer average lifespans and the acceleration of change, two decades may become a very short time indeed. And—however the argument is resolved—it will affect the way he lives and the way he makes a living.

"The modern corporation," states Lee A. Dubridge, president of the California Institute of Technology, "as contrasted with an individual, is a long-lived entity. A successful corporation will, it can be hoped, still be in existence one hundred years hence, after all its existing personnel—and indeed their children and grandchildren too—have gone . . . Therefore an increasing interest is to be found today among corporation executives in trying to peer into the future and ask how company policies today can best be adapted to potential future developments."

For the most part, it appears that "future potential developments" will be determined by the interplay between two numbers. One is a very simple one — the total surface of the earth and the natural resources it contains. It is a fixed number; it will never get any larger. The other number is the world population, which even now is exerting a powerful corrosive force against those portions of the planet that are inhabitable with present techniques and is pressing hard against our known reserve of resources. This is a number that will continue to grow, at least for the next twenty years. Every twelve seconds there is a net population gain of one person in the United States; a net gain of 300,000 persons, throughout the world, every single day.

They create not simply a problem of food (though this is the most immediately pressing) but of clothing, shelter, education, employment, medical care, entertainment, and—most of all—some meaningful goal for their lives beyond mere existence. It has been customary to think of all—or most of these people—as a growing market: for food and metals and rubber and glass and paper and services of all kinds. Under existing conditions they constitute only a potential market, not an actual one.

In the words of Lammot Du Pont Copeland, president of E. I. du Pont de Nemours & Co., "In the very abundance of swelling human numbers, the poverty of most of mankind is rooted. This truth, in the short arc of a dozen years, has etched itself deeply into the minds of scholars and physicians, priests and presidents, leaders of industry and science.

"I confess, like many others, I once took for granted the notion that a rapidly growing population almost automatically meant rising profits and better life for more people. I have learned that for the world as a whole, this is not so. And for America, it will not be so much longer."

There is little that can be done about the population growth in the next two decades, although perhaps afterward there may be. So one turns to the other number — the quantity and quality of our technology and resources — to see if an answer may be found there. Happily, it appears there can, and that neither America, nor the rest of the world, *necessarily* need starve nor downgrade its way of living. And it is to these possibilities that we now turn . . . □

TIME TO RETHINK

"We really have to go through a whole process of national thinking. There is nothing anywhere in American general education that has anything to do with the quality of the physical environment. You can hardly find a word, and this is a staggering gap in a country that thinks of itself as one of the best educated in the world . . ."

GARRETT ECKBO
Landscape Architect

CITY LIVING, COUNTRY THINKING

"I think Richard Hofstadter expressed it best when he said that the American nation was born in the country and has moved to the city. Our thinking to a very considerable degree has remained rural thinking. As cities developed in the United States, we have looked upon them as something abnormal, something undesirable. City lines, county lines, state lines no longer mean very much. We have reached the point where we have to face up to the serious problem of whether the city has outgrown its viable size."

FRANK B. FREIDEL, JR.
Historian, Harvard University

"we wend our way like worms"

A BUREAUCRATIC TRANCE

"Our resource planners operate in a
bureaucratic trance, assuming that the
population of the United States will
double by the year 2000 ... But the time
has already come for thoughtful men
and women to ask themselves some
basic questions about our land-people
equation ... It is obvious that the best
qualities in man must atrophy in
a standing room only environment.
Therefore, if the fulfillment of the
individual is our ultimate goal, we must
soon determine the proper man-land
ratio for our continent."

STEWART L. UDALL
U.S. Secretary of the Interior

WE HAVE CHOSEN OTHERWISE

"We could have a better physical
environment by the simple allocation
of resources. Whether this would be
either healthy or socially valuable is a
question. But in any case ours is a
society that has not chosen to allocate
resources in this way. As a matter of fact
we have institutionalized against it.
Almost everything we do reflects the
unimportance of the physical
circumstances and the design quality
as against the importance of technology.
"We, our society, is prepared to let 30 or
40 million people live in a state not very
far advanced from that on the banks
of the Nile, in a far different country ..."

VICTOR H. PALMIERI
Pres., Janss Corporation
Land Developers

A VERRA FEW PEOPLE

"Thomas Carlyle once said to an
American: 'Ye may boast o' yer
dimocracy, or any ither 'cracy, or any
kind of poleetical roobish; but the
reason why yer laboring folk are so
happy is that ye have a vost deal o' land
for a verra few people.' "

JOSIAH STRONG
"Our Country"—1885

☐ If the world of the next 20 years is, as we have said, largely to be determined by the interplay between numbers — numbers of people and numbers of resources — and if, as we have indicated, nothing can be done about the first, it seems reasonable to examine the second.

We will talk here about numbers as they concern the United States, because, if, with our technology, our untapped resources, our still enormous unused land areas, the vitality of our people, and the investment capital we have, the land-population problem cannot be solved, then it seems there is nowhere else that it can be.

The number we will consider is 1,904,000,000 — the extent of land acreage of the continental United States. It is interesting that once we have that figure, there is not much we can do with it. We understand it quantitatively well enough (as we do most things) but not qualitatively well enough (nor do we most things). We know how much there is, but we do not know too much more about it.

It is a strange and perhaps lamentable fact that as late as 1963, of the land area of the United States, only 65 per cent had been topographically mapped (i.e. as to land features) and only 20 per cent had been mapped geologically (i.e., as to the kind of land it is).

Since the turn of the century, the land of the United States has been used much the same way, as our maps (opposite) show. Nobody planned it that way; there has always been such an abundance of land of one sort or another that planning seemed unnecessary. Today it may be reasonable, if not widely acceptable, that we consider planning land resources for the maximum benefit that we know how.

The place to start would seem to be with some sort of mapping that inventories what we have. Paul D. Spreirigen, in the *Saturday Review,* suggests, "The entire United States should be studied to determine its significant and integral physical sections. These should be delineated according to their characteristic topography, climate and culture. We propose the formation of groups of persons, representing all walks of life and all professions, to study and lay forth a future vision of what these could become at their best."

Considering that this nation has supported such bits of inventory as the International Geophysical Year and the Year of the Quiet Sun, and is spending billions to find out more about the moon, it is interesting that we have not bothered to find out much about what is right here.

The amount of land given to urban use in the United States — and throughout most of the world—is a tiny fraction of the whole. As William Wheaton, director of the University of California Institute for Urban and Regional Development said (early in 1966): "Only about 30,000 square miles of the 3-million-square-mile area of the nation are now devoted

LAND USE IN THE U.S. ■ *Proportionate use of this country's 1,904,000,000 acres continues to change very little during this century, as indicated below. It is interesting to note that grazing, which is a highly inefficient use of land, is by far its largest allocation in the U.S.*

[1900]

Use	Million Acres
■ Urban (cities of 2,500 or more) & Transportation	23
■ Public Recreation	5
Agriculture	449
Commercial Forests	525
Grazing	808
■ Reservoirs	negligible
■ Wildlife	negligible
■ Mining, Wasteland, Miscellaneous	94

[1950]

Use	Million Acres
■ Urban (cities of 2,500 or more) & Transportation	42
■ Public Recreation	46
Agriculture	523
Commercial Forests	484
Grazing	700
■ Reservoirs	10
■ Wildlife	14
■ Mining, Wasteland, Miscellaneous	85

[1980]

Use (estimated)	Million Acres
■ Urban (cities of 2,500 or more) & Transportation	60
■ Public Recreation	76
Agriculture	443
Commercial Forests	484
Grazing	700
■ Reservoirs	15
■ Wildlife	18
■ Mining, Wasteland, Miscellaneous	63

FIGURES OBTAINED FROM "RESOURCES IN AMERICA'S FUTURE" BY HANS H. LANDSBERG, LEONARD L. FISCHMAN AND JOSEPH L. FISHER. PHOTOS COURTESY U.S. FOREST SERVICE AND AGRICULTURAL EXTENSION, UNIVERSITY OF CALIFORNIA.

ONE MAN'S MEAT . . .

"It is, perhaps, necessary only to remember that the American Indians possessed, but benefited little from, the fertile soil which formed an unprecedented source of wealth for the Colonists . . . that the Colonists gained little more than the grinding of their grain from the water power which made magnates of the early industrialists . . . that the early industrialists set little store by the deposits of petroleum and ore which served as a basis for the fortunes of the post-Civil War periods . . . that the industrial captains of the late 19th Century had no conception of the values that lay latent in water power for generating electricity, which would be developed by the enterprisers of the 20th Century . . . and that these early 20th Century enterprisers were as little able to capitalize the values of uranium as the Indians had been five centuries earlier. The social value of natural resources depends entirely upon the aptitude of society for using them."

DAVID M. POTTER
"People of Plenty"

YOU CAN'T RUN OUT

"It is impossible to run out of anything in economic terms. All that happens is that the price goes up, which encourages greater efforts to produce the goods in question and the use of substitutes."

CHARLES P. KINDLEBERGER
Prof. of Economics, M.I.T.
Technology Review, Nov. 1965

to urban use. This is only about one percent of the land area . . . A population of 300 million could readily be accommodated in our present urban area with no more discomfort than is suffered by millions of citizens of Boston or New Haven or Cleveland or Chicago."

But there is at least one problem that may be of concern in the allocation of acreage to urban use. It is that this extension often is at the expense of high-yield agricultural land. Once urbanized (making a parking lot, freeway, housing tract or supermarket out of it), it not only loses its high yield productivity, but it cannot be restored to agricultural use again except at inordinate expense.

One of the reasons our unplanned use of land has been so destructive both in this country (witness the Dust Bowl eras of 1830 and 1930) and elsewhere (the impoverished lands of Greece and Spain, the man-made deserts of Australia and New Zealand, the treeless plains of China and the man-made deserts of North Africa and the Mediterranean basin), is that man's horizon has been so limited, both by terrain and the curvature of the earth, that he could not see himself as a major force at work upon his environment. What he did was expedient and local, but its cumulative effect has been, all too often, disastrous.

"Man and nature," says Dr. E. A. Gutkind in *Our World from the Air*, "are the twin agents of the perennial revolution which shapes and re-shapes the face of the earth and the character of man's activities. This struggle, at times sporadic and violent, at others gentle and consistent, but forever demanding a new response to a new challenge, activates the potential energies of man and nature, molding them in a grand pattern of advance or retreat, of creative interaction or disastrous antagonism, of promise or of failure.

"The conquest of the air enables mankind for the first time in its history to experience this interaction in all its innumerable ramifications. A new scale of time and space has been added to our mental and material equipment. Before this conquest, we were wending our way like worms through narrow passages and seeing only more or less unrelated details. Today, we can look at the world with a God's eye-view, take in at a glance the infinite variety of environmental patterns spread over the earth and appreciate their dynamic relationships . . ."

Until man's instruments began to fly, mapping was a slow, laborious and expensive operation. It was performed piecemeal and it produced a haphazard mosaic with many pieces missing. Today, not only do man's eyes have wings but his vision has penetrated beyond the visual spectrum into a suprasensual world that is almost wholly new to him. Infrared, x-ray, radar, and microwave; radiotelescopes, sonar, underwater television and photography; Geiger counters and scintillometers have opened the doors to a universe as strange to man as a newly discovered planet.

Nor are we anywhere near the end of new extensions of our nervous systems to explore our environment; quite recently the low-powered, continuous wave gas laser altimeter was introduced as a precision tool for high speed mapping. As AeroService Corporation, Philadelphia, reports in its magazine, *Search,* "It has a very narrow beam and an accuracy of better than one foot . . . AeroService tested the laser altimeter at altitudes ranging from 1,000 to 13,000 feet . . . (It) is able to pick out trees, highway surfaces, curbstones at roadsides, and ditches beside a runway . . . The morphology of the ground slopes — boulder sizes, grass height, and so on — will be clearly visible on laser traces."

Of all our planet's resources, the most precious is human awareness; each new device, instrument or technique that increases our receptivity to the stimuli of our natural environment also creates new avenues for the solution of ancient problems whose solution under the pressure of growing population cannot be much longer delayed. What we mine is the mind of man; what we extract are new dimensions of human experience.

For some time now we have had the techniques for inventorying the world's resources, but have not had the industrial nor the political will to implement them. Today, it appears that projects such as the World Resources Inventory, sponsored by Southern Illinois University, and various international cooperation projects sponsored by the United Nations and some international scientific organizations, may make it possible in the next two decades to make better sense of our world than we previously have done.

Even before the time comes when we are able to tuck the first worldwide inventory into our incandescent 20th Century jeans, we already have a sort of an idea about what kind of resources the world has in minerals, metals, chemicals and power generation to meet the challenge of the next twenty years. From such figures as are available, it appears there will be a sufficiency of everything we are likely to need at least through the year 2000. Most analyses of the availability of natural resources ultimately come down to the question, "can we create enough energy to develop them?"

Milton F. Searl, in a report to the U.S. Atomic Energy Commission, sums up the world picture of energy requirements this way: "By the year 2000 a world population twice that of 1960 will consume about five times more energy. At that date the countries of North America, Western Europe and Oceania will account for only about 45 per cent of the world total, compared to 60 per cent in 1960. Over the same period the share

TWO CENTURIES OF COAL

"*. . . coal reserves could supply the entire 450 billion tons that the world is expected to consume between 1960 and 2000 and enough coal would remain in the ground to satisfy the world's total demand for energy for almost another century at the estimated annual level of consumption in the year 2000.*"

Based on estimates by
PAUL AVERITT of the
U.S. Geological Survey—1963

OIL UNTIL 2000 A.D.

"*Present proved reserves of oil are nearly 320 billion barrels, equivalent to 56 billion tons of hard coal, or more than 40 times the worldwide consumption of oil in 1960. The totals for the world's potential of oil and gas, expressed as equivalents of hard coal, are somewhere between 535 billion metric tons (the lowest estimate) and 1,620 billion metric tons (highest estimate) . . .*"

Scientific American
September, 1963

NUCLEAR ENERGY "FOREVER"

"*In the U.S. alone, the potential (known and unknown) uranium sources, comparable in quality to ore now being mined, are estimated by the U.S. Geological Survey to range from 2,100 billion to 6,900 billion tons of coal equivalents. The largest figure is substantially greater than the combined total of the world's known resources of recoverable and potential sources of oil and natural gas. . .*"

Scientific American
September, 1963

OUR PLUNDERED PLANET

". . . We human beings are rushing forward unthinkingly through days of incredible accomplishments, of glory and of tragedy, our eyes seeking the stars—or fixed too often upon each other in hatred and conflict. We have forgotten the earth, forgotten it in the sense that we fail to regard it as the source of our life."

FAIRFIELD OSBORN "Our Plundered Planet"

"We travel together, passengers on a little space ship, dependent on its vulnerable supplies of air and soil . . . preserved from annihilation only by the care, the work, and I will say the love, we give our fragile craft."

From the last speech of ADLAI STEVENSON

of the USSR and Eastern Europe will decline slightly from about 21 per cent to 19. Meanwhile, energy consumption in the rest of the world will have climbed from 20 per cent of the world total in 1960 to about 35 per cent in the year 2000."

It is a characteristic of fuel sources, of course, that they are used up in the process of releasing energy. Thus the world's total useable fuel sources is one of the absolute measures we can apply to our future progress. It is entirely conceivable, and perhaps even highly probable, that before the end of the next two decades new forms of energy release will have been developed and that the efficiency of those we now have can be substantially increased.

Non-fuel minerals — metals and chemicals — cannot, of course, be used up in the sense that fuel sources are; they can only be changed in form. The earth has as much iron, aluminum, copper, zinc, etc. as it ever had, and it will continue to have it in the future. The fact that they may be in forms we cannot economically use with current technology does not mean that they could not, if we desired, be returned to a useful state. We frequently tend to think of processes in terms of linearity — from raw material to finished product to ultimate consumer to oblivion — instead of thinking of the human use of durable materials as only part of a cycle. It would be quite possible to create an economy in which durable materials are recycled over and over again, and to some extent (as with gold and platinum) this is already done. To the extent that it is not, the big city dumps of our present times may well be the "Mother Lodes" of our future years.

Even without changing our wasteful ways, there appears no reason to believe we will run out of vital natural resources in the next twenty years. Julian W. Feiss, of the U.S. Geological Survey, points out: "In spite of the accelerating drain on the world's mineral resources, it is now recognized that they will never really be exhausted. Just as advances in technology have made it possible to exploit today ores so lean they would have been considered worthless only fifty years ago, new advances will make it possible to extract metals from still leaner ores in the future. In effect, technology keeps creating new resources. Meanwhile, new geophysical and geochemical tools have uncovered a remarkable number of unexpectedly rich mineral deposits, which the world, *if it is wise,* can use as capital assets to advance the well-being of all."

The italics and the emphasis are ours. In our use of land areas and natural resources, the barriers no longer are technological; they are in our minds. That we have not always used them wisely in the past does not necessarily mean that we cannot do so in the future. ☐

THE DREAM THAT WASN'T

"We are waking now from the American Dream to realize that it was a dream few Americans lived in their waking hours. The history of the New World has turned out to be not so different from that of the Old. The peril that threatens the last of the American wilderness arises not from the reckless dream, but from the same historic forces of rapacity and cruelty that laid waste the land in the Mediterranean Basin, in Arabia, India and the treeless uplands of China.

GERARD PIEL

SPHERE BY ARNALDO POMODORO ON PERMANENT EXHIBIT AT THE MUSEUM OF MODERN ART, NEW YORK CITY. PHOTO BY RICHARD SAUNDERS.

TRICKS ON A WATER CYCLE

WATER, WATER EVERYWHERE

"The amount of drinking water needed each year by human beings and domestic animals is of the order of ten tons per ton of living tissue. Industrial water requirements for washing, cooling, and the circulation of materials range from one to two tons per ton of manufactured brick to 250 tons per ton of paper and 600 tons per ton of nitrate fertilizer. Even the largest of these is small compared with the amounts of water needed in agriculture. To grow a ton of sugar or corn under irrigation, about 1,000 tons of the water must be 'consumed,' that is changed by soil evaporation and plant transpiration from liquid to vapor. Wheat, rice, and cotton fiber respectively require about 1,500, 4,000 and 10,000 tons of water per ton of crop."

ROGER REVELLE
Scientific American—Sept. 1963

DROP IN THE BUCKET

There is very little fresh water available to man, and much of that is, from his standpoint, in the "wrong" place. Something like 97.2 per cent of the earth's water is in the oceans, 2.15 percent is locked up in ice caps and glaciers, and the remaining 0.65 per cent makes up the earth's lakes, rivers, streams, underground water bodies and atmospheric moisture. Of the 380 billion acre-feet of snow and rain that fall on the earth each year, only about 11 billion acre-feet, or less than 3 per cent, are used to grow all the world's food and fiber products.

BRING YOUR OWN BOTTLE

"I once wrote a story of a society in which fresh water was so scarce that men brought their own pocket flasks of water when they went visiting. They had them filled at municipally run pumps, which charged by the pint. I don't think we'll be anywhere near that point in 25 years, but we're heading in that direction."

ISAAC ASIMOV
"The World of 1990"
The Diners Club Magazine, Jan. 1965

☐ "If there is magic on this planet," wrote naturalist Loren Eiseley, "it is contained in water." We seem, of late, somehow to have lost control of that magic: we know how to perform it well enough, but we have not persuaded enough people to pay to see the performance.

Thus, we have a "water problem" that is very much like the "air problem," in that we have created it ourselves; not because we don't know better, but because we have lacked the economic and political will to apply what we know. It is this kind of mental barrier that gives credence to the statement, "The epitaph of our times may be, 'They found it too expensive to survive.'"

When we peer into the future, we tell ourselves that there will be many more people than there are now; that most of them will be clustered in urban areas; that, hopefully, most of them will be living better than they do now; and that, if they do live better, it will be because they have more food and clothing and shelter than they do today.

If there is a common denominator to this rising tide of human expectations, it is water. If there will, indeed, be more food, more fibers, more materials of all kinds, it will come from the use of water. Again, one can see the next twenty years as the confrontation between numbers; a fixed one — the supply of fresh water available; and a growing one—the rapidly increasing needs of human beings for more and more fresh water. The zeros of both those numbers are as obdurate as the rounded pebbles of some ancient stream bed.

Standing now, the indefinable shape of our future pulsating in our hands, where do we start? We might try by asking if maybe there is more fresh water somewhere. Perhaps we look below our feet, "Is there water underground?" The people who poke about such things reckon that there may be one million cubic miles of water in underground "aquifers" inside the continental limits of the United States, in the first half mile of the earth's crust. We need to know more about it than we do now, and particularly how we can replenish it as we use it.

"During the past few years," commented *Scientific American* in 1963, "evidence has been obtained that large areas in the Sahara may be underlain by an enormous lake of fresh water. In some places, the water-bearing sands are 3,000 feet thick, and they appear to extend for at least 500 miles south of the Atlas Mountains and perhaps eastward into Tunisia and Libya. If this evidence is correct, the amount of useful water may be very large indeed — of the order of 100 billion acre-feet, sufficient to irrigate millions of acres for centuries."

It is believed that comparable bodies of water may underlie the land formations of most continents.

It may be that the search for major underground bodies of fresh water, and the means to develop them, could be as productive as the research now going forward toward making fresh water out of salt water. This is a useful approach, under special conditions, and undoubtedly there will be much more of it in the next two decades. But, as an approach, desalination of sea water runs up against the economic barrier of diminishing returns.

"No matter how much," comments *Scientific American,* "engineers increase the efficiency of desalting, there is one substantial cost element they can do little about. Water from seaside desalting plants will have to be pumped uphill to where it is used; water from rivers and lakes runs downhill and gravity is free. As a matter of fact, if the Mediterranean Sea were miraculously to turn fresh, the cost of transporting its water deep into the Sahara would still be prohibitive."

Perhaps a more promising solution would appear to be to make better use of the fresh water supplies that we have.

Everett P. Partridge, hydrologist, writing in *Consulting Engineer,* sums up much of today's thinking about tomorrow's water problems by saying, "the relatively prosaic program of simply delaying the runoff from the land to the oceans continues as our most immediate and currently most economical means of taking care of the water needs of industry . . . Even when we hoard water everywhere that a dam seems practical, we must transport it, use it and re-use it perhaps many times before we allow it slowly to return to the ocean . . ."

Already in most industrialized countries, water is being used over and over again. "In two score miles of almost any American river today, the same gallon of water may cool a blast furnace or a power plant condenser, bathe a baby, refresh the air of an office building, wash some dishes, spin the blades of a turbine and carry away domestic wastes," comments the Calgon Corporation in *The Challenging Problems of Water.*

"As that gallon of water courses those 40 miles downstream," the booklet continues, "the people and industry along its shore contaminate it with all manner of wastes . . . It must be recleaned to some extent for every use. The dirtier the water, the more it costs to clean it. The quantity of water has remained constant, but its quality has gone down and its cost has gone up."

The crux of the problem, of course, is to create the sort of economic and political environment in which each user will find it to his advantage — as well as being his personal responsibility — to make sure that the water he returns to the river or lake is as free of pollution as when it was taken out. Individuals would do this by supporting programs that provide for municipal water treatment and industrial concerns would

ACCOUNT OVERDRAWN

*" Some federal officials are talking of
the day when river basins will be linked
with each other so that water can be
piped from one part of the country to
another as needed . . . We face a water
crisis that threatens to limit economic
growth, undermine living standards,
endanger health and jeopardize national
security. We live on the edge of
water bankruptcy."*

U.S. News & World Report
August 2, 1965

NO SHORTAGE

*"We have not run out of water;
we have simply run out of new streams
to pollute."*

E. ROY TINNEY
Director, State of Washington
Water Research Center

do it by building into their pricing policies the cost of returning unpolluted water from their plants to the source from which they took it. The problem is that there are, as yet, no uniform regulations, equably applied throughout the continental United States, because pollution laws are, for the most part, locally formed and locally applied.

Since the waterways must flow through some 48 states, 3,000 counties, and the areas of some 117,000 governmental units, the problem of water pollution, like that of air pollution, is predominantly political.

It does not appear to be an economic problem. *Consulting Engineer* has figured the cost of meeting present water service deficiencies, including adequate municipal sewage treatment, as about $3.7 billion per year, with about $2 billion per year invested by industry to remedy its pollution problems. For an assumed average population of 210 million persons, this works out to about $27 per person per year. *Fortune* magazine figures the cost of reducing current levels of air pollution by two thirds would cost about $3 billion a year, or $1.30 per person per month.

Meanwhile, there are other solutions to the water problem, primarily technological ones. The vast losses of water in irrigation can be cut down by lining head ditches with plastic sheets, by spraying growing plants with a thin film that allows the plants to breathe but cuts evaporation losses; by coating the surfaces of ponds and reservoirs to retard evaporation and by diverting irrigation water use from marginal lands to more intensively productive ones.

Still another technological solution to the water problem of the next two decades is to shift the water from where it is plentiful to the areas where it is not. One program which, if implemented, will be among the largest projects between 1966 and 1986, would take water from the Yukon and Tanana Rivers in Alaska, pump it to the Peace River reservoir in Canada, divert part of that to the Alberta-Great Lakes canal to help supply the dwindling Great Lakes, and divert the remainder to a vast 500-mile-long Rocky Mountain Trench, which would receive 74 million acre-feet per year.

Out of the Trench, water would be provided for irrigating Idaho, Oregon, Utah, Nevada, California, Arizona, New Mexico, Colorado, Texas, Nebraska, Oklahoma and, finally, the arid northern states of Mexico. The plan would cost about $80 billion and take some 30 years to complete, which works out to about $2½ billion each year, or less than half of what this nation spends on liquor annually.

Meanwhile, one envisages giant underground bodies of water lying under the continental granite like great whales sleeping beneath the arctic ice . . . ☐

PHOTOGRAPHY BY BOB CONOVER

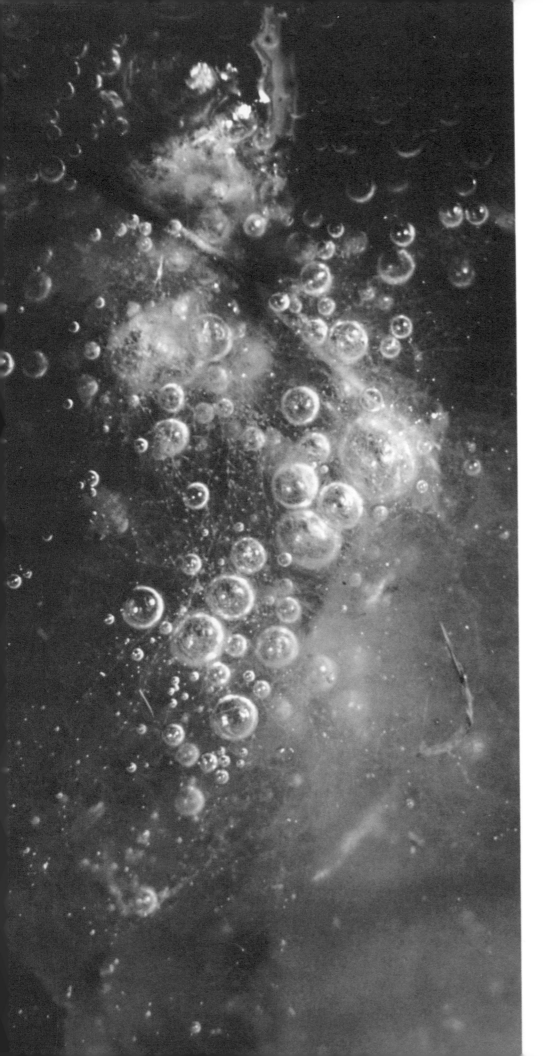

THE LONG VOYAGE HOME

*Perhaps the ocean is itself
a living creature—an organism
so vast that we cannot
comprehend that it is alive.
Trapped by its own enormous
weight in the deeper indentations
of the planet; it reaches out
great tentacles of rivers to scour
the hearts of continents
for the nutrients that give it life.
It may be that the turbulence
where surf meets shore is but the
rippling of the sensitive skin
of the sea-animal, responding,
sometimes angrily, to
the stab of headlands and the
abrasion of wind-driven air.
The waves are but the pulsation
of some unseen giant heart.
And all the skin and hair and
scales and shells that
creep about, carrying their
bags of sea water inside them,
are the ocean creature's way
of protecting its emissaries from
the radiation from some
merciless, far off sun beating
down upon the skeleton of
a dead world. Man, that
"walking bag of sea water,"
is but another way the ocean
has of going ashore.
Now the prodigal returns—
as have the porpoise and
the whale before him—and
the most exciting adventure of
our next twenty years may
be this dramatic homecoming,
after a journey of eight
million years.*

LAND OF THE FREE

*"Yes; I love it! The sea is
everything. It covers seven-tenths
of the terrestrial globe.
Its breath is pure and healthy.
It is an immense desert, where
man is never lonely, for he
feels life stirring on all sides . . .
The globe began with the
sea, so to speak; and who knows
if it will not end with it? . . .
Ah! sir, live—live in the bosom
of the waters! There only is
independence! There I recognize
no masters. There I am free."*

CAPTAIN NEMO—in Jules
Verne's "Twenty Thousand
Leagues Under the Sea"

lure of a lost world

RIGHT NEXT DOOR

*"For tens of thousands of years—
ever since man has possessed the power
to sense and reason—he has been
aware of the seas around him . . . But
never until recently did man seek
great understanding of the oceans,
because he saw little necessity.
There was always a new frontier, an
unexplored land, unexploited territory
. . . Now our view of the seas has
had to undergo a drastic change. We
have always considered them as
barriers to invasion; we must now see
them not only as links between people,
but as a vast new untapped resource."*

PRESIDENT LYNDON B. JOHNSON
USIA ByLiner—November, 1965

REAR VIEW

*"With minerals resting on it, nutrients
sinking into it, geologic history locked
in its sedimentary layers, and petroleum
beneath it, the sea's bottom is at least
as interesting and certainly more useful
to mankind than the moon's backside."*

DEAN ATHELSTAN SPILHAUS
Institute of Technology
Minnesota University

☐ Since first he listened to the legends of the lost Atlantis and mused about Mu, man has never failed to feel that somewhere along the way he has lost a world. Perhaps it was Eden, or only the nostalgic radiance of a Golden Age, but lost it seems to be. It is also possible, of course, that what we lost was not the world, but innocence, and that what we lament is some springtime of our youth when we had April in our eyes.

In any event, today, moon mad and starstruck, we have lingered too long upon the beach, gazing longingly at the sky, when all the time the "lost continent" lay just out there beyond the first line of breakers. When we peered into tidal pools, we saw not the outposts of another world, but only crazy reflections of ourselves.

Joseph B. MacInnis, writing on "Living Under the Sea," in *Scientific American*, March, 1966, says, "It is one thing to glimpse a new world and quite another to establish permanent outposts in it, to explore it and to work and live in it . . .

"The submerged domain potentially available to man for firsthand investigation and eventual exploitation can be regarded as a new continent with an area of about 11,500,000 square miles — the size of Africa. It comprises the gently sloping shoulders of the continents, the continental shelves that rim the ocean basins. The shelves range up to several hundred miles in width and are generally covered by 600 feet of water or less.

"That they are submerged at all is an accident of this epoch's sea level; the ocean basins are filled to overflowing and the sea has spilled over, making ocean floor of what is really a seaward extension of the coastal topography. Geologically, the shelf belongs more to the continents than to the oceans. Its basement rock is continental granite rather than oceanic basalt and is covered largely with continental sediments rather than abyssal ooze."

And so we stumble upon it — nearly half a thousand years after Columbus — the lost world of our fantasy, and a rich continent whose future exploitation may well be the most exciting adventure of the next two decades. Through the alchemy of time, Columbus has been transformed into Cousteau (whose daring explorations in the 1950's showed that we would not really fall off the edge of the habitable world if we just kept diving on and on.)

What is most remarkable about this new continent is that it is contiguous with the already occupied seacoasts of the world. Much of it lies close to already-developed sources of power and distribution; close to the markets its products can serve. And, if it does not abound in ivory, apes and peacocks, it promises a close and exploitable supply of oil and gas, metals and minerals, medicine and food.

Professor A. M. Gaudin, metallurgist at MIT, comments, "Just as open pit mining has revolutionized the mining industry in my lifetime, so undersea mining may do it for our children."

Since the continental shelves are but extensions of the mainland, one would expect to find there much the same sort of thing man has found on land. And, indeed, this appears to be so; even with limited approaches, even with our currently primitive tools.

We might be said to stand today in the "Tin Lizzie" age of undersea technology; the Kitty Hawk of hydrospace. "Our oceanographic activities at this point in time may be likened to our interest in atomic power back in 1948," comments D. C. Burnham, president of Westinghouse Electric Corporation. "Our atomic power organization started with one manager, one scientist and one secretary. Today (1965) we employ some 6,500 persons in our various atomic departments."

Even with primitive techniques, we are beginning to mine the sea. "At least $8 million a year in diamonds is being dredged from the sea floor off the mouth of the Orange River in South Africa," points out *Engineering and Mining Journal*, May, 1965. "The Japanese are extracting 600 tons of iron-ore sand monthly from Tokyo Bay and mining ten million tons of coal each year from undersea mines ranging from 600 to 3,000 feet. Tin ore is being recovered from the ocean shelves and river beds of Malaya, Indonesia and Thailand, to the tune of $150 million per year. Gold has been found in production quantity in Norton Sound, Alaska. Over $15 million worth of sulfur is produced annually from wells in the Gulf of Mexico."

Compared to the world's total land output, this is, of course, minis-cule. But two important forces bear upon the rapid exploitation of the sea in the next twenty years.

One of these is the exponential rate at which both the United States government and industry are beginning to invest in oceanographic research. *Missiles and Rockets* magazine, June 21, 1965, reported:

"Rep. Craig Hosmer (R.-Calif.) ranking House minority member on the Joint Committee on Atomic Energy, estimates that no less than 43 Congressional committees and subcommittees authorize or appropriate funds to be spent on oceanographic programs. He noted the accelerated industry interest in oceanography, now that the field is experiencing an annual growth rate in federal expenditure of 10 to 11 per cent. He estimated that by 1972, the government's oceanographic expenditures will reach $350 million annually, and total expenditures over the years 1962-1972 will have been about $2.2 billion."

That *Missiles and Rockets* should show an interest in hydrospace helps to make our second point about the forces converging to accele-

THE "WET NASA"

"Among the areas in which space know-how uniquely fits the aerospace field to tackle the problems of oceanography are (1) reliability and efficiency requirements, (2) systems management experience, (3) structures and materials, (4) operation in a hostile environment outside the atmosphere, (5) instrumentation and sensors, (6) computer, guidance and power systems and (7) vehicle design and construction."

REP. JOSEPH KARTH (D-Minn.)
Missiles and Rockets
January 24, 1966

OIL ON THE SHELF

"It has been estimated that the rocks of the continental shelf surrounding the U.S. may eventually yield, with modern production and conservation methods, as much as 20 billion barrels of petroleum and 150 billion cubic feet of natural gas."

Petroleum Today
Winter, 1965

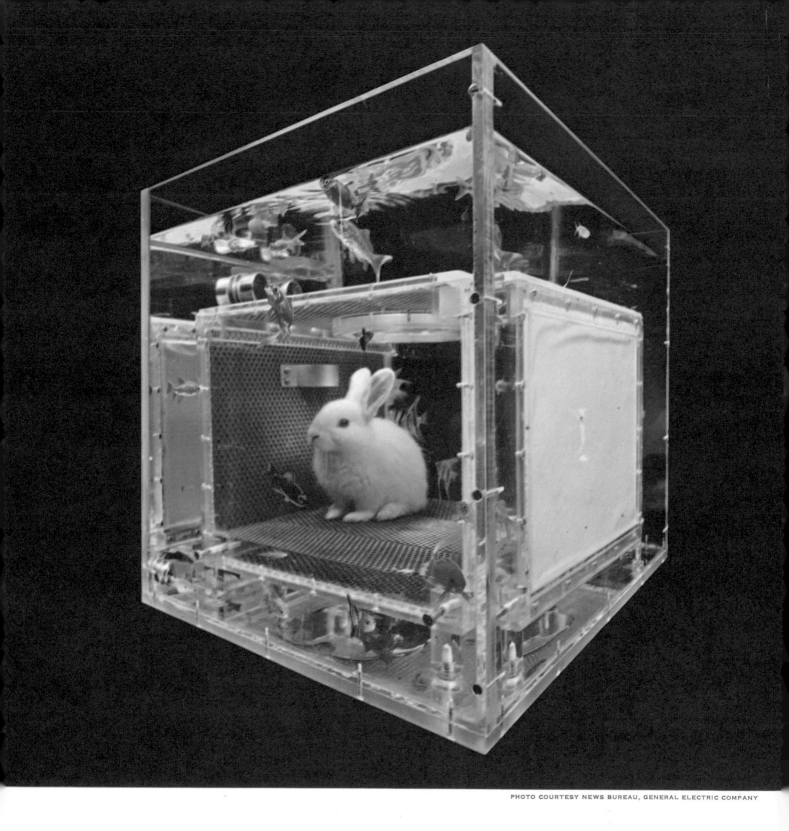

PHOTO COURTESY NEWS BUREAU, GENERAL ELECTRIC COMPANY

Man may soon be able to breathe as naturally underwater as fish, using the same type of artificial "gill" that forms four sides of this rabbit's submerged pen. The "gill" is an ultra-thin membrane of silicone rubber which admits air from the surrounding water and allows the carbon dioxide from breathing to escape. Since water is essentially saturated with air to a depth of many hundreds of feet, man could greatly extend his present ability for doing useful work underwater, freed from today's encumbering oxygen breathing apparatus. It is foreseeable that submarines, underwater experimental stations, construction operations on continental shelves, and even subaqueous cities, could sustain life without air pumping equipment, drawing enough air from the water that surrounds them through permeable membrane skins. Perhaps tomorrow's aquanauts will wear "hydrospace suits," using this synthetic material, to explore, work and perform research.

rate the growth of hydrospace technology—that the exploration of the oceans is very closely related, technologically, to the already established technology of aerospace.

Daniel J. Haughton, president of the Lockheed Aircraft Corporation, says, "Aerospace research has much in common with ocean research. Materials, propulsion, auxiliary power units, guidance, and communications systems are as vital to marine vehicles as they are to aerospace vehicles, and pose many of the same problems . . . It is logical, then, that the aerospace industry should turn its research attention to the fields of the oceans."

In essence, there is very little difference between designing vehicles and structures for use under the sea and in doing the same for aircraft, space rockets and satellites. Similar considerations of light weight, strength and resistance to environmental attack apply. Thus it would appear that the light metals, such as aluminum and titanium, whose characteristics help make possible man's conquest of air and space, may also prove fundamental to the construction of the exploratory vehicles, permanent undersea structures, and surface support vessels of the coming conquest of hydrospace. From the point of view of those who produce or manufacture the light metals, there is the important difference that where aerospace technology is limited to the larger technologically advanced countries, the exploration and development of the continental shelves is open to any country bordering the ocean or sea, and requires relatively small investment because much of the basic development has already been done in aerospace research.

Hull strength requirements for hydrospace exploitation are relatively modest. "A submergence capacity of 1,500 feet would allow coverage of the continental shelf and about 11 per cent of the ocean bottom; 8,000 feet would cover the significant area of the Atlantic Ridge and about 19 per cent of the ocean; 20,000 feet would cover the deep ocean plains and about 98 per cent of the ocean . . ." writes Walter W. Kinsinger, Bureau of Ships, in *Naval Engineers Journal*, August, 1965.

Of materials for use at these depths, Martin A. Krenske, head of the design analysis branch, submarine structures division, David Taylor Model Basin, says, "Very briefly, high strength steel hulls have a depth potential of about 6,000 to 10,000 feet. Use of HY-60 aluminum and NY 110/120 titanium would permit operation to about 15,000 feet. . . ."

When it is added that man has already proven his capability to work and live efficiently, without pressure suits, at depths of 370 feet and that pressure laboratory research shows he may be able to do as well at 650 feet, it would appear that man has not only found his "lost world," but that he already has the capability to claim it as his own. □

A MASSIVE EFFORT

"*The Navy cannot do the job alone. As oceanographic programs expand and develop at the national level, it becomes increasingly evident that the exploitation of the world's oceans requires a massive effort with industry and government working together with common goals.*"

Rear Admiral DENYS W. KNOLL, USN
Oceanographer of the Navy

A WAY OF DRIVING OFF THE SPLEEN

"*I thought I would sail about a little and see the watery part of the world. It is a way I have of driving off the spleen, and regulating the circulation. Whenever I find myself growing grim about the mouth; whenever it is a damp, drizzly November in my soul; whenever I find myself involuntarily pausing before coffin warehouses . . . then I account it high time to get to sea as soon as I can.*"

HERMAN MELVILLE
"Moby Dick"

# of time, space and megastructures

COME NO CLOSER

"Personal space in man seems to be comparable to Hediger's flight distance in animals. A lizard can be approached to within six feet before he flees, an antelope within 60 feet, and an alligator takes off at 150 feet. Man himself carries with him a number of hidden zones that elicit different responses as boundaries are crossed. The behavior appropriate for each zone, the tone of voice used . . . and the distance to each boundary are all a matter of culture, learned early in life."

EDWARD T. HALL
"The Language of Space"

SCENTS OF TIME

"Until the coming of the missionaries in the 17th Century, and the introduction of mechanical clocks, the Chinese and Japanese had for thousands of years measured time by graduations of incense. Not only the hours and days, but the seasons and zodiacal signs were simultaneously indicated by a succession of carefully ordered scents."

MARSHALL MCLUHAN
"Understanding Media"

☐ "If present trends continue," then it is believed that by the year 1986 most of the world's people may well be huddled up together in urban areas. In a subsequent part of this seemingly endless monologue, we are going to suggest that it ain't necessarily so, but for now, we will assume that any rational discussion of the next twenty years will include some appraisal of the texture and quality of urban life, if only because that is where the action is.

We have, as part of our European heritage, a deeply ingrained belief that space is something outside us that can be cut up into little cubes and that time is a one-way street, which we can mark with convenient intersections. Our cubes are the places people live in and our cities are clusters of little cubes, piled up like the blocks of some retarded child. We divide the time of our life into intersections we call hours, and we have established neighborhoods of early morning, noon and afternoon within the city limits of our days, and we recognize (although it has not for many years been necessary) a distinction between night and day — sort of county lines we have set up in time.

That a house or structure is but an extension of our bodies — a new skin stretched out to intercept the wind and rain and cold — simply does not seem to be a part of our thinking. Nor, despite all our physics, are we able yet to think of a space-time continuum in which we are dealing with a continuity of experience that is not, as we experience it, broken up into cubes and minutes, but is a flow. As a result, we often approach the planning and building of human habitation with much the same spirit that a mad scientist might study a stream by pulling a bucket of water from it and then studying what is in the bucket. The belief that by breaking a big problem into little problems, we somehow can solve it more easily, is one of the more pervasive delusions of our time.

It has been said, often enough to become a cliche, that between now and the end of the century, "we must build as many structures as have been built since Colonial times." As an extension of Colonial thought, this is possibly true; by some residual alchemy of third grade arithmetic, we are trapped in the illusion that 2 plus 2 always equals four, and that, if there are twice as many people, then they will require twice as many structures to house them and to provide for their activities. It is as if we believed we understood a stream twice as well by taking two buckets of water out of it instead of taking only one.

But there are other ways that we *can* look at things, and if we really believe that the natural resources of earth and the skills of man will be hard pressed just to provide a doubling of the shelter we have today, we might actually try to look at our problems in a different way.

When it comes to our use of time, we are like poor dirt farmers who have moved to the big city; we bring our farm hours with us. Thus we divide night and day, although, as Marshall McLuhan (among others) has pointed out, "Electric light abolished the divisions of night and day, of inner and outer, and of the subterranean and the terrestrial. It altered every consideration of space for work and production as much as the other electric media altered the space-time experience of society."

Having brought day with us from the country (because, without lights, it was the only time we could work), we divided the daylight hours with three meal periods, because the work on the land was hard and it was good to rest the horses and refuel ourselves in the middle of the long days. It has not, in our urban areas, for some time been necessary to rest the horses, and it is doubtful that in the normal course of our labors, we expend enough energy to require refueling ourselves three times a day. But we continue to do so.

We also divide our time into weeks—state lines whose borders exist, like political state lines, solely in our minds. And so there are five days that we work, and two days that we don't, and these are, for almost everyone in our society, the same days.

The result of this farm-type, Colonial-era thinking is to create the sort of problems that result when everyone goes to work at the same time, eats at the same time, has recreation in the same time, gets up and goes to bed at the same time. The way we solve the problem is to build generating capacity in our power plants for peak hours; to build highways three times as big as they need to be, to take care of peak traffic to and from work, and to overload our parks, resorts, beaches and other recreational areas to the saturation point two days a week, and leave them virtually deserted all the rest of the time. As population increases, and becomes more highly congested in urban areas, the "problems" compound, too, and we are forced into an insensate (and ultimately useless) frenzy of designing and building to take care of urban problems created by rural thinking.

It may be that within the next twenty years, driven to it by taxes and frustration, we will begin to run our lives around the clock, and stagger our days off, and thus reduce peak traffic loads by two-thirds, and use our shopping and recreational facilities the week-around. We have done this during war times; but why does it take a war to make us do so?

In addition to viewing our use of time somewhat differently, there are also possibilities for our viewing the use of facilities in a different way. As things stand today, we find most of our commercial and manufacturing establishments used but one-third of the time. Intensively used, they could perform the same function with one third of the exist-

PHOTO BY WILLIAM JACKSON © 1966

ONE THING AT A TIME

"As a rule, Americans think of time as a road or a ribbon stretching into the future, along which one progresses. The road has segments or compartments which are to be kept discrete ('one thing at a time'). People who cannot schedule time are looked down upon as impractical."

EDWARD T. HALL
"The Silent Language"

BIRTH OF THE MEGASTRUCTURE

"Today's multiple-use buildings may be a mere portent of things to come, as land prices predictably soar to new heights. The end, as prophesied by Jose Sert, dean of the Harvard University Department of Architecture, may be giant 'megastructures,' built to a scale beyond anything thus far conceived, containing everything from parking garages, transit terminals and commercial facilities, to housing units."

Engineering News-Record
April 1, 1965

JUST PLAIN BORING

"A general consideration favoring multiple-use buildings is that living in a 100 per cent residential neighborhood is boring, and people like seeing some other types of the life in the district."

EDGARDO CONTINI
Victor Gruen Associates

ing structures. There is no reason, for example, why Company "A," a business firm, should not use the premises during the "normal" working day; nor why Company "B," a bank clearing house that processes accounts at night, should not use the same premises between, say, 4 p.m. and midnight; and Company "C," an import organization which must do business while it is daytime overseas, should not use it from midnight until morning, until Company "A" comes "on shift." Given the anticipated shorter work week of our immediate future, three six hour shifts would allow three two-hour periods for cleanup and maintenance service between shifts.

If three business organizations who use the same type of equipment —typewriters, desk calculators, computers, telephones, desks, chairs, drinking fountains and coffee dispensers—would join together this way, the investment in equipment would also be reduced by two thirds.

As to the "records" required by each business occupying the same premises at different times, it is not easily conceivable that the 19th Century practice of putting things on paper and then saving the paper will much longer continue in an age that offers direct recording and storage on microfilm and magnetic tape.

A system of multiple-time use of manufacturing (as well as commercial) facilities is also possible; a good example lies in the several major and competing metropolitan newspapers that have agreed to use the same typesetting and press facilities. It is hard for some of us to accept, but a printing press, a rolling mill, or textile mill does not know or care who owns or uses it. There is no real reason why many manufacturing plants should stand idle two thirds of the time. In many industries, productivity could be tripled by multiple-time use.

If some of our problems could be alleviated by using time differently, even more could be alleviated by considering space differently. Not everyone is aware of it, but Americans use space in a different way than many other cultures do. We tend to think in terms of invading space by particularizing it into squares or rectangles.

"Our concept of space," says Edward T. Hall in *The Language of Space (AIA Journal, February, 1961)*, "makes use of the edges of things. If there aren't any edges, we make them by creating artificial lines. Space is treated in terms of a co-ordinate system. In contrast, the Japanese and many other people work within areas. They name "spaces" and distinguish between one space and the next or parts of space. To us a space is empty — one gets into it by intersecting it with lines.

"The American pattern emphasizes equality and standardization of the segments which are used for measuring space or into which space is divided, be it a ruler or a suburban subdivision. We like our components

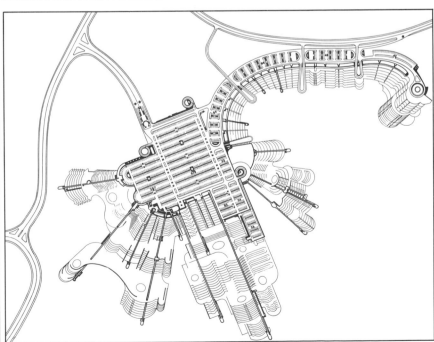

One possible solution to the problem of space and time in our cities is the megastructure. Essentially a city in one vast, continuous building, the megastructure would encompass dwellings, stores, service facilities, offices and recreation centers within one concentrated urban structure. Everything would be within walking or easy driving distance—including the countryside, which would surround the city, not be broken into fragments within it. This concentration would provide a richer, more diverse life than that of suburbia, while preserving the countryside from suburban sprawl. In addition, it would reduce the size of today's metropolis to the more workable, cohesive political unit of under 50,000 population that environmental planners suggest.

The plan for one such megastructure is shown here, a "contour-rise" urban core designed for the Santa Monica mountains of southern California by Cesar Pelli, Director of Design, and A. J. Lumsden, Assistant Director of Daniel, Mann, Johnson and Mendenhall.

GIVE ME DOWNPAYMENT

"Look at every Main Street of every town in America and ask yourself 'who cares?' Nobody cares about community, divinity and humanity, and you can prove it by asking people what they do care about. In terms of shelter they care about downpayment and location. Give me downpayment and location and I'll outsell community, divinity and humanity on any street corner."

VICTOR H. PALMIERI
Pres., Janss Corporation
Land Developers

ROW, ROW, ROW YOUR BOAT

"... the size of a park is directly related to the manner in which you use it. If you are in a canoe traveling at three miles an hour, the lake on which you are paddling is ten times as long and ten times as broad as it is to the man in a speedboat going thirty.... Every road that replaces a footpath, every outboard motor that replaces a canoe paddle, shrinks the area of the park."

PAUL BROOKS
The Atlantic Monthly

standard and equal. American city blocks tend to have uniform dimensions, whereas towns in many other parts of the world are laid out with unequal blocks."

This "set" of the American mind conditions many of our approaches to things. We like standard shapes and sizes; as a result we live in a world of squares and rectangles. Our books and magazines and newspapers are rectangles of standardized size or proportions; so are our windows and movie and television screens. Even our artists, who should know better, restrict their visions to a rectangular canvas. Basically, most of our buildings — residential or commercial — are rectangles, or systems of rectangles joined together.

It is a tribute to the intuition of teen-agers that they look upon us as "squares," or, even worse, cubes, "a square in 3-D." And it is perhaps interesting that they have sought refuge from a life bounded by squares by turning to the only means of escape available to them, the circle in the form of the wheel or the phonograph record.

This way of looking at the world through systems of rectangles leads to some interesting paradoxes; perhaps some of them may be reduced by looking at the world differently in the next twenty years.

The rectangle is not only an awkward shape in which to live, but it forces us into types of construction that require bearing walls and massive use of materials that mostly are there to hold themselves up. We do not usually think of structures as being systems of equally opposed forces in equilibrium.

It is quite possible to base our approach to construction on the natural geometry of space. Buckminster Fuller, whose geodesic domes are only now beginning to proliferate like mushrooms, has been suggesting this for two decades.

Commenting on his ideas, *Time,* January 10, 1964, said, "In the era when the aircraft industry in particular was devising a new technology of lightweight engineering and materials, the traditional building methods seemed to him absurd. Traditional buildings depended on the compression of their walls to support a roof. But modern technology has developed tensile materials which are many times stronger in relation to their weight than compression materials. A house designed to use tension as its basic structural principle could be made infinitely lighter, with fewer materials and, therefore, far more cheaply."

With aluminum, magnesium, titanium and plastics abundantly available in our technology, it is interesting that we still go to the expense and trouble of designing and building structures that are closer to the Egyptians, Aztecs and Romans than they are to modern times. Perhaps, confronted with building requirements that dwarf anything we have faced in the past, we may begin to use some of the technology and materials that we already have.

It is also possible that we are still laboring under the delusion that structures should be designed and built to last as long as possible. But in a changing world, we cannot design structures today that are likely to fit the needs of people ten or twenty years from now. Perhaps, as was suggested at the Aspen International Design Conference in 1965, what we need is a "Kleenex architecture," something that can be used up and thrown away.

"Kleenex architecture" or not, one of the possible approaches to the architecture of the next twenty years may be based on looking at our world as three dimensional instead of two dimensional. It was the invention of the elevator that increased the useful urban surface of the earth by multiples up to 60 times the land surface. It was the electric light that made cities more attractive than the farm because life did not stop at sundown. It is now possible that air conditioning, plus elevators, plus the electric light and television, will lead us to live as far below the surface of the earth as we do above it. We might even be considerate enough to build our "skyscrapers" downward, and leave the surface of the earth as park and farming land. We can.

Malcolm B. Wells, writing in *Progressive Architecture*, February, 1965, says, "I have checked and prodded this idea of underground construction from every angle, and still find only the mildest objections . . . Cost is an unavoidable problem in structures built to carry 4 to 10 feet of earth . . . But have we ever for a minute stopped to realize that what we do each day in the name of architecture is just as ruthless, just as destructive, as the work the buffalo hunters did? Until we've seen ourselves in that light, we'll go on missing the point, always feeling that our work is somehow different, important.

"The simple fact remains, though, that there just isn't any building as beautiful, or as appropriate, as the bit of forest it replaces."

One is tempted to say a loud "Amen." But perhaps it always is difficult to quit when one is ahead. We offer the following observation about an earlier America that may give us some sort of idea of the kind of world we might live in—should we wish:

Donald John Hall, writing in the *Sierra Club Bulletin*, December, 1965, said, "None but the Indians have ever lived in this country, and they existed only as part of it. They have never attempted to assert themselves, but have grown up like trees. It is their food, their drink, their religion and their life . . . They pass through it silently, leaving as little trace as sunlight through wind."

Could we not, if we tried, do as well? ☐

WHAT'S SO GOOD ABOUT A TREE?

"I still think," said a builder, "that it is good to save trees, but I don't understand why."
Dr. Abraham Kaplan, a philosopher, replied, "What is so good about it is that it is not experienced as the product of a design committee nor as the result of the efforts of an association of builders."

"31 Minds Explore Our Environment"—NAHB, 1965

THE PERSISTENCE OF ERROR

"We have accepted the notion that the middle-class American way of life is the ideal, and we don't have any other ideal. We have no experimental kind of living going on here, and I don't know how we are ever going to get it. If you say, 'All right, let's have a new city,' I am afraid it is always going to be forced into the same old bureaucratic pattern."

PERCIVAL GOODMAN, F.A.I.A.
Architect—New York

INDUSTRIAL STONEHENGE

"The great advantage of suburban tract housing is that it is junk and we can throw it away without losing anything. The only bad things are the permanent basements and the monumental barbecues. . . . We live in an industrial Stonehenge—the people are progressive, but all that junk is in the way."

RAYNOR BANHAM
Aspen—1965

"lET THEM EAT CAKE"

☐ There is a legend, or an old-wives' tale, or a superstition, or something that says that a bird can be so hypnotized by a snake that it will fail to make use of its natural ability to escape, and allow itself to be devoured. Whether this has any reality in the biological world has little importance here; its value lies solely in that when the Western, technologically advanced societies face the "food problem," they react very much like the bird transfixed by the serpent. All our soaring jets and orbiting satellites will avail as little as the wings of the bird, if we do not somehow find a way to produce a few ounces of grain or rice for the child who stands barefoot in the dust of his tumble-down village with an empty bowl or gourd in his hands.

Says Dr. Raymond Ewell, of the State University of New York at Buffalo, speaking at the 148th National Meeting of the American Chemical Society in Chicago, 1964: "The food/population problem seems likely to reach such enormous proportions by 1975 that it will dwarf and overshadow most of the problems and anxieties which now occupy our attention, such as the threat of nuclear war, Communism, the space race, racial problems, unemployment, Berlin, Vietnam, the Congo, Cyprus, Cuba and the like. These current problems will fade into the background as the enormity of the world food problem impresses itself on the western world."

Like small children at play, we use the lids of our well-filled garbage cans as a shield, and the T-bone from our latest steak as a sword, and we face this switchbladed Thing in the dark alleys of the world. And it will not work.

Says *Forbes*, March 1, 1966, "The deadly effects of the population explosion aren't for tomorrow. They are here and now. Today.

"One billion people, a third of the world's population, drag themselves through the day weak from hunger, an easy target for disease and frequently for death from starvation. Another billion are badly malnourished, almost on the borderline of starvation. . . .

"The malnourished masses love their children as intensely as well-fed Americans love theirs. They are not about to starve peacefully and quietly, in patience, resignation and fatalism, as their ancestors might have done. They know there is a world without hunger somewhere outside their dusty villages. They have transistor radios, and they have bumped in rickety buses into market towns. They have taken seriously the politician's promises of a better life. They will riot and kill to achieve it. They are doing so right now."

In our country, it is quite possible to make a lot of money writing a book about how to cut down on calories. Someplace, between Metrecal and the sauna bath, we seem to have lost a world. Or almost.

PHOTOGRAPHY BY BOB FRASER

THE OTHER WORLD

"The misery of 2.5 billion persons is beyond the comprehension of the average American. In his book, The Great Ascent, *Robert L. Heilbroner wrote a dramatic passage telling what would happen to an American family if its living standard were to be reduced to that of the underprivileged people of the world:*

" 'We begin by invading the house to strip it of its furniture. Everything goes: bed, chairs, tables, television set. We will leave the family with a few old blankets, a kitchen table, a wooden chair. . . . The box of matches may stay, a small bag of flour, some sugar and salt. A few moldy potatoes already in the garbage can must be rescued, for they will provide much of tonight's meal.

" 'The bathroom is dismantled, the running water shut off, the electric wires taken out. Next, we take away the house. The family can move to the toolshed. Communications must go next. No more newspapers, magazines, books. . . . Next, government services must go. No more postmen, no more firemen. There is a school but it is three miles away and consists of two rooms. They are not too overcrowded since only half the children in the neighborhood go to school.

" 'The nearest clinic is ten miles away and is tended by a midwife. It can be reached by bicycle provided the family has a bicycle, which is unlikely. . . . Finally, money. We will allow our family a cash hoard of $5. . . .' "

HARRY FERGUSON
UPI, Oakland Tribune
December 14, 1965

TWO OUNCES OF GRAIN

"To increase consumption of food grain (in India) by two ounces per head per day . . . will require an increase of nine million tons in annual supplies. This means an increase of more than 10 per cent in domestic production or alternatively, an increase in import expenditures of $750 million, which is more than half of India's total export earnings."

PITAMBAR PANT
Chief, Perspective Planning Division;
Indian Planning Commission

PARADISE ENOW

"Very few Americans, picking and choosing among the piles of white bread in a supermarket, have ever appreciated the social standing of white bread elsewhere in the world. To be able to afford white bread is a dream that awaits fulfillment for billions of the world's population. To afford it signifies that one enjoys all the comforts of life."

ISABEL CARY LUNDBERG
Harper's Magazine, December, 1948

TOO LITTLE, TOO LATE

"The effort required (to feed the world) is far greater than the present combined international, bilateral, foundation, industrial and private assistance to less developed countries. Technical assistance is too spotty, too little, and may soon be too late. The world food gap is still increasing alarmingly, demographic projections are staggering, and poverty and social unrest are the rule, and lower income countries are becoming trapped by increasing dependence on external sources of food and money. The industrialized countries must come to recognize that the application of scientific and technical knowledge to the developing countries requires a concerted and sustained effort of the magnitude of that being given to the conquest of space and a substantial fraction of that devoted to armaments."

The Technology Review
November, 1965

What more is needed as evidence that the serpent has transfixed us with his stare? Says *The New York Times,* July 12, 1965, "The report (by a government task force) observes that 10,000 persons die every day from malnutrition and starvation and that with food production declining and population increasing . . . the world would be hard put to feed itself by 1980. The report estimates that about 70 per cent of the children in less developed countries are undernourished or malnourished. . . . About 50 per cent of all children up to 6 years old and about 30 per cent of the age group from 7 to 14 are labeled as 'seriously malnourished.' It is reported that about half the children in less developed countries including the Latin America countries, never reach their sixth birthday."

Or, *Vision* magazine, May 29, 1964, says, "Without the successful achievement of fantastic—and up to now unforeseeable—economic development, population growth must inexorably convert Latin America into one of the most unfortunate, miserable and devastated regions of this planet."

The evidence pours in upon us with the ubiquity and stridence of television commercials, and we, for the most part, are out in the kitchen getting another beer from our overstuffed refrigerator. In a more reflective moment, we might ask ourselves whether this is really our responsibility, which is another way of asking, "Am I my brother's keeper?" And the answer to that seems to be if we are not, then what in the world are we here for?

"The U.S., Canada and Australia are going to have to feed the world," says Chairman Robert S. Stevenson of Allis-Chalmers, "or we're going to have to help the world feed itself." It is conceivable that we may have to do both; the unthinkable alternatives are, alas, all too thinkable.

Sometimes one hears the expression of a point of view that the only trouble with these people is that they don't really try to help themselves; they stand around waiting for handouts from a rich uncle.

Says Eugene R. Black, former Chairman, the World Bank, "The speed at which a country develops depends largely upon its ability to direct its growing resources to investment rather than consumption, to uses which will raise tomorrow's output rather than satisfy today's demands. A poor society finds it difficult to save at all and will be doing well if it can set aside 10 per cent of its income. But if its population is growing at an extremely rapid rate, it will barely be investing enough to stay where it is. . . ."

Maybe what is wrong is that these people just don't educate themselves well enough to apply the techniques the western technologies have to offer. Says Kingsley Davis, professor of sociology, University of

California; "A rapid rise in the number of people to be maintained uses up income that might otherwise be utilized for long-term investment in education, equipment and other capital needs. To put it in concrete terms, it is difficult to give a child the basic education he needs to become an engineer when he is one of eight children of an illiterate farmer who must support the family with the product of two acres of ground."

"We're caught," says John Gunther, "in a vast, hideous treadmill . . . the more aid we give, the more we shall have to keep on giving, because of relentless population pressure."

Perhaps one of the problems we have in giving, is that we do not really understand what it is that we have to give. It may be that we had the gift boxed and wrapped by the pretty girl at the department store, but we have forgotten what was in it. Perhaps we never knew.

"The assumption," says Margaret Mead, "that men were created equal, with an equal ability to make an effort and win an earthly reward, although denied every day by experience, is maintained every day by our folklore and our day dreams."

"Consistently, throughout our history," says David Potter in *People of Plenty,*"we have assumed that we had a message for the world, a democratic message, and, some would say, a message of redemption. Consistently, we have scanned the horizon, looking for signs that the message was being received . . ."

As we are most uncomfortably aware, the feedback so far has been discouragingly small. It is akin to the messages we hopefully beam into space, thinking perhaps some far off planet in another galaxy will respond. When they do not, we feel that we may not have used the right wavelength. It does not often occur to us that we might have sent the wrong message.

Tune in to David Potter again: "The politics of our democracy was a politics of abundance rather than a politics of individualism; a politics of increasing our wealth quickly rather than of dividing it precisely; a politics which smiled both on those who valued abundance as a means to safeguard freedom and on those who valued freedom as an aid in securing abundance."

Perhaps, in the end, what we have to offer that other world—those other two-thirds of the people on our planet—is not so much a political system, or even individual freedom, but simply how to increase the abundance of material things so that a man can think more about what he believes in than he does about his belly.

And then, it may be that he will choose freedom—as once, given the same choice, we did. ☐

MOTHER HUBBARD

"Once bulging U.S. surpluses are rapidly disappearing. In fact, surpluses of those farm commodities that the hungry nations need are down to or below levels the U.S. Department of Agriculture deems 'prudent' to maintain as national reserves.

"With all this, farm groups . . . are calling for an expanded Food for Peace effort that would free the American farmer from production controls and permit him to go all out to feed the world."

Chemical Week
January 1, 1966

WORLDS IN COLLISION

"The world is on a collision course. When the massive force of an exploding world population meets the much more stable trend line of world food production, something must give. It is high time that we began to fashion our domestic agricultural programs and policies with a view toward the political and economic realities of the developing world food crisis."

DR. EARL BUTZ,
Dean of Agriculture
Purdue University

HOLLOW PEOPLE, EMPTY WORLD

*"If present trends continue, it seems
likely that famine will reach serious
proportions in India, Pakistan
and Communist China in the early
1970's. Indonesia, Iran, Turkey,
Egypt, Brazil and several other countries
will follow within a few years.
Most of the other countries of Asia,
Africa, and Latin America
will fall in this category by 1980.
If this happens, as appears
probable, it will be the most colossal
catastrophe in history. It would
be a completely new situation—not
enough food for the billions
of human beings inhabiting the
surface of this globe . . ."*

DR. RAYMOND EWELL
State University of
New York at Buffalo

*"Remember us—if at all—not as lost
Violent souls, but only
As the hollow men . . .
In this last of meeting places
We grope together
And avoid speech
Gathered on the beach
of this tumid river."*

T. S. ELIOT
"The Hollow Men"

PAINTING BY TOM HENDERSON

THE WHOLE WORLD IN HIS HANDS

IT SEEMS POSSIBLE

"The key to preventing world famine is not distributing food as such, but helping the starving nations learn how to produce their food, using our surpluses to bridge the gap between now and the time when they can produce their own. It seems possible to win the war against hunger within the next 10 to 20 years."

ORVILLE FREEMAN
Secretary of Agriculture

WE KNOW HOW NOW

"Man's capacity to go without food and his ability to eat food are both limited —1,500 calories a day is a starvation diet, but 3,000 calories is generally too much, so a well-fed man can eat only twice as much as a starving one, a ratio of two to one ...

"During almost all of man's time upon this earth he had to struggle for food. Forty years ago we would not have known how to feed the whole world. We know now."

JONATHAN GARST
"No Need for Hunger"

☐ The connoisseur of change, desperately searching the present to find some clue to the future, might do well to take a look at a place called Rothamsted, about 25 miles north of London. This is one of the world's oldest agricultural experimental stations and the facility to look for is Broadbalk Field, an 11-acre parcel of land planted in wheat.

For nearly a century, now, this little experimental field has been beaming out its message of hope for the world's hungry and there is indication that at last the message is getting through.

Broadbalk Field's acreage is divided into three strips. On one of them is put a heavy dressing of barnyard manure; a second gets a treatment of chemical fertilizers; and the third gets no "help" at all. For a hundred years, the results have been the same; the "naturally" fertilized field and the chemically fertilized acres yield richly, and in the same amount. The unfertilized acreage is a poor producer; about one-fiftieth of the other strips, or what one would get from similar untreated soil in most of the developing countries in the world.

The message is simple, and it is clear. The way to increase the world's production of food from existing acreage is through the application of relatively inexpensive chemicals that can be mass produced in factories. The results can be dramatic.

What is still often not recognized about farming is that it only incidentally involves the use of the ground or soil. What *is* involved is solar radiation, water, carbon dioxide and very small quantities of chemicals. The classic experiment along these lines was made by Jean-Baptiste Van Helmont, who described his experiment in *Ortus Medicinae,* published in Amsterdam in 1652:

"I took an earthen vessel in which I put 200 pounds of soil dried in an oven, then I moistened it with rain water and pressed hard into it a shoot of willow weighing five pounds. After exactly five years the tree that had grown up weighed 169 pounds and about three ounces. But the vessel had never received anything but rain water or distilled water to moisten the soil when it was necessary, and it remained full of soil, which was still tightly packed, and lest any dust from outside should get into the soil, it was covered with a sheet of iron coated with tin, but perforated with many holes. I did not take the weight of the leaves that fell in the autumn. In the end I dried the soil once more and got the same 200 pounds I started with, less about two ounces."

Here, in this elegantly simple experiment—in two ounces of chemicals that became a willow tree more than 400 years ago—was at least one of the answers to the world's food problem in the next two decades; but the message has only started to arrive. It says the same thing as that little field of wheat at Rothamsted; namely—that it takes so little in

PHOTOGRAPHY BY BOB FRASER

NOT BY BREAD ALONE

*"Man is more than animal. He has
mental, emotional and spiritual needs
that go far beyond bare necessities,
creature comforts and material
resources. Every man deserves at least
the chance to lead a life of satisfaction
and purpose, to achieve in life more
than mere existence.*

*"Even if science by some magic could
show the way to feed new billions of
people, we still would not have solved
the 'population problem.' The quality
of life cannot be omitted from
the solution. Indeed, there can be no
true solution until society can offer every
individual an opportunity—in the
fullest sense—to live as well as
to survive."*

JOHN D. ROCKEFELLER, 3rd.
Chairman, Board of Trustees
The Population Council

chemicals to make so much in food.

Recently the United Nations Food and Agriculture Organization (FAO) summarized the results from more than 9,500 fertilizer field trials in 14 countries in North and West Africa, Central and South America, and the Near East. "There can be no doubt," said Dr. H. L. Richardson, who directed the FAO fertilizer program, "that when farmers in developing countries use fertilizers—even without improved farming methods—the results will be good."

Based on these trials, the FAO estimated that the average increase in agricultural production for all countries, worldwide, all varieties of crops, and all seasons, using the most economical fertilizer treatments, is 74 per cent. Economic analysis of the results indicated that 93 per cent of the trials demonstrated satisfactory returns from moderate amounts of fertilizer.

Similar trials have been conducted in India, Pakistan, Taiwan, the Philippines, Mexico and other countries. The value/cost ratio varied from 2.3 to 7.0, corresponding to economic returns of 130 to 600 per cent on the investment in fertilizer.

But it is only when the statistics are brought down to earth that the really dramatic nature of this solution can be appreciated. John Couston, economist with the FAO, relates: "One small farmer in Guatemala, through the use of chemical fertilizer alone, increased his annual income 20 times from 1960 to 1964. Formerly, this small farmer grew only enough food to furnish his family's requirements. Profiting from the application of fertilizer, this farmer has built himself a separate house and uses the old hut to cook in. For transportation now, he owns a brand new bicycle."

It is still rather widely believed that the reason "poor" countries are poor is because their soils will not support the degree of productivity that would enable them to advance. "But," says geochemist Harrison Brown in *The Next Hundred Years,* "difference in agricultural productivity in different regions do not appear to be primarily attributable to inherent differences in soil fertility or climate. They reflect rather the technological level of the culture and the density of its population.... This is very clearly shown in comparisons which concern a single measure of the extent to which technology is applied to agriculture—namely, the use of fertilizer..."

He goes on to point out that, "Europeans apply over twice as much fertilizer per acre per year as do Americans. The rate of application in Japan is again twice that of Western Europe. In India, on the other hand, fertilizer is used but little since it is not available in quantity nor is the Indian farmer well informed concerning fertilizer application."

Based on the caloric content of the potential food per acre per day, there is a direct relationship between what different nations produce on their acreage and the amount of fertilizer that they use. In the U.S. it is about 4,500 calories; in Asia, the average is 4,000 calories per acre per day; in Western Europe it is 7,000 to 8,000 and in Japan it is 13,000 calories.

Whether he would be willing to recognize the description or not, the farmer in any country in the world is a radiation chemist. His historic problem has been that the radiation is abundant, and free; the chemicals seldom are either one. Thus, in most areas of the world, the farmer's ability to feed the increased world population is directly related to the degree to which heavy industry can produce and deliver chemical fertilizers.

"The capital cost of fertilizer facilities per acre fertilized is not high," says Jonathan Garst, in *No Need for Hunger*, "Probably $10 per acre in fertilizer factories would provide enough plant food to add 50 to 100 per cent to the low yields in the hungry countries of the world. In the non-Communist countries where food is short, there are about 1.5 billion acres of cultivated land, so around $15 billion will be needed. This would be equivalent to adding at least 750 million acres to the crop area of these countries. It would be like discovering another, bigger North America. This is just the kind of spectacular boost these countries need."

Chemical Week, in its June 26, 1965, issue, says that "To feed a population estimated at 3.5 billion by 1980 (compared with 2.4 billion in 1965), Asia, Africa and Latin America must increase use of fertilizers from today's 4-million tons/year to 15-millions tons per year in 1970 and 30 million tons in 1980."

Food population expert Dr. Raymond Ewell figures the cost of building enough fertilizer plants to produce 30 million tons of fertilizer would be about $5 billion—ten per cent of the cost of putting a man on the moon. "Historians of the future may remark on whether it was more important," he observes, "to have devoted our resources during the 1960's to putting a man on the moon or to have devoted our resources toward averting the world famine of the 1970's."

He goes on to say that total world fertilizer production should be approaching at least 100 million tons of plant nutrients in 1980, compared with the 30 million tons at present. Yet, there is nothing on the horizon to indicate that anywhere near that amount of new productive capacity is going to be built.

Once again, as with the land use "problem," the water "problem," and the air pollution "problem," the basic difficulties do not appear to relate to shortages of resources nor to lack of technical know-how, but to the deficiencies of outmoded political thinking. "A great deal more

LEACHING THE FUTURE AWAY

"Though the U.S. is not threatened by starvation, rapid population growth does threaten—and is already crippling—our individual freedom and quality of life. It is leaching away the future, too, by making potential gains in our standard of living increasingly hard to achieve. Inevitably, continued population growth means higher taxes for welfare, health and education, as well as increased police, fire, sanitation and highway costs."

"The Poverty of Abundance"
World Population Council

AND NOW, FISH FLOUR

"Halifax scientists recently developed a
process for making high quality fish
protein concentrate .... Made from cod
fillets, filleting line scraps and other
marine organic odds and ends, fish
protein concentrate or 'fish flour' is an
odorless, tasteless white powder similar
in appearance to wheat flour, but
containing up to 96 percent
high quality protein . . ."

C-I-L *Oval*, Summer, 1964

ALGAE ICE CREAM

"It has been estimated that the annual
fish harvest of 35 million tons could be
increased tenfold. Challenging and more
visionary is the possibility of harvesting
minute plants and creatures of the sea,
such as the mass cultivation of sea water
algae for foodstuff. Japanese scientists
have prepared algae bread, algae
noodles, algae soup and algae ice cream.
Those who ate these algae foods found
them palatable and nutritious;
to some they were delicious . . ."

CAPTAIN W. J. CHRISTENSEN, USN
Naval Engineers Journal, June 1965

must be learned," said *Chemical Week* in the June 26, 1965, issue, "if U.S. investors are to contribute to and profit from the world's burgeoning need for fertilizers."

The area for potentially profitable investment is further limited by political thinking in many countries that make the terms of "outside" ownership too risky to attract large scale investment.

The problem of producing chemical fertilizers is, of course, tremendously complicated by the equal problem of finding ways to distribute it in countries where terminal facilities are lacking or inadequate; where inland transportation routes are unequal to the task of getting the fertilizers into the farms or getting the resulting produce out; where there is, at present, no available capital to carry the farmers on credit until the magic of the fertilizer can begin to work; where centuries' old approaches to agriculture must be changed in the minds of men. We have had the technology to solve these problems for nearly three decades; what is lacking is not the way, but the will.

There are many other contributing solutions our present technology can make to the world food problem of the next 20 years:

. . . We can change the kinds of food that are raised; from cereals to higher yield varieties like potatoes and sugar beets, thus getting a higher caloric output from the same amount of land and effort.

. . . We can give up processing vegetables through domestic animals (with a 90 per cent loss) and go directly from, say, alfalfa to protein. The difference between feeding it to a steer and transforming it directly is the difference between 43 edible protein pounds per acre per year for raising cattle; or 1,500 edible protein pounds per acre per year by direct transformation.

. . . We can recycle cottonseed meal, cornstalks and other residue (together with molasses and urea) back through livestock as feed instead of burning it or throwing it away.

. . . We can reduce spoilage through better design and use of food storage bins and containers; through wider use of refrigeration and irradiation and packaging design.

. . . We can reduce the amount of foodstuffs lost (it is one third of the world's production) to insects, vermin, fungus and various plant diseases through the intensive use of herbicides, pesticides and insecticides.

. . . We can, through irrigation and fertilization, bring approximately one billion more acres of the land surface into the kind of agricultural productivity that Europe has today. Estimates are it would take about 30 to 50 years and an investment of $500 billion.

BUT THAT WAS WHERE I STOOD

"It may not strike you as a marvel. It would not, perhaps, unless you stood in the middle of a dead world at sunset, but that was where I stood.

Fifty million years lay under my feet, fifty million years of bellowing monsters moving in a green world now gone so utterly that its very light was traveling on the farther edge of space.

The chemicals of all that vanished age lay about me on the ground. Around me still lay the shearing molars of dead titanotheres, the delicate sabers of soft-stepping cats, the hollow sockets that held the eyes of many a strange, outmoded beast.

Those eyes had looked out upon a world as real as ours; dark, savage brains had roamed and roared their challenges into the steaming night.

Now they were still here, or, put it as you will, the chemicals that made them were here about me on the ground. The carbon that had driven them ran blackly into the eroding stone.

The stain of iron was in the clays. The iron did not remember the blood it had once moved within, the phosphorus had forgot the savage brain. The little individual moment had ebbed from all those strange combinations of chemicals, as it would ebb from our living bodies into the sinks and runnels of oncoming time . . .

Like men from those wild tribes who had haunted these hills before me seeking visions, I made my sign to the great darkness. It was not a mocking sign, and I was not mocked . . ."

LOREN EISELEY
"The Immense Journey"

PHOTO BY WILLIAM JACKSON © 1966

. . . We can substitute an agricultural approach for our present hit or miss hunting approach to harvesting the products of the sea. It is estimated that the world's annual fish harvest of 35 million tons could be increased perhaps as much as fivefold without destroying the self-perpetuating "food chain" of the ocean's living economy.

. . . We can produce high protein concentrates that can be added to low protein diets.

Nevin S. Scrimshaw, head of the Department of Nutrition and Food Service, M.I.T., writing in *Technology Review,* November, 1965, says "After the seeds of soy, cotton, sesame, peanut and sunflower plants are commercially pressed, the resultant meal contains approximately 50 per cent protein, and the oil can be sold to pay much of the cost.

"One third of a properly processed oilseed meal mixed with two-thirds of cereal grain gives a mixture whose quality and concentration of protein is adequate for all human needs. Over three million pounds of the low-cost, protein-rich vegetable mixture, Incaparina, developed on this principle by the Institute of Nutrition of Central America and Panama, will be sold in Columbia and Guatamala this year to make a drink with the protein value of milk, at one-fifth the cost."

One of the most promising advances in developing low-cost, high protein additives may be the discovery that bacteria which feed on petroleum may be turned into protein concentrate that is tasteless, odorless, and might be mass-produced inexpensively.

The bacteria eat the paraffins out of the petroleum, leaving the remainder for further processing. One pound of paraffin produces a pound of protein. A properly-fed 1,000 pound steer stores up just one pound of protein a day. In the same 24 hours, a half ton of selected micro-organisms, feeding on oil, increases in size and weight by five times, and half this gain is useful protein—2,500 pounds of it.

Alfred Champagnat, manager of the Societe Internationale de Recherche BP, which developed the petroleum-protein process, has estimated that 20 million tons of pure protein could be produced per year from 40 million tons of crude oil, a small fraction of the world's annual production of crude oil.

There are, in short. many contributions we can make toward solving the food problems of the next twenty years, although none seem as promising of immediate results, all things considered, as the production and wide-spread use of chemical fertilizers.

But today we stand knee deep in our own garbage on this neon-lit intersection of the world, waiting for the next bus to the moon. That sound in the background is not Muzak; it is the rising, angry clangor of empty rice bowls. ☐

TIME OUT OF MIND

*"Carriages without horses shall go,
And accidents fill the world with woe.
Around the world thoughts shall fly
In the twinkling of an eye
Under water men shall walk,
Shall ride, shall sleep, shall talk;
In the air men shall be seen
In white, in black, and in green."*

MOTHER SHIPTON'S PROPHECIES
(17th Century)

NEW DIMENSIONS

"Certainly we can hardly hope to block the seemingly inexorable march of post-historic man by clinging to obsolete institutions and archaic forms of the human self, fabricated by earlier cultures . . . What we need to confront the threatening omniscience and omnipotence of posthistoric man is to cultivate powers equally god-like in a quite different part of the personality. Must we not cultivate a force that came late even in man's conception of godhood—the force that Henry Adams prophetically summoned up in opposition to the dynamo? I mean the force of love."

LEWIS MUMFORD

TELEMOBILITY

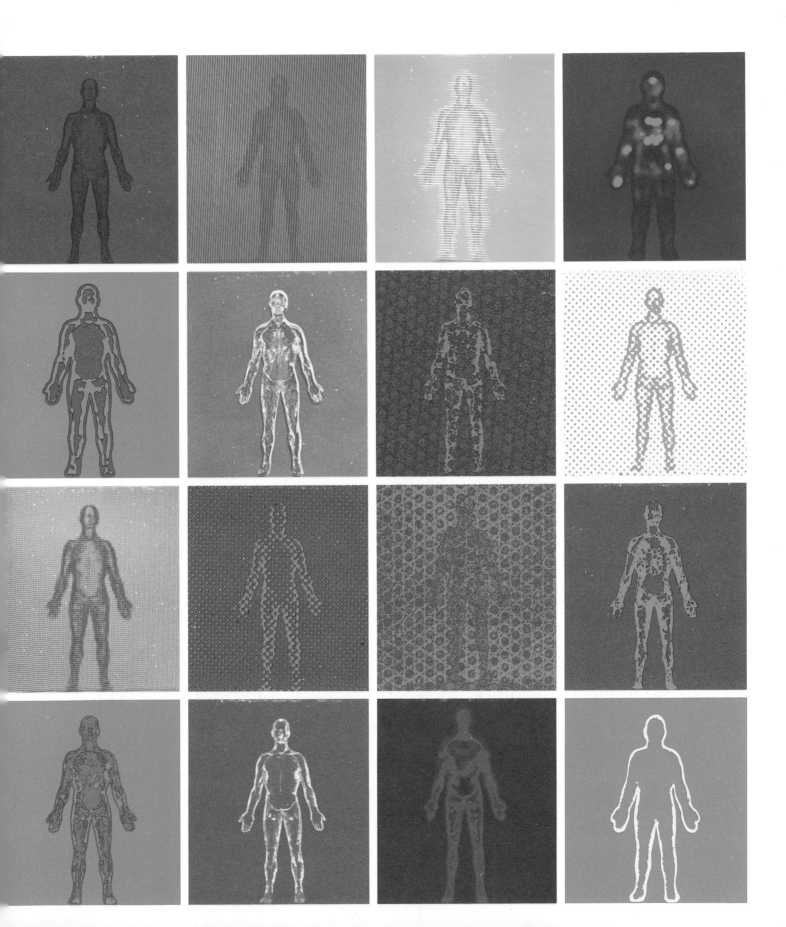

THERE ARE RANGES of mountains so vast—the Atlas, the Sierra, the Himalayan, the Andes—that even when we have negotiated the passes and crossed to the other side, we are not aware that we have, in truth, crossed them. In our time now—in the years immediately ahead—the human species is crossing such a divide. We are beginning to move from a mechanically fragmented world, a thing of bits and pieces, into a process world, where the wave is more important than the drops that make it up. Like "Alice Through the Looking Glass," we have begun to immerse ourselves in an electromagnetic environment—where the White Rabbit is always late (because there is no time) and where the White Queen is ever running faster, just to stay in one place. When we annihilated time and space through the human use of the electromagnetic spectrum, we began to cross The Great Divide.

4

a day for killing time

THE DIVINE THOUGHT

"Movement is very old. It is older than the earth, the root, tongue, hoof, nerve. All the choir of heaven, 'the mighty and most elegant structure of the earth and all the earths of night,' the galaxies and super-galaxies, the oceans and rivers are pushed on the driving wheel of this device . . . Blood runs. Even the fixed forms which seem so still have something within them that is not still. This holds for the electron, too, 'in perpetual motion at the rate of several thousand miles per second.'

"Distance is a fine thought, even a divine thought. Stretching and reaching out one morning in the great tedium for a ray of light—reaching farther, farther— the little paramecium made the great stride from a wave swinging her, to the pull of Self; and from what it is to be safe in a snug harbor of your own, to the world of experience and experiment; and what it is to go on a road . . ."

MADGE JENISON
"Roads"

THE WORM IN THE GARDEN

"The story of Eden is a greater allegory than man has ever guessed. For it was truly man who, walking memoryless through paths of sunlight and shade in the morning of the world, sat down and passed a wondering hand across his heavy forehead. Time and darkness, knowledge of good and evil, have walked with him ever since . . ."

LOREN EISELEY
"The Immense Journey"

WIDE, WIDE WORLD

"Imagine a series of clear plastic domes, one within another. You can only see them from the outside; from the inside they are invisible. You become aware of an environment—one of those domes that surrounds you—only when you get outside of it. At that point you can see it. But you can't see the one which is now *about you."*

HOWARD GOSSAGE
Ramparts—April, 1966

☐ Whenever we look for the beginnings of things—the triggers that release the avalanches of change that sweep whole worlds into churning debris—what we find is almost always something small; some small, furtive thing whose actions, if observed at all, catch but the corners of our Olympian gaze. Some small thing.

It must have been that way for the dinosaurs. Pounding and bellowing upon the jellied swamp of a world they ruled for 120 million years, they did not notice the little shrew-like, furry things that ate dinosaur eggs. Whatever their other charms, the dinosaurs were poor mothers; they left their eggs lying about as casually as a spoiled and wanton child might scatter her dolls before time to nap. The little, shrew-like things, perhaps a distant progenitor of us all, ate most of them up. After a while—no dinosaurs.

Or, contemplate the Philadelphia Exposition of 1876. The dinosaur of *that* time—and the showpiece of the Exposition—was the monstrous Centennial Corliss engine; a Gargantua of pulleys and belts and drive shafts, crowning glory of 19th Century mechanical technology. But three years earlier, the dynamo for generating electricity and a motor for converting the electricity into mechanical energy, had been demonstrated— hardly noticed—at the Vienna Exposition. In the end, the dynamo was to eat the Corliss engine up, and nearly all its breed; not unlike the furry things that ate the dinosaur's eggs. Always—some small, unnoticed thing.

Should one want to find the beginning of the new age we now have entered, watching our dials, clicking our shutters, pulsing our lasers in the radiant ectoplasm of the mid-20th Century, he might go back to a summer's afternoon at a country house called Lacock Abbey, not far from Bath, England.

On a sunny day in the year 1835, a man who was at once a scientist, country gentleman and a "mathematician of means," could be observed placing small boxes—no bigger than mousetraps (and it is said that his wife did call them "his little mousetraps")— about the green mansions of his grounds. William Henry Fox Talbott, the father of modern photography (for it was indeed he) would wait a while and then, "After the lapse of half an hour, I gathered them all up, and brought them within doors to open them. When opened, there was found in each a miniature picture of the objects before which they had been placed."

That was the day that time was killed, for the passing world could now be preserved for all posterity. As an instrument for achieving immortality, the pyramids had been swept away and all the gilt-framed paintings of famous kings. Now, even the common man could be passed, in silver chloride effigy, from child's hand to child's hand down the tumbling years. Time had had its stop in those little photonic mousetraps. They

PGS. 2-3, PHOTOGRAPHY BY BOB FRASER, KAISER GRAPHIC ARTS

were such little things, those photon-catching mousetraps in the sun.

But something else had happened as well. For here, in a little box you could hold in the palm of your hand, was a major advance in the luminous science of photochemistry. The subsequent efforts to improve the Lilliputian image in the mousetraps helped lead to the discovery of the photon and the interaction between waves of light and the physical world. For the first time, man had begun to use a portion of the electromagnetic spectrum as a *tool* rather than just something "out there." This discovery opened the road to the motion picture, television, the electronic computer, maser, laser, microwave, radar, Telstar and Early Bird, and foreshadowed the obsolescence of the wheel as the major component in man's mobility upon earth. The creatures of the electromagnetic world are hungrily eating up the eggs of the clockwork dinosaurs that roam about us, the last of the progeny of the Corliss engine.

With the invention of the photograph, we killed time; and with the invention of the telegraph, we abolished the space that separated man from man. In our days, a hybrid of the two—the photograph joined to the telegraph—has given the world an instantaneous vision of itself that stops the wheel in its tracks, may relegate the freeways to empty loops of concrete spaghetti, and may even leave the central city core a wasteland of empty glass and metal tombstones. Oh, not yet; not for a while. But in time. Swarms of electrons are nibbling away the mechanical world we all grew up in.

In the pages that follow, we will talk about a subject that is a little analogous to something we mentioned earlier. We talked then about "action at the interface;" how, at the boundary layers between different neighborhoods of men and ideas, our social institutions—the codified visions of ourselves—were being abraded away. Now we will talk about "involvement at the overlap," for we see our times, and those of the next twenty years, as the action resulting from the overlapping of the mechanical age and the electromechanical age; a coexistence, if you like, between the wheel and the electron. And we will say that the wheel will not wholly disappear, nor will freeways and cities, but that they will, in the period we discuss, be of far less importance to us.

We will begin to live more and more in the shock wave that is created when an electron drops to an orbit closer to the nucleus. We will begin, more and more, to ride the waves of the oscilloscope; to swim in the blue-green phosphors of our television screens.

We no longer have places to go; we only have places to bring here. We will exchange the wheel for the dance of the photons, as once we traded the horse for the wheel, and it will be another world, altogether, when we do that. □

THE STOP ACTION LIFE

"The brain is a billion lens motion picture camera shooting and coordinating billions of frames a second. The 'imprint' system is one of these frames— stopped—upon which man's perception and symbolic thinking develops. Man's mind imposes upon the variegated flow of energy one static model— years out of date, kept current only by the slow process of conditioning and association . . . What happens outside or inside, we perceive in terms of our mental imprinting system. We live in a dead world—cut off from the flow of life and energy."

TIMOTHY LEARY
"Languages: Energy Systems
Sent and Received." ETC.

DIAGNOSED AS THROMBOSIS

"We doubt whether it is realized how fundamental is the influence of transport on the shape and growth of a nation's economy. When it is a question of the stimulation of underdeveloped economies in other parts of the world, it is a truism that transport is one of the two great 'nation-building' influences (education being the other), which are basic to everything else.

"What does not seem to be so readily accepted is that a mature economy is equally sensitive to the condition of its transport system. If the coming flood of vehicles means freer and easier transport of goods and persons, it cannot help but be beneficial. If, however, it leads to clogging of the arteries of transport, it may lead to a general thrombosis."

"Traffic in Towns"
Her Majesty's Stationery Office, 1963

ballet of the clockwork dinosaurs

☐ For quite some time now, say 600 million years, there's been something moving around out there.

As we reconstruct it from such faint and fragmentary images as we have so far found imprinted on ancient rocks, we see first some small, nameless organism detach itself from the bottom ooze and swim blindly upward toward the light—mobility had become a way of life. In another picture, obviously taken later, a trilobite stirs sluggishly in his shallow, Cambrian pond. Somewhat later still, tall grass lifts its head above the surface of a sun-drenched lake and shoots spores, like missiles, at the neighboring shore; life's first aerospace venture had been launched. Long, long after, some fishlike thing with stubby fins crawls painfully the few feet from its dried-up waterhole to one with water in it.

That uncertain journey beneath the burning radiation of a sun too young was the first step toward a time when, as Loren Eiseley has described it, "Tyrannosaurs, enormous bipedal caricatures of men, would stalk mindlessly across the sites of future cities and go their slow way down into the dark of geologic time. In all that world of living things— nothing moved except with the grave, sleepwalking intentness of the instinct-driven brain. It was a world of slow motion . . ."

Motion, nonetheless. In time, a warmer blood suffused the living world, stretched fins into wings and legs, and the tempo of life upon the planet quickened. But, slow or fast, the motivation of all those millions of years did not change; always some living thing attempted to move toward some new experience; something to eat, to drink, to breathe, to love. Some ancient wisdom imprinted on those primitive networks of nerves told them that there is a "somewhere else" and that by the expenditure of energy they could move there.

The knowledge that we can move in space through the purposeful expenditure of stored energy is thus among the most ancient of our heritages; implicit in the image we have of ourselves and the environment that surrounds us. Much newer is the discovery that we can move the experience to us; such a concept probably did not enter the world until some furry or feathered thing, assuming responsibility for small copies of itself too defenceless to move about safely in an alien world, brought food for its young back to the cave or nest.

By the time man made the scene, shambling into the afternoon of a world already old and wise, he was pre-programmed for both types of mobility. The hunter was thus, in this sense, the prehistoric precursor of the horseman, the motorcar, the jet liner and the orbital satellite. And the farmer, who did not pursue his quarry but raised it next to his cave or hut, became the progenitor of all those means we have of bringing

PHOTOGRAPHY BY ROBERT A. ISAACS

ADVENTURES OF A
STEEPLECHASER

"When the motorcar was new, it exercised the typical mechanical pressure of explosion and separation of functions. It broke up family life, or so it seemed, in the 1920's. It separated work and domicile as never before. It exploded each city into a dozen suburbs, and then extended many of the forms of urban life along the highways until the open road seemed to become non-stop cities.

"The motorcar ended the countryside and substituted a new landscape in which the car was sort of a steeplechaser. At the same time, the motorcar destroyed the city as a casual environment in which families could be reared. Streets, and even sidewalks, became too intense a scene for the casual interplay of growing up . . .

"This is the story of the motorcar, and it has not much longer to run . . . Witness the portent of the crosswalk, where a small child has the power to stop a cement truck . . ."

MARSHALL McLUHAN
"Understanding Media"

45-MINUTE WORLD

"For the first time in history, the ultimate in transportation is in sight. By the early 1980's travelers may zoom from the U.S. to any point in the world in less than 45 minutes. Man simply can't travel any faster. Speeds higher than this would defy gravity and hurl passengers and their craft into orbit . . . Exotic as it may seem, a preliminary design for such a craft already has been drawn up by Douglas Aircraft Company engineers. The 'Pegasus' is a rocket transport capable of whisking 170 passengers, their baggage and 18 tons of cargo high above the atmosphere from continent to continent at 17,000 miles per hour. Douglas engineers believe it could start coming off the assembly lines and into commercial service in 15 to 20 years . . ."

News-Front—October, 1965

X, Y, Z—WHERE ARE YOU?

"It will soon be possible to obtain reliable topographic and planimetric maps from which all forms of photogrammetric data can be obtained without further field work. The controls for these maps will have been established by, and referenced to, space satellite stations following a specific orbit. Ground orientation would be accomplished by simultaneous satellite and ground observation electronically relayed to a computer by micro-wave transmission. "Maps for route determination will be restricted to aerial photographs reproduced and rectified to scale for visual inspection. The economics of the route will be determined through the use of airborne instruments recording the x, y, z triordinates in digital form and transmitted directly to the computer by microwave transceiver. The computer will then develop alternate routes for the class of highway desired. All existing and forecasted traffic data will be immediately available through the continuous use of photography and electronic equipment."

WILLIAM A. BUGGE
"Highway Transportation After 1975"
Civil Engineering—January, 1962

experience to us; his small plot of planted ground was the ancestor of television.

That was only yesterday, geologically, and in the few hours since we have invented vehicles, which are mechanical tools for moving the body toward an experience, we have discovered ways to manipulate electromagnetic waves—a way of bringing experience to the body.

All this past is but the prologue to the drama that is now unfolding before us. Man has always had the choice between two kinds of mobility, but he has for the most part concentrated on means for moving the body to the experience. In doing so, he became enchanted with the vehicle—the horse, the chariot, the raft, train, automobile, airplane—each in its time the magic carpet that transported his neural network to the scene of its desire. So enraptured did he become with the vehicle that he began to confuse the *means* of mobility with the *meaning* of mobility.

In the end he overlooked, and ultimately almost forgot, the essential purpose of human movement, which is to confront the sensory system with a new array of stimuli. As a sight and sound experience, there is nothing to choose between sending a man to New York, or sending New York to him.

Already the car in the garage and the television set in the living room —both of them tools for communication—are in direct competition for man's time and energy, and this is but the beginning of the beginning. As he moves more deeply into the electromagnetic world, more and more "making the scene" will mean not stepping on the starter, but switching channels.

But the ten-thousand-year enchantment with the vehicle is far from over; the mechanical sculptor in his technological studio is still deeply involved with his clockwork Galatea. He brought her to life and in his exultation refuses to admit, what in his heart he knows, that the definition of life is that it is mortal.

The love-affair continues. The daily press is full of talk about supersonic transports traveling three times the speed of sound; of 150-mile-an-hour automobiles; of trains traveling at 300 miles per hour; of transports that can carry 600 people and their baggage at sonic speed; of a rocket liner that can carry 170 passengers at 17,000 miles per hour, connecting any point on the globe with any other in 45 minutes.

There is much talk of these things. There is little talk about the implicit assumption that our future world will be so poorly organized that delivery of anyone—or anything—on a global basis in 45 minutes would be necessary. In a computer controlled technology, won't we plan better than that?

Nevertheless the trend of all our future projections is toward larger and larger vehicles, faster terminal-to-terminal speeds, greater road-ability (as in the hydro-foils, the ground-effect machines, vertical take-off aircraft, pneumatic tube rapid transit). There is no doubt we can build all these if we want to, but one gets the feeling, somehow, that the right questions are not being asked.

In a world where passengers and cargo can be moved from any spot on earth to any other spot on earth at 17,000 miles per hour (with vertical takeoff and landing by rocket), where is the need for a super-sonic transport system that goes at 2,000 miles per hour? More importantly, where experience can be brought to the human sensory system with the speed of light, what is the point of transporting the nervous system to the experience at earth-bound speeds at all? Of all our hallucinations, the most pernicious is that we think we know what we are doing.

Our infatuation with the vehicle has also led us to neglect to create the environment in which it can function most efficiently. It has been said—sometimes loudly enough to hear—that this country has "the greatest transportation system in the world." The only people who disagree with this are those who have tried to use it. In fact, we do not have a transportation system but—thanks to concentrating on the vehicle—a number of sub-systems of different sizes, speeds and capabilities.

They sometimes meet, almost by accident, at places called terminals which are not really terminals at all but staging areas where the traveler tries to figure out how to get to the next system's terminal so that he can continue his often dubious venture. This is not a system, it is a random dispersion of accidental meetings. What holds the non-system together is the automobile; it draws the little lines from terminal-point to terminal-point. The result is a rude caricature of a transportation system, much like those little "connect the dots" games one sees in the children's section of the Sunday papers.

Let us be completely ridiculous and suggest that the purpose of a transportation system is to move a person from where he is to where he wants to be. It is not enough to get him, say, from Spokane to Chattanooga—but from where he is in Spokane to where he wants to go in Chattanooga. A fully systematized transportation network would take care of the traveler, with a single ticket, from the moment he puts the cat out and closes the front door until, all smiles, he walks up to the reception desk at his ultimate destination and presents his business card. We do not, as yet, have anything remotely resembling such a system. Not for people, anyway.

What holds the system we *do* have together is, as mentioned, the passenger automobile and bus, and they are in trouble. "Vehicular traf-

VTOL ANYONE?

"A Northeast Corridor air commuter network using VTOL (Vertical Takeoff or Landing) aircraft or STOL (Short Takeoff or Landing) aircraft and linking 50 terminals in 38 population centers could be developed between 1970-80 for $500 million, according to a study sponsored by the U.S. Commerce Dept.

"The study, conducted by the Massachusetts Institute of Technology, concludes that aircraft could be developed that would operate at fares of 5 cents/passenger mile over 100-mile lengths . . .

"The MIT study is the latest in a series of systems-type research projects being financed by the Commerce Dept. on the transportation needs of the Northeast Corridor. The program includes prototype development of a high-speed train which would cut 30 min. off the present 4.5 hour rail-time between Washington and New York.

"Other studies concern improved means of speeding automobiles and bus traffic between city centers and into residential suburbs. Scope of the studies is almost unlimited, touching such advanced possibilities as trains or ground-effect vehicles operating in tubes or troughs, and electronic regulation of personal automobiles on automated freeways . . ."

JAMES R. ASHLOCK
Aviation Week & Space Technology
April 4, 1966

PASSENGER PIGEON

❧ or ❧

"YOU CAN'T HARDLY GET THERE FROM HERE"

(A play in Three Acts and One Scene—the Scene is at the airport when you find your luggage has mistakenly gone to Alaska, our 49th State.)

ACT ONE

Walk from house to car	30 seconds
Drive car to express bus stop	4 minutes
Wait for bus	3 minutes
Express bus to bus terminal	32 minutes
Taxicab to airlines terminal	7 minutes
Wait for airport bus at terminal	5 minutes
Airport bus to main airport terminal building	24 minutes
Wait and check-in at ticket counter	7 minutes
Walk to Gate 22, Concourse "C"	4 minutes
Wait for flight to be called	15 minutes
Walk to and board aircraft	1 minute 30 seconds
Wait for all passengers to be loaded; keep eye on stewardess	10 minutes
Taxi to end of takeoff strip	3 minutes
Wait to take off	7 minutes
Takeoff	30 seconds

Distance traveled—**25 miles**
Time required, **2 hr. 3 min. and 30 secs.**
Average speed, **12.2 mph.**

ACT TWO

Fly 347 miles at 347 mph. Keep eye on stewardess; offer to share your seat belt with her. If refused, read **Mad** magazine — **60 minutes**

ACT THREE

Taxi from runway to terminal, wait for exit steps to be fumbled into place	9 minutes
Unbuckle seat belt and/or stewardess, descend steps and walk to Gate 99, Concourse 348; three-quarters of a mile from baggage claiming area	30 seconds
Walk from gate to baggage claiming area	6 minutes
Wait for luggage; it is either there, or mistakenly en route to Point Barrow, Alaska, our 49th state	7 minutes
If luggage is not in Alaska, pick it up and carry to airport bus stop	30 seconds
Wait for bus to load and leave	5 minutes
Airport bus to downtown airlines terminal	40 minutes
Cab from bus terminal to hotel	7 minutes
Check in hotel, take elevator to room, discover lights don't work Call room service	10 minutes

Distance traveled, **25 miles**
Time elapsed—**1 hour 25 minutes**
Average speed, **17.7 mph**

total miles traveled	397
total time elapsed	4 hr. 28 min. 30 sec.
average mph. for trip	88.7
stewardess' name	unavailable

fic," says Evan Herbert in *International Science and Technology*, (May, 1964), "consists of independently controlled units. When they are densely concentrated, drivers' whims gel into a cooperative fluid . . .

"You can't really turn to the laws of motion to describe mathematically the way cars move down the road. While it is evident that vehicles in traffic no longer move as a matter of the driver's free will, but as a cooperative phenomenon—the cooperation is a psychological one that is better described by stimulus-response equations. Drivers respond to the cars in front, to the cars behind, and to the cars alongside. The closer the proximities, the tighter the coupling of stimulus-response. In fact, a theoretical model of vehicular follow-the-leader movements might conceivably describe the behavior of a school of fish or a flight of birds . . . There may be some ways to describe this traffic fluid which will prove useful in solving real problems on the highway."

Fluid moving in a pipe; messages moving along a wire . . . most of our roadways are designed as if they constituted an environment for traffic, but what they really establish are the parameters for vehicular movement. The real environment is created by the vehicles themselves in relation to each other. Highway designers build the frame; drivers create the picture that goes in it.

Are there ways we can approach this differently? One way might be to apply the sophistication of aerospace technology to the movement of vehicles on the roadway. The problems are not dissimilar—an object moves in time and space; it can be controlled.

"Space-age transportation," says *Metropolitan Magazine* in an article, "Aerospace Technicians Tackle Tangled Transportation," (November, 1965) "has come down to earth to use its fountainhead of talent, technology and technique to help untangle traffic for us earthlings. Thus far, the contribution of the space-age engineers is a transportation study that was jointly sponsored by the State of California and North American Aviation, Inc.

"The broad sweep of this comprehensive approach is neatly packaged in six 'sub-models.' Three are basic models—population, econometrics, and land use. These feed into a fourth model which allocates demand to transportation modes. This information passes into a fifth, used to simulate existing or possible transportation networks. The sixth model evaluates improvement in existing transportation modes or new transport ideas."

Models are the games technicians play. It is quite possible that the outcome of the games may be important to us insofar as we are like a school of fish darting down the freeways. But there does seem to be something missing: the subject is not just vehicles—bits of information

GET THERE BEFORE YOU LEAVE

"*Los Angeles to Tokyo in 5½ hours. You'll be able to leave New York at 9 a.m. and arrive in San Francisco at 8 a.m. Just in time for a second breakfast.*

"*And that's not too far off. The first test flight of a U.S. supersonic transport is scheduled for 1969. It should be certified for flight in 1974 . . .*

"*The supersonic transport will carry 266 passengers and cruise from 1800 to 2000 mph . . . Industry economists foresee that the SST program will equal in size the Apollo lunar landing or the Polaris combined submarine and missile systems . . .*"

The Iron Age
April 14, 1966

THE QUIET REVOLUTION

"*By the time supersonic transports start burning up the airlanes in the early 1970's, another high-powered innovation in transport technology will be phasing more quietly into general service. If all goes as predicted, computers will by then be managing the rating, routing, sizing, packaging, billing and auditing of freight movements by all modes of transportation. By so doing, they will have far wider and deeper effects on transportation than the glamorous SST's.*

JOSEPH M. S. COYLE
"Traffic and the Computer"
Traffic Management, April, 1966

THE TRAFFIC GENERATORS

"Still another aspect of the traffic problem is revealed each time a new road is built. New traffic comes forth and creates congestion. Why? Because roads are connecting links to human activities. Road systems inherited from the earliest days of travel are direct links from town center to town center. And, in towns and cities, traffic is a function of buildings in which human activities take place. Buildings generate traffic and are destinations for it."

EVAN HERBERT
International Science and Technology
May, 1964

moving along a channel—there are people in them. There have been many studies of automobiles and traffic, but not too many about the kind of people who drive automobiles.

It may be that the main reason a man drives his car all alone to work is that it gives him the only times during his day when he can be free from the social, emotional, and psychological pressures of family, relatives, neighbors and business associates. In all his active working years, he usually has but two refuges for privacy; driving his car alone or locking himself in the bathroom. Perhaps it might be possible to design bathrooms that offer the visual experience of a car moving along the highway. But then, he'd probably never go to work.

We do not, as yet, have a true "traffic science," nor do we, as yet, have laboratories in which to study people driving cars. England has at least one; the Road Research Laboratory of the Department of Scientific and Industrial Research at Crowthorne. Here there is a full scale mockup of a highway interchange, into which scores of different kinds of vehicles and drivers can be fed at different speeds. Instruments measure what happens and from this traffic engineers can get some basis for estimating what effect differences in design and traffic control might have.

This is different from more conventional test tracks, where skilled drivers propel the most recent model cars around and around a track. As we experience it, traffic is not like that. A good test mix in a traffic laboratory would include all sizes, ages and kinds of vehicles (although it is as ridiculous to have commercial vehicles moving on passenger car highways as it would be to have passenger vehicles allowed to run along railroad lines; yet we do it all the time.)

The test drivers would include teenagers, elderly people with badly fitted bifocals, alcoholics, drug addicts, timid old ladies, salesmen late for their next call, bus drivers running five minutes behind schedule; and big-rig truck drivers with a date that night in Des Moines. Liberally interspersed should be station wagons acrawl with small children, a St. Bernard who keeps trying to get in the driver's compartment, ice cream all over the seats, and oranges rolling about the floor.

Perhaps if we set up some of these laboratories and operated them under all sorts of weather and visibility conditions, we might begin to understand what the highway traffic problem is all about. Perhaps, someday, we will.

Aside from the fact that we still, contrary to all reason and experience, design roadways on which drivers going in opposite directions can approach each other at high speed, there is mainly the problem of how vehicles can move safely and comfortably from one roadway system to another. This is sometimes called "the problem of nodes"—the point-spaces where systems join. Included among nodes are "merging traffic" where vehicles, sometimes all too violently, "merge" as one fish tries to join the school of fish flying down the highway; the intersections where, for reasons that escape almost anyone who thinks about it, right angle traffic "crosses the 'T' "—an old naval strategy that has littered the bottoms of oceans with the hulks of warships—and the movement of vehicles down a street so intersected that it is like traversing the alimentary tract of a worm that has been chopped into bits by some future Nobel prize winner.

We usually place our traffic signals at the nodes; too little and too late to avoid calamity if our timing is wrong. Wolfgang von Stein, in the traffic department at Düsseldorf, Germany, has experimented with pre-signals set 100 feet *before* the signal at the intersection. He also has tried putting "speed signals" along the roadways leading to an intersection, suggesting what speed should be maintained in order to get through the intersection safely with the light, or to slow down leisurely for a stop. He reports that the percentage of vehicles passing through an intersection without stopping, when using this system, has increased from 55 to 77 per cent.

It is a common experience to sit in a car at an absolutely empty intersection, waiting for the red light to change. The programming of these signals was frozen into a timing pattern based on a previous traffic flow. But that traffic has long since dispersed and its passage is no longer relevant. We sit and wait anyway. Why?

In Toronto, a Univac 1107 has been hooked up to take data simultaneously on what ultimately will be a 1,000-intersection system. Detectors report on the passage of all the vehicles in the system by scanning them at 64 pulses per second, and the data is fed into a central computer. The computer figures out the quantity, speed, and position of the traffic and activates the intersection lights to keep the traffic flowing smoothly. Here is the marriage of the wheel and the electron; they interact, each influencing the other. And, perhaps, in the next twenty years, that is the way it will be.

If traffic-actuated control will not work, perhaps the solution will be to monitor the movement of the vehicles electronically. W. A. Bugge, then Director of Highways, Washington State Highway Commission, writing on "Highway Transportation after 1975," in *Civil Engineering,* (January, 1962), suggests, "With the pressing need to reduce traffic fatalities and costly accidents, traffic control will have to be fully automatic, positive and sufficient to give full coverage at the fingertips of engineers, maintenance forces and enforcement officers. The freeway and other high speed sections, whether intra-city, inter-city, or inter-

THE CREWLESS ENGINE ROOM

"The major costs of operating ships today are the handling of cargo and the payment of crew. We may therefore expect that in the future great efforts will be made to decrease both these items. Cargo-handling costs can be cut by improved crane facilities, side-loading ports, conveyor belts, the use of containers, train ferries, and so on.

"The reduction of crew costs can only be achieved by a reduction in the numbers of the crew, and this means the introduction of some degree of automation. As an example, the running behavior of the engines can be monitored automatically, the information being displayed on a central control console in the engine room, while the maneuvering and general control can be carried out on the bridge, and these and similar changes could result in an appreciable saving in crew numbers . . ."

DR. F. H. TODD
Superintendent, Ship Division
National Physical Laboratory
Shipbuilding and Shipping Record—
1962

GET A HORSE

"Motor trucks average some six miles an hour in New York traffic today, as against eleven for horse-drawn trucks in 1910—and the cost to the economy of traffic jams, according to a New York Times business survey, is five billion dollars yearly!"

"The Poverty of Abundance"

THE HIEROGLYPHICS THAT MOVED

It is interesting, perhaps even significant, that in a world increasingly involved with motion, we have not yet developed a symbolism by which it can easily be expressed. The drawings of architects, highway designers and rapid transit engineers alike are static frames of frozen moments like single frames from a motion picture.

It should, however, be possible to devise a system of notation—much like a musical score—which preserves the sense of motion, and yet is transferable from discipline to discipline; for example, from ballet to highway engineering, or even from human beings to computers.

Lawrence Halprin, landscape architect, has worked out such a symbolism, which he calls "Motation." It is too complicated to describe fully here, but a little of what it has to offer is shown on this page. A more complete description may be found in the July, 1965, issue of Progressive Architecture.

The illustrations at the right show how the movement of a person moving through a plaza might be annotated. The film strip shows the beginning of the walk; one set of drawings shows the general environment in which the walk is taking place; and the other set shows how personal experience of the environment changes as he moves through it. Photos and frames read from the bottom up, and some of the symbols used are described immediately below. Although the frames depict the entire journey through the plaza, the photos relate only to the first five frames.

"MOTATION" BY LAWRENCE HALPRIN. EXCERPTED FROM PROGRESSIVE ARCHITECTURE MAGAZINE.

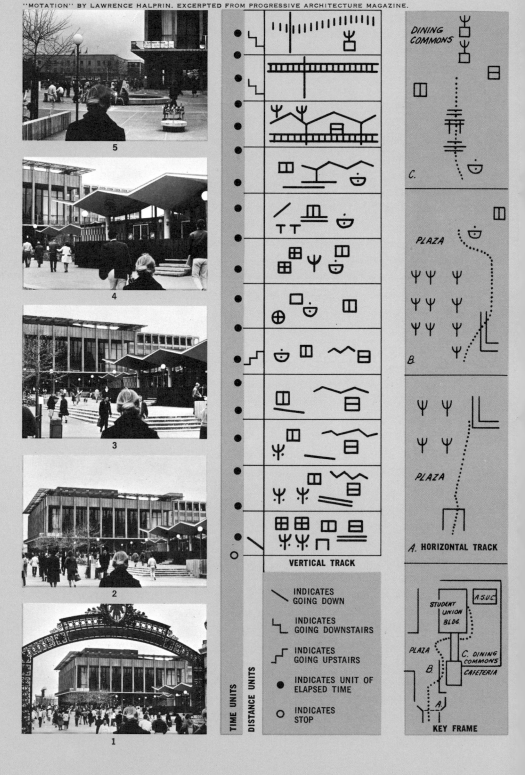

VERTICAL TRACK

A. HORIZONTAL TRACK

DINING COMMONS

C.

PLAZA

B.

PLAZA

TIME UNITS

DISTANCE UNITS

INDICATES GOING DOWN

INDICATES GOING DOWNSTAIRS

INDICATES GOING UPSTAIRS

INDICATES UNIT OF ELAPSED TIME

INDICATES STOP

KEY FRAME

STUDENT UNION BLDG.

A.S.U.C.

PLAZA

C. DINING COMMONS

CAFETERIA

B

A

MOTION SYMBOLS

| | VERTICAL ELEMENT
| — | HORIZONTAL ELEMENT
| \ | DIAGONAL ELEMENT
| ⊞ | HIGH BUILDING
| ⊟ | LOW BUILDING
| ⊞ | MEDIUM BUILDING
| ⊓ | DOOR OR GATE
| ⏝ | FOUNTAIN

| Ψ | TREE
| • | HUMAN
| ⊕ | BIKE
| > | DIRECTION OF MOVEMENT
| ⌞ | BELOW EYE LEVEL RIGHT
| ⌝ | ABOVE EYE LEVEL LEFT
| ‖‖ | FENCE
| ▥ | RAILING
| ⊤ | TABLE

Dot on both sides of symbol indicates plural

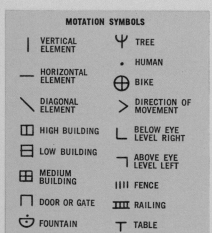

5

4

3

2

1

state, must be provided with a means of positive traffic control. This will be done by guidance systems in the vehicle. There will be television surveillance of every mile of highway so that a dispatcher can anticipate problems and correct them before congestion builds up, or take remedial action after an accident has occurred.

"The driver's position in relation to other vehicles within one mile of him, together with his position on the roadway with respect to all points of conflict, will be shown continuously on a small television viewer, available to him at the flick of a switch." While he's watching TV, who is watching the road?

The next step, of course, would be the completely computerized, electronically controlled movement of automobiles on freeway and turnpike systems. Such control systems will be well within our technology in the next two decades; they almost are now. What is overlooked in the implementation of such systems is that people *like* to drive their own cars. In an increasingly fragmented and regimented society, driving one's own automobile may be one of the few experiences left where the individual feels he is still able to control something; still personally involved. If this psychological satisfaction is removed by automatic controls, why not take public transportation to begin with, and pick up a rental car for transportation to the specific destination after the freeway journey is ended?

Other problems of our broken-wheeled age may be partially helped by the electron. Today, we see the spectacle of huge buses running almost empty along their routes during "off" hours. This is analogous to the automatic red light at an intersection where no traffic is crossing; and just about as useful. It should be within the range of our technology to take the big rigs off the streets, except during peak hours, and substitute smaller carriers—jitneys or microbuses.

People who want to ride to somewhere else would simply dial a number on their phones. When sufficient numbers close together had been accumulated, a jitney or microbus would be routed by computer, along the most economical route, to the various residences, pick the passengers up at the door, and take them to the closest terminal that connects with other systems. It is true, this would involve some waiting on the part of the passengers calling in. But have you ever waited at a bus stop, with the present system, during the off-peak hours?

There has been the suggestion, in recent years, that private automobiles be barred from central core areas of major cities because of the increasing traffic congestion and lack of parking space. An extension of this idea might simply be to have people drive their cars to the closest transit terminal, park them, then take the mass transit to a central city

THE 3000-MILE ELEVATOR RIDE

"*Travel has changed drastically, and I don't mean that it's just faster. Travel, for the most part, is no longer travel; it is a process which has a beginning and an end but virtually no middle. Travel is not an experience so much as a suspension of experience. Flying in a plane from San Francisco to New York is nothing more nor less than a horizontal elevator ride. One imagines if we had buildings 3,000 miles high, there would be a young woman on the elevators offering us coffee, tea or milk . . .*"

HOWARD GOSSAGE
Ramparts—April, 1966

THE CiTY THAT MOVES

"*Environments change their qualities with the variation of speed they generate. As we move through them, they move around us. On our freeways and rapid transit systems the variation in environmental speed becomes clearer when we observe the contrast between the high-speed foreground and the low-speed background . . .*
"*As another example, an automobile can be defined as an instrument for moving you to the city, but it can also be defined as a means of moving the city to you. In terms of the individual, whose only true continuity is his own awareness, it can be said, with all psychological justice, that the environment moves . . .*"

LAWRENCE HALPRIN
Progressive Architecture—July, 1965

INCOMPATIBLE GEOMETRY

"There is an incompatibility among the geometry of roads, the vehicle-driver complex, traffic controls, and the law. But research leading to a theory of traffic flow may provide a more realistic basis for designs of roads, vehicles and controls that may resolve the conflicts.

"Even without a theory, there is promise of some relief of congestion in computers that adapt the timing of signals to real-time traffic demands on a city street system. Long range, the very causes of movement can be manipulated by rearranging building placement to simplify circulation patterns among these traffic generators . . ."

EVAN HERBERT
"Traffic"—International Science
and Technology—May, 1964

PASS WITH CAUTION

"According to projections by the long-term planning group of Stanford Research Institute, the communications industry will overtake the transportation industry in dollar volume in the U.S. in 1977, to reach a volume of $50-$60 billion per year.

Missiles and Rockets
January 31, 1966

terminal and be picked up by taxicab to go to their destination.

The taxicab would be part of the mass transit system and would be supported in the same way that other forms of public transportation are, through individual fare collections and public subsidy. Meanwhile, the streets would be open to the use of commercial vehicles and mass transit, and parking lot areas could be returned as bases for high-rise buildings, a portion of whose tax returns would be used to defray the expense of the taxicab fleets.

There also is the question, asked more frequently in recent years, why there is any charge for transporting people horizontally in city core areas at all. We would be outraged if we had to pay a fare each time we took an elevator in a high rise building, yet the horizontal movement of people is just as important as their vertical movement. Perhaps we just need to think about turning the elevator system on its side and provide free horizontal transport for people downtown.

Perhaps, too, we might begin to find, in the next twenty years, the application of some of the already advanced technologies we have for the movement of goods to the movement of people. No manufacturer would put up with a system in which his product has to be repackaged at each change of carriers. One might look at the camper-back or the travel trailer, with their compact comfort, and ask if they could not be adapted to a system of "people-tainers." When the family wants to go on a long, involved trip, the transport service provides the "people-tainer," complete with its fold down beds, toilet facilities, closet space, view windows, etc., whose dimensions have been standardized for handling over the whole system. The "people-tainer" is pulled up to the family's front door, the kids, bedding, food for snacks, toys, etc. are stored in it, and away they go to the closest terminal, to be picked up by forklift and placed, with similar units on a flat bed railroad car, a highway rig, or a super-air transport. Luggage would be about as necessary as high-button shoes. The "people-tainer" could be handled—just as containerized cargo is today—on all parts of the system; and when it arrives at its destination, it would simply be lifted by elevator into open compartments in hotel or apartment house frames, where the "people-tainer" becomes one of a complex of rooms connecting with eating, recreational and other facilities.

It might not happen, and most likely it won't, but it is an example of what we have been trying to say here: even in a wheel-dominated technology, there is no reason why we should not live better than we do. The choreography for the "clockwork dinosaur" is yet to be written. When it is, people will move through space as gracefully and meaningfully as dancers in a ballet. Perhaps, in twenty years, it will happen. □

DRAWING BY MASAMI MIYAMOTO

WHAT IS MAN?

*"A self-balancing, 28-jointed
adapter-base biped; an electrochemical
reduction plant, integral with
segregated stowages of special energy
extracts in storage batteries for
subsequent actuation of thousands of
hydraulic and pneumatic pumps
with motors attached; 62,000 miles
of capillaries . . .*

*"The whole, extraordinary complex
mechanism guided with exquisite
precision from a turret in which
are located telescopic and microscopic
self-registering and recording range
finders, a spectroscope, etc.; the turret
control being closely allied with
an air-conditioning intake-and-exhaust,
and a main fuel intake . . ."*

R. BUCKMINSTER FULLER
"Nine Chains to the Moon"
J. B. Lippincott Co., 1938

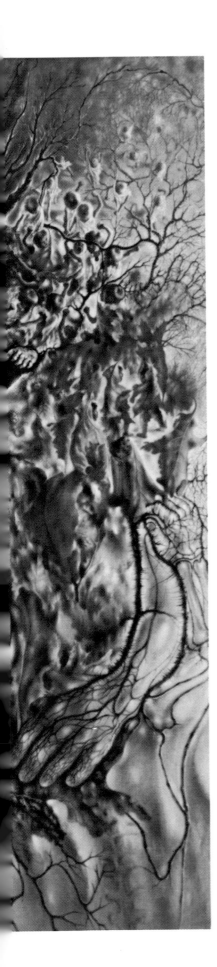

riders of the electronic surf

☐ A journey—any journey—is a lonesome thing. However long or short the way, it inevitably involves the traveler in experiences that are not shared by those he left behind. Whatever he may have been when he left, the traveler returns—to some extent—a stranger. The tribal cohesion of the early hunters, whose individual weakness led them to roam in packs, and of the early farmers, who for mutual protection tilled their plots within shouting distance of each other, was fractured when the first traveler turned his back on them all and set off on his lonely journey.

The vehicle itself is a capsule of loneliness, its passenger-carrying ability limited by the capacity of its power train. The people who take a trip together are never quite the same as those who did not take it, and their number is always limited by the size of the vehicle. When man began to travel in vehicles—whether on horseback, raft, or dugout canoe —he began a process of separation which, amplified over the centuries by advances in vehicular technology, broke society into little pieces, and made strangers of us all.

In recent years, this fragmentation has been attributed to the invention of printing, with its formalized breaking down of human experience into standardized bits and pieces that can be arranged into linear sequences. This, it is said, was later translated by advancing technology into the standardization of parts (pieces of type), the assembly line for mass production (sentences on a printed page), and the specialized and repetitive actions of workers, which was reflected in the separation of our arts and science; in the compartmentalization of our formal education, and the over-specialization of our economic lives. The result was the breaking down of what had once been the continuous, flowing interaction between organisms, each other, and their environment, into static, standardized bits and pieces. Our intellectual, emotional, social and economic lives had been reduced to a series of "still" pictures which, if sequenced properly and run through the machine at the "right" speed, gave us the illusion of life, but not the feeling of it.

We thus have finally begun to reap the harvest of our affair with the vehicle—a sometimes bitter harvest. But it is possible that we are coming to the end of this long and lonely journey and that we may embark upon a quite different one. Our new electronic technology offers us, at least in theory, the possibility that all of us can share in the same experience simultaneously. The hard glow of the television tube may weld our fractured world together, and offers us the opportunity to restore identity, process and continuity to our inner lives. It may be that *this* is the road we will take—together. Someone has referred to this as "an insurmountable opportunity." Perhaps it is—but if we keep in mind the long way we have come, and the way we may go, it may not be so insur-

DETAIL FROM "HIDE AND SEEK" BY PAVEL TCHELITCHEW—MUSEUM OF MODERN ART, NEW YORK. MRS. SIMON GUGGENHEIM FUND.

DEATH OF THE CITIES

"Arthur Clarke, who still keeps a fatherly eye on the multimillion-dollar system he proposed in Wireless World *in 1945, foresees sweeping changes touched off by communications satellites. Cities, he thinks, may disappear. Their principal reason for being is to cluster people closer together where they can see and talk with each other, a process that is not always enjoyable. When an executive can instantly reach all his contacts, wherever they may be, by television, he will have little reason for leaving home . . ."*

Time, May 14, 1965

A MEMBER OF THE FAMILY

"Television's biggest impact has been on the American home. Before TV, it looked as if Detroit might turn the suburban home into an appendage tacked onto the two-car garage; a nice place to sleep but you wouldn't want to stay there. Television changed all that.

"This winter (1965-66) Americans will spend more time watching TV in their living room than doing anything else except sleeping . . .

"The astonishing thing about television in the home is its boundless variety. In the course of a single broadcast day, TV is many things to the average family—a visual newspaper to glance over at breakfast; a baby-sitter for pre-school children; a cordon bleu *cooking course; a friendly visitor for shut-ins, retired people and harassed housewives; a free ticket to the ball game for sports fans; an afternoon at the movies for the kids; a source of after-dinner relaxation for the father; an education in current history for the family, and so on . . ."*

Electronic Age
Summer, 1965

mountable, after all . . .

In the preceding pages we have discussed the movement of the human sensory apparatus to a point in space and time where it can experience a new array of stimuli. We have suggested that the application of already existing electronic technology to the established but non-interconnecting subsystems for bodily transport could help us achieve, during the next twenty years, a supertransportation system that could move the human organism from experience to experience as smoothly and easily as schools of fish move through water.

Now, we are going to discuss the reverse process, which we believe will take place during the same two decades; the increasing ability of our technology to move the experience itself—in sound and color and full dimension—to the human nervous system. We are going, further, to suggest that it is in the interplay between these two developments— the movement of the body toward the experience, the experience toward the body—that much of the excitement of our next twenty years will be created.

We will also suggest that during this period of overlapping technologies, the city, as we have known it, may be transformed into something else that we can now but dimly see; that some highways and networks of roads for human transport may sink back into the natural landscape; that the pattern of our workaday lives will undergo profound transformations; that our social and political and economic worlds will become something quite other than they now are.

And, finally, we will conclude that there will come a point—perhaps in the next two decades—when the human sensory apparatus will no longer easily be able to distinguish between an electronically created experience and an in-person one. At that time, we believe, the human organism will increasingly choose in favor of an electronic experience over a "real" experience, and we will have begun to move deeper and deeper into the electromagnetic spectrum . . .

Let us imagine a particular space and time circa 1986: a home in the suburbs of Phoenix. A man is sitting in the middle of a circular room and on the curved walls around him he can see the ocean—surf breaking over the rocks and foaming up the beach; a fish hawk trembling in the luminescent sky. Across from him sits another man, and the two of them are talking to each other. Once in awhile, the boom of the bursting surf and the cry of the hawk intrude upon their conversation.

Let us now say that the room is underground and has no "real" view at all; that what is experienced on the curved walls is an image on a "flat wall" television screen, pre-recorded in Hawaii, and now being replayed electronically. Let us further say that the first man is "real," but that the second man is being broadcast by laser beam from a satellite and recreated, in color and full dimension (you could walk around his image and see the back of his head) by "holography," so that though he is "there" in Phoenix at the moment, he is "in reality" at the same moment sitting in his study at the University of Edinburgh.

Where, in this situation, does "reality" begin and end? This will be a question that—by 1986—we will, individually, be asked to answer. There is nothing in the situation just described that does not appear to be perfectly feasible within perhaps the next ten years; certainly within the next twenty. We have *already* entered a new world of experience.

It all began about a hundred years ago, but what it comes down to is the advent of television, just after World War II.

"To observe *really* fast growth, *really* swift change, one must leave the land of housing starts, heating ducts, and the plug-in stove. The classic case in point for growth must be observed in its natural habitat— the living room. There she sits, in all her flickering grandeur, maybe a one-eyed monster, maybe not, but no matter what it is called, television adds up to *change*," says Ben J. Wattenberg in his superb study of the 1960 census figures, *This U.S.A.*

"In 1940, the number of television sets in American homes could probably be counted on the fingers of one hand. By 1947, 14,000 families had television. In 1948, there were 172,000 families owning a set. By 1949, there were still fewer than a million families with television . . .

"In 1948, fewer than one household in each *two thousand* had a set; in 1960, *nine out of ten* families owned a set. By 1964, fully 93 per cent of American households had television . . .

"Already children ask their young (very young) parents, 'What was it like growing up in the days before television?' . . . Already it seems difficult to remember the bygone era when the population was divided into those who had television sets and those who did not . . .''

Sometime in the 1950's, the American people made a commitment; something like the decision to migrate westward a hundred or so years earlier; they began a mass trek toward electronic experience . . .

"No other single phenomenon in American life has ever met with such acclaim as television," says Desmond Smith, writing in *Electronic Age* (Summer, 1965). "It took 80 years for the telephone to be installed in 34 million homes. It took 62 years for electric wiring, 49 years for the automobile and 47 years for the electric washer to reach the same number of homes. Television made the giant stride in 10 years.

" 'People who deny themselves television deny themselves participation in life today,' says author and critic John Mason Brown. 'They are self exiled from the world.' "

FACSIMILE BY TELEPHONE

"CHICAGO: — Magnavox Co. will introduce later this year a low-priced facsimile device that transmits printed material over ordinary telephones . . . "The new facsimile device, called Magnafax, is a desk-top unit used with regular telephone systems. An office worker dials the number of another office and then can transmit to it letters, signatures, blueprints or other printed material . . ."

The Wall Street Journal

TV PIX FROM RECORDS

"PITTSBURGH: — Westinghouse Electric Corp. said it has developed an electronic system that plays television pictures from a phonograph record. The new system, called Phonovid, produces up to 400 still pictures and 40 minutes of voice and music from two sides of a 12-inch, 33⅓ recording . . . "Audio and video signals both are present in the grooves of the 'Videodisc' and both are picked up by the phonograph needle . . . Pictures on the television screen may be line drawings, charts, printed text or photographs . . ."

The Wall Street Journal

SCULPTURED BY LIGHT

"Television has within its power to decide what kind of people we become. Nothing less."

Rt. Hon. W. F. DEEDES, M.P.

THE BANK-A-PHONE

"Imagine this sequence of events when you sit down to pay your electric or fuel bills. Instead of writing and mailing a check, you simply would stick a colored plastic card into a special slot at the back of your modernized telephone and dial your bank's computer number.

"Next, you would 'dial' the amount of the bill—using the regular telephone digits. Within seconds, an electronic voice would inform you that $18.43 had been transferred out of your checking account into the utility's account— and that would be that."

SYLVIA PORTER
"Your Money's Worth"
May 5, 1965

ONE ELECTRON, ONE VOTE

"... the business of voting in America— the most important business in a democracy—is slow, cumbersome and primitive," says CBS President Frank Stanton. "If we ran our factories, conducted our communications and nurtured our health at the same rate of scientific and technical advance as we conduct our political affairs, we would be taking weeks to make a pair of shoes, delivering the mail by Pony Express, and treating pneumonia by bloodletting."

"Toward Voting as a Positive Pleasure," Time, Dec. 10, 1965

Someplace, somehow, something new has entered our lives. And not only ours:

"...Television is booming all over the world," says John A. Schneider, speaking as president of the CBS television network. "Set ownership rose from 164 million last February to 173 million in July (1965). It is interesting to note that this country accounts for less than one-third of all the television sets in the world. Western Europe has 48 million receivers, eastern Europe has 21 million, the Far East has 19 million."

The trek toward the phosphors is not an American phenomenon, it is a turning of the human species away from the personal biological confrontation of experience to the introspective experience of electronic waves. If ever there was an avenue of approach to the "one-world" concept—this appears to be it. The world is becoming a village.

So far we have discussed television in the broadest sense—the sort of thing we experience in our living rooms—broadcast television. From some central transmitter it balloons out over an area of approximately 50 miles, or is ricochetted from microwave tower to microwave tower, pours through the walls of our houses, streams through our bodies, and a part of it is picked up by antenna and becomes a pattern of dots on a screen, moving so fast they appear, to us, to be a picture.

But there are other forms of television, and, in the long run, these may transform our lives more than the monster in the living room.

"There are two television services; one visible and the other invisible to the general public," said Nathan L. Halpern, President, Theatre Network Television Inc. (TNT), at the University of Pennsylvania, January 31, 1966. "Better known as broadcasting and closed-circuit television, the two media co-exist, with each providing services to its own audience.

"Closed-circuit TV is a dynamic part of the mid-20th Century explosion in communications. It is composed of a wide and varied range of separate and private communications. Largely unknown to the public, it might even seem like 'unseen television.' Yet it is increasingly and powerfully an essential communications medium serving the expanding special needs of our society.

"It is an authentic television whose true role perhaps has been overshadowed by the omnipresent broadcast television. Still growing, closed-circuit TV is an emerging medium on the new frontier of communications..."

Here, in the "unseen world of TV" is a person to person, firm to firm media that annihilates space and time, makes the corporation president as close to his regional manager, 3000 miles away, as if they were in the same room; brings the economic and business life of our country into full, instantaneous sight and sound communication. Already, the memo

PHOTOGRAPHY BY ROBERT A. ISAACS

FLAT WALL TV

"One of the dreams of the electronics industry is to make a television screen that will hang flat on the wall. It's an idea to which everybody responds enthusiastically—everybody but the men who would have to design the set.

"Imagine what such a TV receiver would be like. There would be no tube to form the picture; instead, the screen would be a mosaic made up of thousands of separate light elements. If the screen were three by four feet, and the pictures were to be as clear as today's television picture, there would have to be at least 700,000 separate elements for black-and-white, almost three million for color. And each one would have to be separately controlled.

"Those control circuits, if built from today's components, would take up all the room in an average-size house. That's what gives the engineers such headaches when they think about on-the-wall TV. But it won't be too long, things continuing as they are, before the electronics industry will be able to fit such a tremendous complex of control circuitry into a package no bigger than today's portable television sets. Microelectronics is the reason . . ."

FRANK LEARY
"The Impact of Microelectronics"
The Exchange—January, 1965

is a paper dodo; tomorrow, the blizzard of corporate paper will melt against the immediacy and warmth of the televised experience.

"We tend," continues Nathan L. Halpern, "to think of television as pictures. Much of closed-circuit TV presents pictures, like broadcasting. But some closed-circuit techniques have developed display systems to present alpha-numeric characters, symbols and graphs; the languages of our most sophisticated technologies of today."

In the business world, we mostly go places to "see" people, or to "see" things. When what we want to "see" can be brought to us, why should we go? This has profound implications for the corporation headquarters, where mostly the people are there to "see" each other, or "see" reports, or what not. Why not let everybody stay home, dispense with the enormous investment in "headquarters," get rid of the tiresome, expensive and unproductive "commuting" period twice each day, and simply conduct business from our homes?

But if we do that, what happens to the central city "cores" when the daily tide of thousands and perhaps millions of businessmen, stenographers, secretaries, and file clerks no longer flood—like the tide of effluent into a tidal pool—into the central city core every morning? What happens to the beauty shops, the little coffee places, the expense account restaurants, the bars, the shoe shine parlors—all the scores upon scores of businesses that depend on this human tide washing in?

And what happens to the mass transportation systems—if huge waves of humanity are not rolling in from the suburban beaches? And the freeways? The "city" becomes not a head-and-shoulders skyscraper matrix, but a thin film of electrons spread over the countryside. It would be a quite different world—to live in and work in.

"The day may come," says Morris J. Gelman in an article called "Will Wire Take Over?" in *Television Magazine* (December, 1965), "when there are no regular over-the-air television stations in the country. It's conceivable that the nation's TV sets will be so accessible by wire that networks will affiliate exclusively with cable systems.

"Wire TV, the intruder who's knocking on broadcasting's status quo, wears the guise for the nonce of community antenna television. This is an industry of weed-like growth which operates by receiving and distributing signals by cable into the home on a subscription basis. What it may become tomorrow has frightened or flipped, bedeviled or beguiled—depending on their viewpoint—a great many people for a great many hours."

If the downtown city core disappears, robbed of its main support of the tide of business people washing in and out every morning and night, what happens to the department stores?

"There's almost no limit to this thing (wire TV). I can even see a marketing service evolving from it," says Tom S. Gilchrist, Jr., vice-president and general manager of WESH-TV, Daytona Beach, Florida. "Suppose as this thing grew it developed into a two-way communication proposition where something advertised on a TV program is followed by a code number. If some viewer wanted to order it, all he'd do is go to his television set and dial a number and the merchandise is delivered to him in nothing flat."

Why department stores in high rent, high tax central core locations? Why not warehouses and studio-type showrooms outside the city and televised "showings" of today's specials directly into the home?

And so, putting all the pieces together—no commuter tide downtown, no flood of people moving in and out, no office buildings, no shops, no department stores. Where did the city go? Perhaps it has gone back to the country, to relatively small—50,000-persons or so units—that are completely self-contained. Where did business go? To a cottage-type industry, where all but operational personnel function from home studios, equipped with three-dimensional TV, magnetic tapes, round-the-clock recording devices. Perhaps the great migration to the urban areas, the creation of megalopolis, will be halted and reversed. Perhaps . . .

It would not happen all at once, nor even everywhere. But the erosion of the city-oriented social and business community as we know it would increase over the years, and gradually the wheel would be traded in on the electron.

Nearly all we have suggested so far can be done with conventional television systems; open broadcast or closed circuit, using current technology. What then if we add the global dimension of synchronous satellite TV transmitters? Now the local and the private becomes worldwide and public. Something more happens to us then.

There seems to be no real doubt that current and immediately foreseeable technology can provide us with a global system for instantaneous communication, but there certainly are some doubts as to whether we actually will implement the technology.

Among those who are optimistic that such a system will be created is David Sarnoff, Chairman, RCA, who, in *Electronic Age* (Summer, 1965), said, "Within a decade, and possibly less, I believe it will be technically feasible to broadcast directly into the home from synchronous satellites. All of the basic components and technology already exist for radio and television broadcast transmitters to operate in space . . .

"Placed in synchronous orbit over the equator, each satellite could broadcast to an area of one million square miles, covering such nations as Brazil, India, Western Europe and the United States. These satellites

GO MICRO WAVE

"The better solution (compared to nuclear powered satellites) to the problem is to use a microwave converter on the home receiver. I don't think the cost of the converter for the receiver is going to amount to very much in the future and the advantages of using the microwaves are so great. From a frequency allocation point of view the number of channels available, for example, would be considerable. I think that if direct broadcasting ever comes about it will operate completely in the microwave band. I also think that's the way it should develop."

Dr. HAROLD A. ROSEN
Hughes Aircraft Co.

HOW BIG THE MOON?

"You have to look at the circuit. You have a satellite and it's pumping power down to some sort of receiving antenna and television receiver. Now whether it's in the home or where it is, this is the problem. You ask yourself, what is the cheapest way to do this?

"Well, you size the satellite and you find the bigger you make it, the smaller you make the receiving antennas. Then it becomes a matter of how many receiving antennas. If you're talking about the home, well, what do we have—about 60 million television sets in this country. So each receiving set costs, say, $100 for the antenna and everything else. That's six billion dollars worth of ground equipment. So you say if I make a few of them—200 or 300, and make them bigger, I can do it for $50 million and I can give the signal to the local TV station and let them send it to the home. The satellite could probably be smaller and the overall investment kept down to about $50 million."

SPENCER SPAULDING
Comsat

THE TIME TRAVELERS

*When photography was invented,
the artist became unemployed.
Searching about for other things
to do, he discovered the future,
buried in his own subconscious mind.
He's been describing it ever since.*

*In the illustrations at right, we trace
one of these lines of exploration.
Georges Seurat, whose painting appears
at the top, was among the
"pointillism" artists of the 19th Century
Impressionists. He broke the human
visual experience down into "point
sources" that had to be reassembled by
the viewer into a meaningful pattern.*

*In doing this, he anticipated the
"halftone" printing process which was
introduced as a mass-production
way of recreating visual experience in
1888. This art form, still used today,
foreshadowed the dot and line
pattern on today's television screens.*

*All three techniques are logical
extensions of a technology that breaks
down human experience into bits and
pieces; the dots and dashes of telegraphy,
the 0 or 1 input of computers, words
on a page. These are the natural
offspring of a mechanical age and are
closely allied to the standardized
parts and assembly line techniques
of contemporary industry.*

*With the introduction of laser
holography which recreates a visual
experience in full dimension, we
may begin to return to a much more
ancient way of experiencing our
movement through space and our
duration in time. Process and flow may
replace bits and pieces. The ray of
the laser beam may melt our fragmented
world back into a cohesive experience
again; and the artist will have to
find some new dimension to explore.*

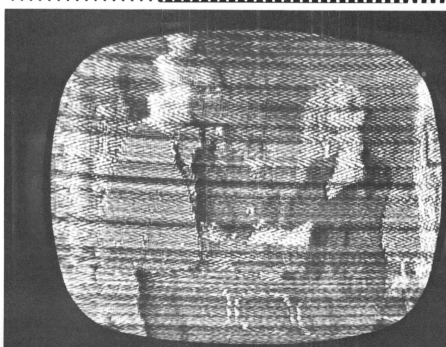

would operate in the UHF-TV band. To receive them would require only minor modification in the home receiver and redirection of its antenna. A six-foot antenna would be sufficient to receive a clear television signal in the home..."

There is little or no dispute over whether we *can* do this; there is argument as to whether we will.

"Despite the many enthusiastic forecasts, however, there is evidence that direct satellite transmission into the home is at least ten or maybe many more years than that away. It might never come. Economics and politics stand hugely in the way," says Morris J. Gelman, in an article, "The Invisible Shield," in *Television Magazine* (February, 1966).

"In ten years," says Spencer Spaulding of the Communications Satellite Corporation, "the technology could conceivably advance to where it was economically feasible to broadcast directly to the home from a satellite. When we're talking economically feasible, we're talking specifically about this country at this moment...

"It is difficult to see how you would replace all of the present network-affiliate setup by going directly to the home. You'd lose a lot of the broadcast structure in the process. Also, in this country, you have a tremendous investment in the local broadcast stations... what are you going to do with the local TV station?"

John F. White, president, National Education Television, says, "Anybody who talks in terms of 20 years about satellite broadcasting directly to the homes is kidding themselves. There's going to be considerable resistance. The resistance will not involve whether we put a satellite up, but how we use it. I think the chances of any network of any kind being able to program out of New York or Hollywood straight into homes is a remote one because the national investment and the national economy are based on individual stations. I think they will have to feed from the satellites to individual stations and then out again ..."

In addition to economic barriers, there may also be a political one. "I see direct broadcasts to the home as practical scientifically," said Leonard H. Goldenson, president, American Broadcasting Co., "but it would be completely impractical politically. I can't imagine any government, including our own, permitting satellite transmissions direct to our homes... I can't see anything changing politically where the Congress of the United States or the ruling body of any country is going to permit unlimited propaganda from orbital stations to come directly into the home without supervision..."

And so we find, as we have in earlier discussions, that the economics of the established order, and the little political cages that enclose our minds, lag far behind what we can do technologically. It is the same with

MY UNCLE THE CHAIR

"...*I predict that within the next ten years the networks, be there three or ten, will realize that programming is becoming banal. When 'Beverly Hillbillies,' which has already spun off 'Petticoat Junction,' which in turn spun off 'Green Acres,' spins again and out comes another bumpkin background which this time fails ...*
"*When 'My Mother the Car' spins off 'My Uncle the Chair'; when 'Gunsmoke' and 'Bonanza' deteriorate into 'Frontier Dentist'... then at last something will be done about the programming problem.*
"*And do you know what I think they will finally get around to doing? They will do what every other kind of business does as a regular way of life— the networks will start spending real money on research and development for the product they sell.*
"*They will establish training courses in the creative arts, schools for writers and directors and even actors ... They will schedule workshops on the air to give these untried talents a chance to be seen. And they will sustain these workshops as necessary, without complaining that advertisers won't support them with sponsorship ...*"

RICHARD A. R. PINKHAM
Senior Vice President
Ted Bates & Co., Inc.

THE ELECTRONIC CITY HALL

"There are five million television receivers in New York devoted to the reception of commercial and educational channels . . . When 280 receivers in the firehouses, 81 in the police stations, 120 in the hospitals, 60 in the libraries, health centers and welfare centers of this city can affect the public interest, safety and advantages so directly, think what we could do with 5,000 receivers otherwise strategically placed!

"With all the power of the commercial system of broadcasting in this country to move merchandise from the shelves . . . with all the great usefulness of educational television . . . I submit that for purpose and continuity, it is Metropolitan TV which provides a direct improvement in municipal services . . ."

SEYMOUR N. SIEGEL
Director of Radio Communications
City of New York

OF BLUSH AND NUANCE

"In order to remove the need for the majority of the personal contacts at present necessary in most business operations . . . telecommunications must provide a form of high-definition color television associated with high quality audio channels—every blush and nuance needs to be accurately conveyed. Looking into the even more remote future, it may not be too fanciful to imagine that other senses will be simulated remotely."

J. D. CLARE
Standard Telecommunications
Laboratories, Harlow, England

air pollution, water pollution, land allocation, growing food, renewing our cities . . . The same old story, over and over again.

"The most notable aspect of our world of novelty and rapid change," said philosopher W. H. Ferry in a talk in Los Angeles in 1965, "is the unwillingness of economists and political scientists to perceive it, and their hostility toward those who do. We chiefly suffer from a failure to sense the human possibilities of our technical accomplishment."

For the moment, we might consider that technologically we can, if we desire to, set up a system of global communications through satellites that will—or could—weld the entire world into a single community. We might also consider that neither economic nor political apathy will, for many years, be able to keep this from happening; they fight a delaying action, but not a terminal one. Having decided this, we might concern ourselves with a much more important question: once given a world-wide communication system, do we have anything to say?

Shortly after our first communications satellite, Telstar, was launched John Crosby wrote, in the New York *Herald Tribune:* "Telstar, as you know, is that complicated ball that whirls through space, transmitting television broadcasts, telephone messages, and everything except common sense. When it was first cast aloft, trumpets sounded. Continents would share each other's intellectual pleasures . . .

"The fundamental flaw in this communications miracle is the same one that has bugged every communications miracle since they started carving hieroglyphics on stone tablets. What do you say on it? . . .

"All the networks were ordered to say something, anything, on the miracle instrument . . . CBS combed Europe and came up with a sausage-eating contest, which was duly sent back via the miracle ball, although that particular news could have gone by camelback without losing any of its essence . . ."

Still, given this technology, we should be able to find something to put inside the glowing, global frame.

"Programming . . . here lies the heart and soul and guts of the future," says Richard A. R. Pinkham, senior vice president of Ted Bates & Co. Inc., speaking on "An Agency Man's Views on the Future of TV" at the A.N.A. 56th annual meeting, November, 1965. "Because the name of the game we're discussing is really programming. That's what television is all about. That's what turns the set on, be it a two-inch portable in a teenager's pocket or an eight-foot screen hanging on the living room wall . . ."

When we assume a global responsibility for what appears on television screens, programming becomes even more crucial. There has been much talk about using global television for educational purposes; but what is it that we have to teach?

PHOTO BY WILLIAM JACKSON © 1966

QUO VADIS?

*Here he comes, stumbling down
his ten thousand technological
years—the fragmented man;
a thing of bits and pieces
cast upon the mudflats of the
20th Century by wayward
tides and waves too high.*

*This is a mosaic that walks,
wearing all his yesterdays
like tattoos. Little, or nothing,
in all his ancient heritage fits
him for this moment.*

*There is always something
coming ashore, and he is doing
so now. He strides into
the spectrum as once the lonely
horseman rode into the sunset
of another time and place.*

*And no one knows what new
adventures await him now.*

PURVEYOR OF TRASH

"Consider, for example, the behavior of literate people when they confront that total communication weapon, television. Most of them know that by the standards they would normally apply to a medium of communication, TV is an unparalleled purveyor of trash; the most extraordinary documentary, for instance, provides less information—in the usual sense of the word—about a subject than a very ordinary article in a slick magazine.

"Yet we sit there, eyes glued to the set, watching this explication of the obvious in hateful fascination and even find ourselves compelled to stay tuned to whatever follows ... Consciously, we despise ourselves, yet we are as fascinated ... as any savage before his totem."

RICHARD SCHICKEL
Harper's Magazine, November, 1965

HYSTERICAL

Eric Hoffer, among others, has pointed out that throughout history literate men have reacted hysterically to each new extension of literacy, seeing its growth as a threat to the favored positions their special knowledge has created for them.

RULE BY PIFFLE

"The democratic thesis is that of consent, participation and improvement. Citizens agree to the basic structure and direction of the nation. They take part directly and indirectly in its governance, and have no choice except to do so. The commonwealth is supposed to move onward and upward as a result.

"But if the customers of mass communication decide what they want to see, hear and read, and if the customers appear to want mainly piffle, what happens to their competence for self-government? What if the tendency of mass communications is to make difficult and in some cases impossible the conditions for self government?"

W. H. FERRY
"Masscomm as Educator"
The American Scholar—Spring, 1966

"President Johnson has his aides putting the finishing touches on a spectacular program to teach the more than 2-billion underprivileged of the world not only how to read and write but also how to grow the food they need and to control the population explosion," reports *Business Week* (December 25, 1965). "The plan is to pipe educational information into the backward villages of Africa, Asia, Latin America and elsewhere via a communications television satellite ... The program as it is being worked out envisions the erection by recipient countries of small ground stations—really little more than powerful antennas—in villages where people would gather for daily TV classroom instruction."

It is quite possible, of course, that this can be done, but the concept, circa 1966, overlooks some rather interesting considerations. Among them—the delusion that people of other cultures "see" the world the same way we do and that they interpret what they see in the same way. This is not necessarily true. (It is said that one of the difficulties in getting "natives" to understand TV pictures is that people on the screen keep "falling off the edges." In the real world, people disappear by getting further and further away or by moving behind some object that gets in front of them. But where do people go when they fall off the edges of the screen?)

"I doubt," says Joseph Goldsen, sociologist, RAND Corp., "if more food will be grown in India, even if every village gets a television set with lecturers teaching new agricultural techniques every hour. It takes generations to change customs and traditions..."

What it really amounts to is that—with our television/satellite technology we have the frame, but we are not at all sure of the picture we should hang in it.

Domestically, the case for televised education is already well established. Whether accomplished by closed circuit, or, ultimately, by satellite, it has the advantage that it can bring audio-visual instruction of a very high quality into areas where, otherwise, quality instruction would be almost impossible to obtain. More and more, in the years we are entering, the school system will become an electronic network.

And not only for the young people, growing up, but for adults as well. "Aristotle provides the point: 'Men by nature desire to know.' They do not cease desiring to know at sixteen or twenty-one or twenty-five," says W. H. Ferry in "Masscom as Educator," *The American Scholar* (Spring, 1966). "Learning proceeds through life, willy nilly. The means of learning change and become more informal. What is learned changes. For most people, mass communications provide the means of their continuing education, for good or ill; and mass communications' choice of topics and emphasis decides, for most people, what is learned ..." □

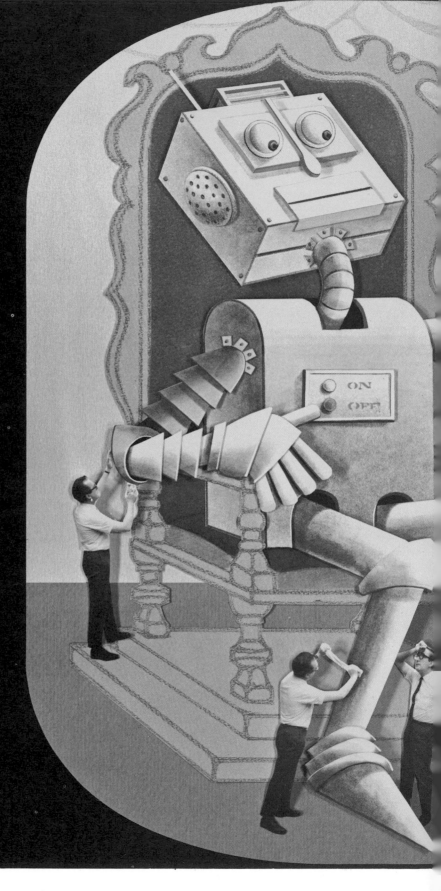

TH' WORKIN' MACHINE
by Jimmy Sherman

I was workin' real hard on my job one day
When my boss came on the scene
He said, "Son go in an' get yo' pay—
An' make way—for th' workin' machine!"

I rolled my eyes; I sho' was sore,
My boss he sho' was mean
He said, "Son you know I don't need
    you no more
You're fired!—Cause I've got a machine."

Well, I got another job, that followin'
    day
A' working harder than you've ever seen
'Til I heard my boss in a loud voice
    say
"Look out!"—It was another machine.

Now, I'm workin' like a slave, an'
    doin' real fine
I'm gettin' these floors so clean
An' I'm hopin' to keep this job of
    mine
Away!—From th' workin' machine.

REPRINTED BY PERMISSION OF THE AUTHOR

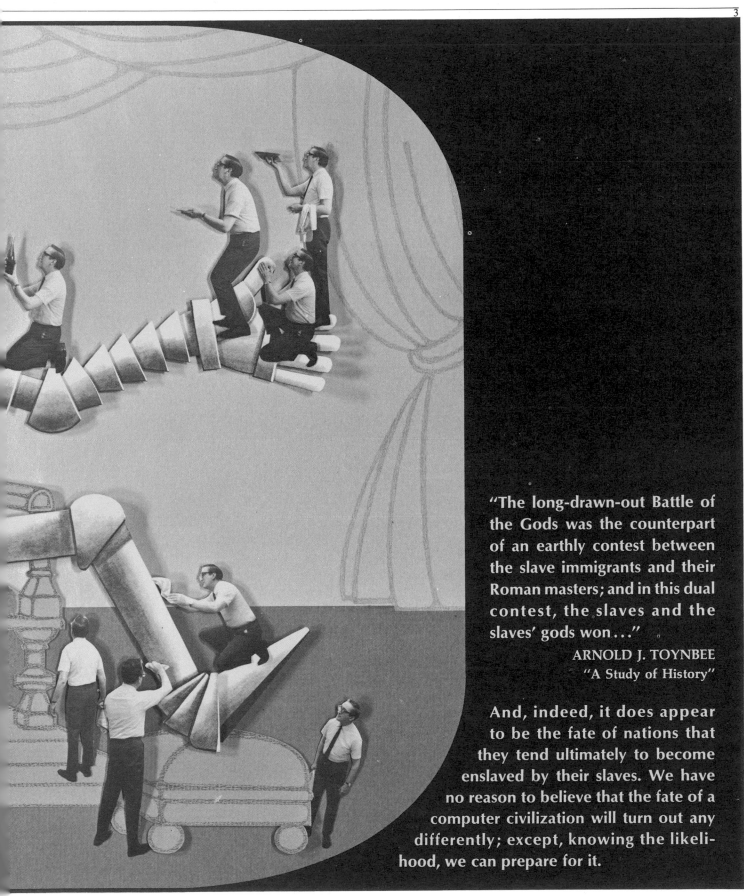

"The long-drawn-out Battle of the Gods was the counterpart of an earthly contest between the slave immigrants and their Roman masters; and in this dual contest, the slaves and the slaves' gods won..."

ARNOLD J. TOYNBEE
"A Study of History"

And, indeed, it does appear to be the fate of nations that they tend ultimately to become enslaved by their slaves. We have no reason to believe that the fate of a computer civilization will turn out any differently; except, knowing the likelihood, we can prepare for it.

ARTWORK BY MASAMI MIYAMOTO

ON THE TRAIL OF THE dolls THAT dANCED

GOLEM (gō'lŭm)

[Heb.,=embryo or anything incompletely developed], in medieval Jewish legend, an automatonlike servant made of clay and given life by means of a charm, or shem *[Heb.,=name, or the name of God]. Golems were attributed in Jewish legend to several rabbis in different European countries. The most famous legend centered around Rabbi Low, of 16th- century Prague. After molding the golem and endowing the clay creature with life, Rabbi Low was forced to destroy it after it ran amuck.*

© THE MACMILLAN CO.

"For you see, ladies and gentlemen, and, above all, your Imperial Majesty, with a real Nightingale one can never calculate what is coming, but in this artificial bird, everything is settled. It is this way, and no other! One can explain it; one can open it and show how it's almost human; show where the records are, and how they play and how one thing depends on another—!"

HANS CHRISTIAN ANDERSEN
"The Emperor's Nightingale"
Odense, Denmark—1835

☐ It may be only because we are so lonely—so awfully lonely. We scan the sky with radar and radio telescope; we probe the planets with rocket-borne instruments that simulate men. We listen and we hope. And no voice answers.

In despair we make effigies of ourselves; something that simulates life and can share with us the extraordinary experience of being alive.

"And God said, let us make man in our Image, after our Likeness." (Genesis I, 1). It was the fifth day.

But even an image can be lonely. And so it came to pass that somewhere east of Eden, on a day not wholly specified, "The Lord God said, 'It is not good that the man should be alone: I will make an help meet for him . . .'

"And the Lord God caused a deep sleep to fall upon Adam, and he slept: and He took of one of his ribs, and closed up the flesh instead thereof; and of the rib, which the Lord God had taken from man, made he a woman, and brought her to the man." (Genesis, II, 2).

We have been making dolls and effigies ever since, of which the latest — but certainly not the last — is the electronic computer.

Says Norbert Wiener, who more than anyone else seems to be the spokesman for the cybernetic world, "At every stage of technique since Daedalus or Hero of Alexandria, the ability of the artificer to produce a working simulacrum of a living organism has always intrigued people. This desire to produce and study automata has always been expressed in terms of the living technique of the age.

"In the days of magic, we have the bizarre and sinister concept of the Golem, that figure of clay into which the Rabbi of Prague breathed in life with the blasphemy of the Ineffable Name of God. In the time of Newton, the automaton becomes the clockwork music box, with the little effigies pirouetting stiffly on top.

"In the 19th Century, the automaton is a glorified heat engine, burning some combustible fuel instead of the glycogen of the human muscles. Finally, the present automaton opens doors by means of photocells, or points guns to the place at which a radar beam picks up an airplane, or computes the solution of a differential equation."

It is indeed a long, long trail that leads back through our heritage of dolls that dance: through Pygmalian and his blushing Galatea; through Pinocchio; through the Emperor's Nightingale; through Dorothy's adventures with the Scarecrow and the Tin Woodman in the Land of Oz; through The Nutcracker Suite and the toy soldiers that marched upon the midnight; through Alice and the playing cards that came to life at the mad Queen's party; through Frankenstein's monster and the picture of Dorian Gray.

Today the effigies with which we play are the little darts of light that dance across the plexiglass screen, deep in a mountain at Colorado Springs, where the North American Air Defense Command scans the world for signs of mechanical monsters on the move.

Says Grey Walter, in his essay, *An Imitation of Life:* "In the dark ages before the invention of the electronic vacuum tube, there were many legends of living statues and magic pictures. . . . One has only to recall the importance of graven images and holy pictures in many religions to realize how readily living and even divine properties are projected into inanimate objects by hopeful but bewildered men and women.

"Idolatry, witchcraft and other superstitions are so deeply rooted and widespread that it is possible that even the most detached scientific activity may be psychologically equivalent to them; such activity may help to satisfy the desire for power, to assuage the fear of the unknown or to compensate for the flatness of everyday existence."

The genie in the magic bottle of our times, whom we summon forth to do our "thinking" by a mere push of the button, differs from all the other effigies that have suffused our history in one important respect: we know *why* it works. All the other dolls of our past and present were empirical; they were shaped from such materials as were at hand, and if they happened to be put together right, they worked. Not so with today's computers; their construction, and their use, is solidly built on information theory, on modern mathematics, and on logic. Given this substratum, we can construct as many kinds of automatons as we desire, or that our technology allows.

It is, in some respects, a frightening prospect—we have created the Sorcerer's Apprentice and set him to work. Unfortunately, perhaps, we have only learned how to turn him on — and not how to turn him off.

There are so many ways we could talk about automation and cybernetics and the computer "revolution." One is reminded of the tale that Aage Peterson relates in his *The Philosophy of Niels Bohr*—a favorite story of that famed physicist.

"In an isolated village there was a small Jewish community. A famous rabbi once came to the neighboring city to speak and, as the people of the village were eager to learn what the great teacher would say, they sent a young man to listen. When he returned, he said, 'The rabbi spoke three times. The first talk was brilliant; clear and simple. I understood every word. The second was even better; deep and subtle. I didn't understand very much, but the rabbi understood all of it. The third was by far the finest; a great and unforgettable experience. I understood nothing and the rabbi himself didn't understand much either."

That's kind of the way it will be on the following pages . . . □

© THE MACMILLAN CO.

CHAPTER I: How it came to pass that Master Cherry, the carpenter, found a piece of wood that laughed and cried like a child . . .
CHAPTER II: Master Cherry makes a present of the piece of wood to his friend Geppetto, who takes it to make himself a wonderful puppet that shall know how to dance, and to fence, and to leap like an acrobat.

"The Adventures of Pinocchio"
by C. Collodi (Carlo Lorenzini)

The latest and perhaps most sharply symbolic of our living dolls is a little black box that one can buy in novelty shops. Push the lever that turns it on, and it whirs, and a moment later a little plastic hand emerges and pushes the lever to shut itself off. Here, in this doll-like effigy, we have the shorthand expression of our times; that, like the atomic bomb, we can, and do, build mechanisms whose sole creative act is to destroy creation.

wiNd ME up ANd i'll TuRN ON

☐ "Let us consider the activity of the little figures which dance on top of a music box," suggests Norbert Wiener.

"They move in accordance with a pattern, but it is a pattern which is set in advance, and in which the past activity of the figures has practically nothing to do with the pattern of their future activities. . . . There is a message, indeed, but it goes from the machinery of the music box to the figures, and stops there. The figures themselves have no trace of communication with the outer world, except this one-way stage of communication with the pre-established mechanism of the music box. They are blind, deaf and dumb, and cannot vary their activity in the least from the conventional pattern."

And this is, indeed, a perfect description of what is meant by mechanization — a robot world, pre-programed for a Newtonian clockwork universe that repeats its past mindlessly into the future. Recently a new dimension has been added—machines that are capable of learning from their past and thus can create new patterns of response in their futures. Cybernation is *not* the mere extension of mechanization and automation; it is a new way of thinking about ourselves—and about machines.

"There is much truth," says John Diebold in *Beyond Automation*, "in the quip that it is as hard for a group of businessmen to define automation as it is for a group of theologians to define sin."

But Ted Silvey of the AFL-CIO has done it very well. In *Automation: the Three-Legged Stool,* he says:

"When a person works or engages in any of the activities of living, he uses the marvelous mechanism which is his body and brain in three specific ways. The first is the exercise of physical strength and manual dexterity, called skill. The second is the functioning of the five perceptive senses . . . and the personal control that is exercised therefrom. The third is the use of the brain, both in its decision-making capacity and in the information storage system we call memory.

"The new industrial technology being called automation is an extension and, in many ways, a replacement of these three human performances: (1) highly engineered *mechanization* extends and replaces physical strength and dexterity; (2) instrumentation and *automatic control* extend and replace the perceptive senses and personal control; (3) the *electronic computer* replaces the simple repetitive decision-making functions of the brain and has a memory. It is these three processes together which constitute automation . . ."

Here we shall speak of automation and cybernation as the non-biological replacement of human nerves and brains in the affairs of men. We are not dolls, nor do we dance atop a music box. And our computers don't either. They are a new race that shares this planet with us—for good or for ill. ☐

TIME'S A VANDAL

"This is mechanical music—music made by watchmakers and artisans. It has on it the stamp of man, of man when the pace of life was slow and its sound calm, and perhaps it is this we recognize when we find ourselves nostalgic for a world we never knew . . . Everyone has his own long ago and far away, and it is of this that the music box sings . . . Its music reaches us exactly as it was first fashioned, undimmed by the vandalism of time. It is a message, surviving intact, from another time which is almost another world. It is delight, it is innocence, it is perfection. We are nostalgic for our beginnings, for the simplicity of our dreams."

HELEN AND JOHN HOKE
"Music Boxes, Their Lore and Lure"

PHOTOGRAPHY BY BOB FRASER   MUSIC BOX COURTESY MR. & MRS. A. HACKER, ST. LOUIS, MISSOURI

THE TURN OF THE SCREW

☐ You may not think of it that way, but the device you are wearing on your wrist is a combination digital and analog computer. It counts each catch and release of the teeth on the escapement gear, and translates the number of counts in a circular motion between gear and gear until, in the end, the hands of the watch stand at an angle that represents how many clicks have occurred since the machine began to operate.

The angle of the hands is an analog "read out" and the "input" is a digital click, click, click. We put such store by this little device that we run our personal, social and business lives by it.

There are many analog devices in our machine world. The pilot who flies your jet liner does so by watching an array of analog readouts; they transform discrete numbers (gallons of fuel in the tanks, pressure per square inch in the hydraulic system, number of feet above sea level as units of barometric pressure) into continuous measurements (the angle of hands on a dial, the height of a column of fluid in a tube).

"In an analog machine," says John von Neumann, in *The Computer and the Brain,* "each number is represented by a suitable physical quantity, whose value, measured in some pre-assigned unit, is equal to the number in question. This quantity may be the angle by which a certain disk has rotated, or the strength of a current, or the amount of a certain (relative) voltage."

An easy way to distinguish between analog and digital processes is offered in Jeremy Bernstein's *The Analytical Engine* where he says, "The analog machines represent number by some analogous quantity, such as length or size. A child might learn to add by assembling blocks of various sizes; a block of a given size would be the analog of 1; a block twice the size would be the analog of two, and so on. . . .To put it briefly, an analog device measures, while a digital computer counts."

Now, analog devices are important to our general thesis, which is that we can — and do — build machines that simulate, if not duplicate, human reasoning processes. One of these processes is analogous. It is characteristic of analog processes that they are only approximate; they indicate high probability but not exact accuracy. They say, "it's about like this."

A fairly familiar analog device is the slide rule, which can give approximate answers to numerical questions that are accurate within two—at the most, four—decimal places. It translates numbers into positions. For greater accuracy, we go to the desk digital calculator.

The next time you turn your head to watch a pretty girl go by, you have transformed certain digital inputs into an analog that is expressed by turning your head. We can design machines to do the same, but, one assumes, the experience would be different for the machine. ☐

PHOTOGRAPHY BY BOB FRASER

MESSAGES from THE infinite telegraph office

THE LOGARITHM OF BITS

"Information is a measure of one's freedom of choice when one selects a message. If one is confronted with a very elementary situation where he has to choose one of two alternative messages, then it is arbitrarily said that the information, associated with this situation, is unity. . . . The concept of information applies not to the individual messages (as the concept of meaning would), but rather to the situation as a whole . . .

"To be somewhat more definite, the amount of information is defined, in the simplest cases, to be measured by the logarithm of the number of available choice. . ."

WARREN WEAVER
"The Mathematical Theory
of Communication"

THE HARDWARE NEURON

"Networks of . . . idealized neurons can be made capable of computing more and more complicated relationships, and, as McCulloch and Pitts showed in their celebrated paper, 'A Logical Calculus of the Ideas Immanent in Nervous Activity,' any functional behavior which can be defined logically, strictly unambiguously in a finite number of words can also be realized by such a formal network."

HEINZ VON FOERSTER
"Perception of Form in Biological
and Man-Made Systems."

☐ Imagine, if you will, that there is an infinite telegraph office. At the base of its service, let us say, you are allowed to send one of two messages — "Yes" or "No." The probability that you will send either "Yes" or "No" is exactly equal. In sending either one, you assume a high degree of risk. If either one fails to get through, there is no statistical pattern from which the recipient can reconstruct what you have sent.

The physical world appears to be a "yes" or "no" universe; it can only be reconstructed through a large sampling of yes's and no's. Our experience of it thus becomes a simple process of addition and the application of statistical disciplines.

Let us now imagine that at this same telegraph office you also can send 26 messages—but only one at a time. Now the chances that you will decide to send any particular one, at a particular time, are 1 in 26; in short, the English alphabet. The probabilities that a particular message will follow another message can be computed statistically, if you are sending in the English language, and if you want your recipient to be able to understand what you have said.

Say that you decide to send the combination, "LOVE"—a word the world needs badly. Out of the 26 choices confronting you, you make one at a time, and the sequence of choices indicates what the message is. In sending this combination, you have confounded nature, and reversed entropy from high probability to low probability, and thus reached out and changed the world.

Essentially, this is what all living organisms do. Out of an infinite number of choices, made finite by their particular point in time and space, living organisms make one-at-a-time sequential selections. This is true whether they pick wave-lengths to look at, channels to switch to, a place to move to or from—any purposeful act we perform reverses entropy. (We use entropy here in the sense that all systems in nature tend toward disorganization — to an equilibrium that is the state of highest probability because, without outside intervention, it is the most likely to occur. Think of a deck of cards being shuffled; each shuffling makes it less likely that any two cards will appear in sequence. When you pick up your poker hand, and arrange the cards in it to form a one-to-five sequence of the same suit, as in a straight flush, you have reversed entropy, and have sent a message.)

The more complex the sequence of yes-no choices, the lower the probability that it will occur. The lower the probability, the more chance the message has of getting through. If you send, "I love you," the chances are that it *may* get garbled enroute, due to noise (such as static on the radio, "snow" on your television screen, etc.) "Noise" is entropy rearing its ugly head; it is the universe's way of getting even with us.

But if you should happen to send something as complex as, "Now is the winter of our discontent made glorious summer by this son of York," there is a pretty good chance that enough of the message will get through that it can be reconstructed statistically. Only one man ever sent that message—it has traveled for 400 years without significant loss of meaning. It is the function of poets that they send messages of such low probability that they cannot easily be misunderstood.

One reason the English language has managed to last so long and pervade so many cultures is that it is 50 per cent redundant; even if half the message is lost, the message can still be reconstructed, providing the message is long enough.

"Messages are themselves a form of pattern and organization," says Norbert Wiener in *The Human Use of Human Beings*. "Indeed, it is possible to treat sets of messages as having an entropy like sets of states in the external world. Just as entropy is a measure of disorganization, the information carried by a set of messages is a measure of organization. . . . That is, the more probable the message, the less information it gives. Cliches, for example, are less illuminating than great poems."

Warren Weaver, in his essay, *The Mathematics of Information*, says: "Information, we must steadily remember, is a measure of one's freedom of choice in selecting a message. The greater this choice, the greater is the uncertainty that the message actually selected is some particular one. Thus greater freedom of choice, greater uncertainty and greater information all go hand in hand.

"If noise is introduced, then the received message contains certain distortions, certain errors, certain extraneous material, that would certainly lead to increased uncertainty. But if the uncertainty is increased, the information is increased, and this sounds as though noise were beneficial!"

One cannot help but be reminded of the madness that beset Don Quixote, who lost what little wits he had trying to decipher, "The reason of the unreason with which my reason is affected so weakens my reason that with reason I murmur at your beauty." As Cervantes commented, "Over conceits of this sort the poor gentleman lost his wits, and used to lie awake striving to understand them and worm the meaning of them; what Aristotle himself could not have made out or abstracted, had he come to life again for that special purpose."

A message, then, is a structure made up of a sequence of yes-or-no choices. It can be the dot-dash of the telegraph key; the on-off of a light globe; the puff, no puff of an Indian smoke signal; the hole-no hole in a punch card; the turn black-don't turn black of a molecule in a photographic film emulsion. It most particularly, for our purposes here,

A MATTER OF DIGITS

"*The most immediate observation regarding the nervous system is that its functioning is* prima facie *digital.*
"*The basic component of this system is the nerve cell, the neuron, and the normal function of a neuron is to generate and propagate a nerve impulse. This impulse is a rather complex process, which has a variety of aspects—electrical, chemical and mechanical. It seems, nevertheless, to be a reasonably uniquely defined process; i.e. nearly the same under all conditions; it represents an essentially reproducible, unitary response to a rather wide variety of stimuli.*"

JOHN VON NEUMANN
"The Computer and the Brain"

ELEMENTARY, MY DEAR WATSON

"*See if you can read it, Watson,*" *said he with a smile. It contained no word, but this little line of dancing men.*

𝍐𝍐𝍐𝍐𝍐𝍐𝍐𝍐𝍐𝍐𝍐𝍐

"*If you use the code which I explained,*" *said Holmes, "you will find that it simply means 'Come here at once.' I was convinced that it was an invitation which he could not refuse . . . "And so, my dear Watson, we have ended by turning the dancing men to good when they have so often been the agents of evil . . ."*

SHERLOCK HOLMES
"The Adventures of the Dancing Men."

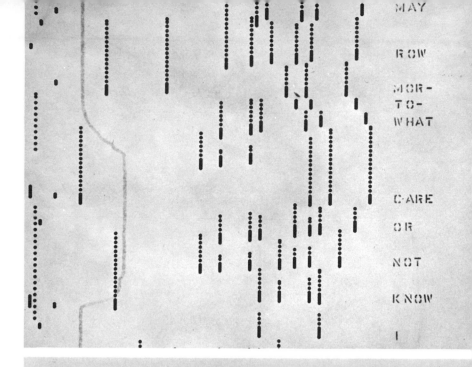

"IT'S GOTTA BE YES OR NO"

*The player piano roll was the direct
descendant of the escapement wheel on
a clock. Both are "go" and "no-go"
systems. The teeth on the clock wheel
said "hold me on" or "let me go."
The player piano roll said to the wind
that fingered its face, "Pass" or
"Don't Pass." And the compressed air
that moved searchingly over the surface
of the roll would find an aperture,
flow through that, and activate a
diaphragm for a hammer, which would
strike a note on the strings.
The punch card is the lineal descendant
of the player piano. It said,
"Charge" or "No Charge" to the
electrical brushes that passed
across its otherwise impassive face.
Thus it is with all digital systems—the
electronic computer, the desk
calculator, and most impressively,
photographic film, where each
molecule in the film emulsion can say,
"Black" or "No Black."
We have recorded this chapter on
film as an illustration of the
tremendous amount of information
that can be contained in a small
space, purely by "Yes" and "No."*

EVERYMAN'S LIBRARY

*"Among artificial memory devices
the most efficient is the photographic
emulsion. Not only can it pack a
great deal of information into a small
area, but each spot is capable of
recording about 10 distinguishable levels
of intensity. Microfilm in particular is
a very effective means of storing printed
or pictorial information. Ultimately,
every man may have on microcards a
library as large as he likes . . .
"If translated to binary code and
recorded as black and white spots on
film, all of the words in all the
books of the Library of Congress could
be stored in a cubic yard."*

GILBERT KING
"What Is Information?"
Automatic Control

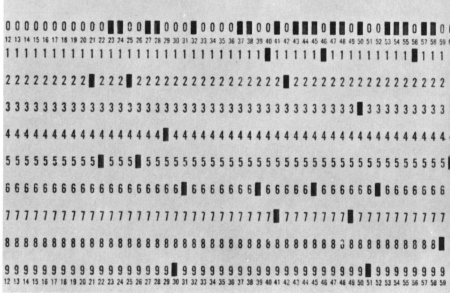

can be the "pass" or don't pass" of an impulse moving along either an organic or mechanical nervous system.

As John von Neumann explains it, ". . . the message·system used in the nervous system . . . is of an essentially statistical character. In other words, what matters are not the precise positions of definite markers, digits, but the statistical characteristic of their occurrence."

What is relevant here as regards "mechanical brains" is that they can reduce the infinite telegraph office to a whistle-stop "yes-or-no" office. But with this difference — computers can make "yes" or "no" choices so rapidly, in billionths of a second, that they can build a high statistical probability into low probability sequences.

Man can do this, too, but he would have to spend a million years in a telegraph office. And you know what that would be like.

"The brain cipher," says Grey Walter in *An Imitation of Life,* "is even simpler than Morse code; it uses only dots, the number of which per second conveys all information. Communication engineers call this system 'pulse-frequency modulation.' It was 'invented' by animals many millions of years ago. . . . The engineers who have designed our great computing machines adopted this system without realizing that they were copying their own brains . . .

"In the language of these machines there are only two statements, 'yes' and 'no,' and in their arithmetic only two numbers — 1 and 0. They surpass human capacity in their great speed of action and in their ability to perform many interdependent computations at the same time."

It's all very simple, really. As we look at men, animals or automatic machines as information processing devices, we find:

an input—the selection of a particular incoming message at a given moment in time

a process—the addition of this message to all the previous messages that have been selected and stored

an output—a sequential selection of "yes" or "no" that is unique, highly improbable, and statistically determined.

Whether the biologic neural apparatus actually works in the same way as computers is something to be discussed later; the point here is that computers can simulate the arithmetical and logical processes of the human mind with incredible speed and remarkable accuracy. Thus the computer becomes an extension of the human brain just as surely as the telescope and microscope become extensions of the eye, the telephone becomes the extension of the mouth, and the steam shovel becomes the extension of hands and arms.

The modern digital computer is an infinite telegraph station; we can send any messages we can think of at the speed of light. We have somehow found a way to translate mathematics into life. □

"TURN ME ON"	⬛⬛
HAMLET	"to be or not to be"
COMPUTER LANGUAGE	0—1
COMIC BOOK	(YES) (NO)
ARISTOTLE	either—or
BIOLOGY	♀ ♂
LIGHT GLOBE	♀ ♀
SILVER CHLORIDE ON FILM	◨ ◧
AVIATION	flaps up—flaps down
ASTRONAUTS	go—no go
CRAP TABLE	come—no come
CHARTIST	x, y
CHESS	P-K4, P-Q3

It's a Barnum and Binary World
Just as ideatic as it can be,
But it would only be make-believe
If it wasn't for you and me.

'STEERSMAN, mind thine oar!'

☐ We have described two processes that appear to apply equally to organisms moving in an environment and to machines—that numbers can be translated into measurements (as in the analog process) and that experience is a function of addition (the digital system). There is only one more process we need in order to understand computers — it has been called "feedback."

Perhaps the best way to describe feedback is to say that it is a subtraction process. Think about picking up a glass of water. You have willed the action, and your arm and hand respond to the will. You determine how close you are to your goal by subtracting the motions you already have made toward it. In the end, the result is zero; no more impulses are needed, because you have reached the glass.

This self-correcting process is what is meant by feedback. When this principle is added to digital and analog processes, we have all that we need to simulate almost any action of an organism in its environment.

Norbert Wiener, in *Cybernetics*, describes feedback very simply. "An extremely important factor in voluntary activity is what the control engineers term feedback. . . . When we desire a motion to follow a given pattern, the difference between this pattern and the actually performed motion is used as a new input to cause the part regulated to move in such a way as to bring its motion closer to that given by the pattern."

As usually happens, the Greeks had a word for it. Wiener explains, "We have decided to call the entire field of control and communication theory, whether in the machine or in the animal, by the name *Cybernetics*, which we form from the Greek word for 'steersman.'

He goes on to point out that, "the steering engines of a ship are indeed one of the earliest and best developed forms of feedback mechanisms."

It is hard to over-estimate the importance of the feedback principle in the development of "thinking machines."

"So with the feedback principle," says John Diebold in *Beyond Automation*, "historians do not have to search for particular mechanical devices to show its prior existence, for we are all aware of the interaction of our sense perceptions and brain — true feedback circuitry. What is new is our conscious awareness of the potentials of this idea, and what will be revolutionary will be the effects of the application of this technology on our society."

So simple: three things — analog, digital processing and feedback. Put them together and you can go out in the backyard right now and out of some old bits of wire, a flashlight battery, and discarded beer cans you may be able to build a creature that can do almost everything the dinosaurs ever did—or you, for that matter. ☐

PHOTOGRAPHY BY BOB FRASER

Adventures of an unemployed motorcycle rider

☐ It does appear that we can, through the application of information theory, mathematical procedures and feedback design, create machines that respond to their environment not unlike living organisms.

Three questions immediately arise: Does a machine think? Does a machine have a soul? Can machines replace men in the mental world as they have in the muscular world?

The first two questions founder on semantic shoals; their wreckage is strewn on the beaches of our current journalism. If we could define, in a universally acceptable way, what we mean by "think" (or even what "really" really means), or if we could define "soul," then perhaps we could apply these definitions to what a machine does and come up with some sort of an answer.

"Let us ask," says John P. Kemeny in his essay, *Man Viewed as a Machine:* "What could a machine do as well or better than a man, now or in the future? We shall not concern ourselves with whether a machine could write sonnets or fall in love. Nor shall we waste time laboring the obvious fact that when it comes to muscle, machines are far superior to men. What concerns us here is man as a brain-machine."

You see? Already the question has squirmed and turned over in our hands. It is not, "Are machines as good as men?" but "Are men equal to machines?"

"We are familiar with power machinery, and we take for granted its superiority to human muscles," comments Louis N. Ridenour in his article, *Information Machines.* He goes on, "We are not yet familiar with information machinery, and we are therefore not prepared to concede its superiority to the human nervous system. Nevertheless, a digital information machine can surpass human capabilities in any task that is governed by logical rules, no matter how complicated such rules may be."

Perhaps it is that we are not asking the right questions, or that we are not phrasing them in a meaningful way. Alan Turing, a brilliant English mathematician, found a better way to ask whether machines think or not. He suggested that we ask, "Are the responses to questions made by a given computing machine indistinguishable from the responses to the same questions made by a given person?"

All we ever can know of another person is the responses he gives to the stimulus we provide; and when his responses are acceptable to us, we say that he "thinks." Turing suggested a game in which a computer in one room, and a man in another room, are asked questions by a third party, who tries to distinguish which answers come from the machine and which from a living human being. In the theoretical simulation of "Turing's Game," it is possible to ask a series of questions whose answers from man or computer would be indistinguishable from each other.

A MATTER OF IDENTITY

(AP)—RIVERSIDE—*Police here today said they had taken into custody*

...................................., *age 26, on charges of disturbing the peace. He gave his occupation as "unemployed motorcycle rider"...*

LEARNED SOMETHING, ANYWAY

"Quite a different approach in the life sciences is the study of living nervous systems to see how they differ from machines in processing information. Because of its simplicity, the crayfish has been a valuable subject for experiment. Thus far, little has been learned that can be applied to computer technology, although the computer has aided biologists considerably in understanding the crayfish."

GILBERT W. KING
Director of Research
IBM

SEAT OF THE PANTS

"The study of the dynamics of the man-machine interface, where the efforts of man and machine converge—is arousing intense interest in industry.

"One design engineer predicts that the day will come when 'seat of the pants' control of a crane or lift truck, for example, will be exactly that. The seat, he believes, could contain devices tied in with the machine's system. The signal would feed back from the system to the operator in the form of a nudge, a tingle, or possibly a light shock ..."

"The Inevitable Science of Human Engineering."
Dun's Review—October, 1965

"However one may feel about attributing intelligence to computers, it must be clear that with their rapid development a new force has come into the world," says Jeremy Bernstein in *The Analytical Engine*. "The history of electronic computers is only twenty years old, and they are still sufficiently simple for one to have a sense of understanding in detail how they work, and therefore of being controlled. (Someone has remarked, 'You can always pull out the plug.') But computers are already being used to design other computers, and it is quite possible that future generations of machines, which have been designed by machines, or which are not organized to an entirely deterministic plan, may be beyond our complete understanding."

That day may not be far away — perhaps it will come during the next twenty years. When it does, we may become the pets and playthings of mechanistic organisms who tolerate us, but do not really need us.

But that day is not yet, and on the basis of superficial characteristics, the human central nervous system appears in some respects to be superior to current electronic brains (someone has referred to the latter as "the brilliant idiots").

For one thing, the human brain occupies very little space (about one-third of a cubic foot); it uses very little energy — about ten watts. It has under normal conditions no heat dissipation problems; and it has a tremendous memory storage system for its size. The brain can, according to John von Neumann's calculations (based on the assumption that no organic experience is ever really forgotten) store the inputs of a sixty-year lifetime, amounting to 2.8×10^{20} "bits" of information, a figure that if written out is 280,000,000,000,000,000,000. This is considerably more than we can now store with the current generation of computing devices, but since storage area in machines is simply additive, there probably is no reason we cannot design machines in the future that have memory banks that far exceed those of man.

The chief advantage of the machine brain is its speed—even current machines can process 55 billion additions per second; human brain responses are considered to be timed to the scanning process (that is, the time it takes us to pick up an input and filter it from other possible inputs from our sensory apparatus, and to pass the input through the system, either to store it in memory banks or process it as an output). This time appears to be approximately a tenth of a second, which is comparable to the "scan time" of the image on your television screen, and resembles the periodicity of the alpha waves that our brains give off, as recorded in electro-encephalograms.

Theoretically, machine brains can be built that operate at very nearly the speed of light. For human nervous systems, the information "bit" travels through its processing at a relatively slow pace, allowing

HE IS THE VERY MODEL

"The designer is essentially a solver of problems, problems presented to him by the nature of the task, of the materials he is using, of the people who will be using his design, and of the market for which it is being produced.

"The model of man which emerges when we consider him as a problem solver— whether his problem is to land an aircraft or design a coffee percolator—is a data processing model. These words are operational, they define concepts in terms of what is done.

"Man is seen as a hierarchy of systems in which he receives data, processes data, and puts out data . . .

"This does not imply in any way that a man's mind works like a digital computer—though it does not deny the possibility. It does say that the relations between what goes into his head through his eyes and ears and what comes out through his voluntary muscles, often suggests what he does."

E. LLEWELLYN THOMAS
"Problem Solving in Design"
from *Design and Planning*

NO LONGER SOULLESS?

"Two great trends characterize our times, says Richard R. Landers, chief of reliability, Thompson Ramo Wooldridge Inc., Cleveland. One is to mechanize humans; the other is to humanize machines. 'The ultimate' he says, 'will be for the two trends to cross— for the man machine to be identical to the machine man. At that point, would God give the machine man a soul?' "

STEEL
November 25, 1963

MAN, LIKE LOVE?

"I don't know if it's because it
builds your ego so much or because of
the feeling, *the physical feeling;*
it overwhelms you, y'know, it's like
really exaggerated . . . uh . . . love
kind of thing, y'know. Power, and . . .
oh, man . . . and what?"

NO YADIYADA

"There is nothing more machinery than
a motorcycle . . . it's all there,
there's nothing covered up; the engine's
doing the engine things right there.
There is an intimate contact between
man and machine; there aren't
any plush seats, or pedals to push or
all this yadiyada . . ."

IN SEARCH OF IDENTITY

"What an easy way to . . . ah . . .
define yourself, what an easy way to
establish your difference from other
people. Y'know, the point is you don't
just ride a motorcycle, you pick up so
much with it . . . you pick up the clothes,
you pick up an attitude . . . a sound . . .
I mean your whole life could be defined
simply by riding a motorcycle . . ."

HENRY S. STONE, JR.
"Youths and Motorcycles"
The Man-Made Object
Vision & Value Series, 1966

PHOTOGRAPHY BY STEPHEN FRISCH

for the fatigue factor at each synaptic gap—the time lag required for the neural complex to regain an electrochemical/mechanical state that will enable it to pass, or not pass, the next impulse along. The machine mind does not, ordinarily, have the fatigue factor to slow it up.

Accuracy is another thing the machine displays better than the human mind. Human minds are accurate to only about two decimal places. We can build into a machine any degree of digital accuracy we desire, just by adding more digits to the other side of the decimal point. Given such speed and accuracy, it is conceivable for an operator to ask a machine brain a question of considerable mathematical complexity, and to have the answer back before his nervous system can move his finger from the last pushbutton.

Speed, high accuracy, and virtually unlimited memory are characteristics of such machine brains as we have today. With the application of micro-miniaturization and solid state technology, the size of machine brains has been steadily shrinking (in relation to their ability); the power requirement has been steadily lowered, and with it the heat dissipation problem. As this process continues, the advantages the human system now enjoys over machine systems will be steadily reduced.

So, what happens then? What happens when the "little black box" on your bedside table is intellectually superior to you?

This brings us to another question—what is the interaction that takes place between a human organism at the interface where it joins the machines it designs, builds and operates?

Historically, we have always learned to live with our artifacts. The motorcar, which once frightened men as well as horses, has become so much a part of our daily lives that to remove it now might destroy us utterly. Radio and television, other machine systems, have become the chief sources of our experience of the auditory and visual worlds. (To realize how much we have integrated machine systems with human living, just try, as this writer once did, to live completely alone for ten days without any people or any of these machines. It is a shattering and decomposing psychological and emotional experience.)

In this section, we have used the image of the motorcycle rider as a symbol of the man/machine symbiosis. Here, man and machine share life and death together; each becomes the expression of experience for the other.

Someday—not too far from now—people will "ride" their personal computers with all the excitement that the motorcycle rider feels when he storms down the long tunnel of the night. We will, with computers, explore our mental world with a something that shares, amplifies and defines our experience. In doing so, it will help us define ourselves as human personalities. □

A GAME OF CHESS

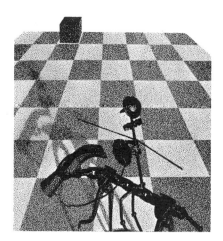

LIKE WHAT?

"A typical computer program may involve many thousands of detailed steps. A program is broken into small steps simply because a computer cannot remember whole procedures as we do. We glance at an individual and know in a flash that it is a 'woman.' A computer, however, would have to be given the anatomical details before it could make the identification 'female.' An evaluation of 'how much' a female would depend on more specific information."

STANLEY L. ENGLEBARDT
"Computers"

☐ If one were asked to try to capture the essential spirit of the last half of the 20th Century in a single picture, he might well consider as his background a vast chess board that stretches to the far corners of the world. On one side of the board, he might place a forlorn, bemused, hopelessly romantic Don Quixote, the White Knight of an age long gone, mounted on a mechanical Rocinante that is a bit swayed in the back by the weight of time and going to pieces a little bit here and there as the aging rivets that hold it together give up their ancient grip.

Facing this symbolic relic of the past—whose dispirited lance already droops in foregone defeat — at the other side of the board, there is an enigmatic little black box. In its calm inscrutability it seems to have crept out of the world of the future. And perhaps it has. One feels instinctively that the confrontation between these two is reflected on the thousand squares and diagonals of which our world is made; and that whatever move the Knight makes now, it will be the little black box that makes the last one.

"The computer," writes Dr. Jerome B. Wiesner, Dean of Science at the Massachusetts Institute of Technology, in the *New York Times,* "with its promise of a million-fold increase in man's capacity to handle information, will undoubtedly have the most far-reaching social consequences of any contemporary technical development. The potential for good in the computer, and the danger inherent in its misuse, exceed our ability to imagine . . ."

The editors of *Automatic Control* say, "There is going to be more and more automatic control in our lives. It is the means by which we will carry on big business and big government, production, finance, communications, trade and distribution in the complex and centrally organized civilization of our times. As citizens, we may hope to manage this revolution democratically and so to our advantage. We had better develop a clear understanding of what the term stands for and of the changes it implies in the way we make our living and conduct our affairs."

It has all happened so fast that many—perhaps most—people don't realize it has happened at all. There still appears to be an impression that computers are something that a very large and sophisticated corporation might use, or an advanced physics laboratory at some technical institute. But as we have seen on the foregoing pages, the simple simulation of the processes of addition, measurement and feedback creates a sorcerer's apprentice that will move in to share our lives, whether we live in a cold water walk-up flat on the Lower East Side, or a penthouse overlooking Lake Michigan, or on a farm in Minnesota.

"At least a dozen of the 20,000 computers in the U.S. have touched your life since you woke up this morning," comments Jerry Carlson in *Farm Management,* July, 1965. "They're processing your checks, keeping your credit card accounts, figuring the averages you hear on the market news, blending your livestock concentrates, helping predict tomorrow's weather and formulating your breakfast sausage. All this in ten short years since the computer age began."

Now, what is particularly interesting about this statement, other than that the little black box is becoming as much of the farm scene as Bossy the cow once was, is that although written a little over a year ago, the figures are already out of date by a wide margin.

The new figures are given by General David Sarnoff, chairman of the board of the Radio Corporation of America, in an article in the July 23, 1966, *Saturday Review* ". . . one fact is absolute: the incredible growth of the computer in numbers, power and availability.

"In just ten years, the typical electronic data processor has become ten times smaller, 100 times faster, and 1,000 times less expensive to operate. These trends will continue, and our national computing power, which is doubling every year, will soon be sufficient to make the computer a genuinely universal tool.

"In 1956, there were fewer than 1,000 computers in the United States. Today there are 30,000, or more than $11 billion worth: and by 1976 the machine population may reach 100,000. And these figures will, of course, be greatly increased through the growth of data processing in other nations.

"A decade ago, our machines were capable of 12 billion computations per hour; today, they can do more than 20 trillion; and by 1976—a decade from now—they will attain 400 trillion—or about two billion computations per hour for every man, woman and child. Quite evidently, the threshold of the computer age has barely been crossed."

We seem always — in our times — to be crossing one threshold or other, but here, instead of proudly carrying our mechanical bride across this threshold with firm stride and a glint in our eye, we seem to have stumbled headlong into an enormous room peopled with strange creatures whose language is as unintelligible to us as a Martian dialect. We instinctively feel that the voices are kindly in tone, but we hardly understand a word of what they say.

On the following four pages we present some of the voices in the enormous room. It might be well to listen to them, for we're going to spend the rest of our lives here, with a little black box at our side. It will understand—but will we? □

ALICE, REVISITED

"For the existence of any science, it is necessary that there exist phenomena which do not stand isolated. In a world ruled by a succession of miracles performed by an irrational God subject to sudden whims, we should be forced to await each new catastrophe in a state of perplexed passiveness.

"We have a picture of such a world in the croquet game in Alice in Wonderland; *where the mallets are flamingoes; the balls, hedgehogs, which quietly unroll and go about their own business; the hoops, playing-card soldiers, likewise subject to locomotor initiative of their own; and the rules are decrees of the testy, unpredictable Queen of Hearts."*

NORBERT WIENER
"Cybernetics"

REVERSE LOGIC

"A famous philosopher admitted that his liking for chess involved a paradox. Theoretically a philosopher ought to admire chess because it leaves nothing to chance, because reason and logic triumph. But again and again, after having done his best to find the strongest move, his own reasoning had proved unreliable. His conclusion was that he liked chess for its uncertainties. For him it held the charm of the unforeseen."

EDWARD LASKER
"The Adventure of Chess"

"Automation's greatest consequence to business will be the enormous social change resulting from it. The entire role of business, its relation to human wants and its way of satisfying those wants depends upon society. Fundamental changes in society fundamentally change the role of business. Buying patterns, consumption habits, and other social attitudes will be radically affected by the technology, and they, in turn, will produce decisive changes in business operations and methods."

JOHN DIEBOLD "Beyond Automation"

TRAFFIC CONTROL—Already installed in several urban areas are computer-controlled traffic systems. Sensors in the streets measure the number of cars and a computer analyzes this data to regulate traffic lights. The system has speeded rush hour traffic 38% and sharply cut accidents. (Reported in NEWSWEEK)

PSYCHIATRY—Computers can now aid psychiatrists in rearranging a patient's random experiences and concepts into a logical, more meaningful order, so that the patient can understand them better. Assimilating a mass of data, the computer can swiftly reshuffle it into an ordered pattern. (Reported in PAGEANT)

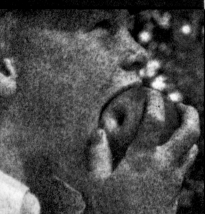

TEACHING—Students can now share a digital computer that adapts lessons to their individual needs and to performance standards of various instructors. Each student receives text and diagrams, test questions and answers at his own pace, and can even erase answers. (Reported in INTERNATIONAL SCIENCE AND TECHNOLOGY magazine)

CRIME—As well as storing names and records (including aliases) of persons and stolen vehicles for instantaneous checking by policemen "on the beat," computers are also helping to solve crimes by assimilating facts and comparing fingerprints to single out suspects from thousands of records. (Reported in BUSINESS WEEK)

LAW—One computer can do the work of many lawyers by locating appropriate precedents for court cases, sifting through thousands of cases electronically in minutes. Legislators are also being aided in recodification by computers that pinpoint records referring to or affecting a law under revision. (Reported in BUSINESS WEEK)

WAR STRATEGY—The Army has designed a computer that can stage a full-scale "battle" against an enemy. Pre-programed with such data as weapons capabilities and battle plans, the computer will accept and carry out military commands and predict their eventual "success" or "failure." (Reported by Army News Service)

PUBLISHING—Extremely high-speed photocomposition is being accomplished by computers which prepare finished copy at the rate of 1000 characters per second that is of lithographic or magazine quality. (Reported in NEWS FRONT)

ANIMAL BREEDING—Many thousands of dairy farmers in all 50 states are participating in a program of electronic storage of production records for hundreds of thousands of cows. In this way, the best milk producers can be pinpointed to produce better herds by selective breeding. (Reported in THE WALL STREET JOURNAL)

"The new mathematical methods of automatic control, a subject sometimes called cybernetics, have been developed now because this is a time when communications and control have in effect become forms of power. These inventions have been directed by social needs, and they are useful inventions, yet it was not their usefulness which dominated and set light to the minds of those who made them."

"Science and Human Values"   J. BRONOWSKI

ASSEMBLY—Among its many uses in automated manufacturing, the computer now can control assembly of radios from component parts at the rate of a thousand a day. Another device can assemble half a television receiver chassis in seconds. (Excerpted from THE REPORTER)

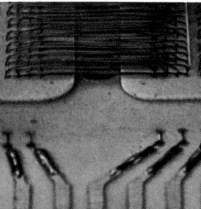

ROBOT—A man-like machine has been developed that can perform space or underwater exploration, handle delicate instruments and act as a military vehicle. Equipped with limbs, a sense of "feel" and electronic "eyes," the robot is guided from inside or remotely by a man, whose movements it copies. (Reported in NEWS FRONT)

BRAIN DISORDERS—An eerie-looking pair of huge eyeglasses with built-in photocells can measure light reflected from the wearer's eyes and feed the information into a computer that diagnoses brain disorders with great precision. (Reported in NEWSWEEK)

REPAIRS—A virtually "immortal" telephone switching system has been devised that fixes itself temporarily if a part fails. In the meantime it figures out what went wrong and tells a maintenance man about it, never allowing itself to stop operating. (Reported in BUSINESS WEEK)

LITERATURE — Probable authorship of disputed manuscripts can be quickly studied and determined by computers. Using certain key words and phrases, a computer recently matched the Federalist papers with various authors and selected James Madison as the likely author. (Reported by ELECTRONIC AGE magazine)

DISEASE DIAGNOSIS—High-speed computers are being programed to automatically culture and analyze bacteria, viruses and other infectious agents in order to immediately identify infectious diseases and enable hospitals and laboratories to begin treatment sooner. (Reported by U.S. Information Service)

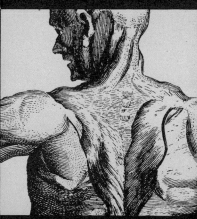

MANUFACTURING—Manufacturing firms are linking their plants to sales offices with computers for instant transmission of production statistics and data, as well as location of the closest availability of products in inventory. Customers are thus getting better, quicker service. (Reported in AMERICAN METAL MARKET)

COMMUNICATIONS — All forms of information—oral, written, photo, or drawing, whether on paper, film, radio or TV can now be translated into identical electronic impulses which can be processed and either stored or transmitted anywhere in the world in less than one-seventh of a second. (Reported in THE QUILL)

"Another portentous (computer) development is simulation. . . . The inventory game, by simulating a real inventory system, allows the player to study its faults and to correct them with computers. In much the same way, simulation is being applied to management problems. Professor Jay Forrester, of M.I.T., using one minute of computer time, has simulated the operation of an entire business over a period of 400 weeks."

GILBERT BURCK "The Computer Age"

HIRING—The federal government has adopted an advanced scientific hiring system that uses a computer to sift through many thousands of prospects for federal positions and can in a moment produce a list of persons qualified (on paper, at least) for these positions. (Reported in NEWS FRONT)

BRAIN—A baby electrochemical brain has been constructed which works like that of a human. The brain is taught by "spanking" it (giving it electrical shocks) each time it gives a wrong response. These shocks cause dendrite growths exactly like those in the human brain, and modify its future behavior. (Reported in STEEL magazine)

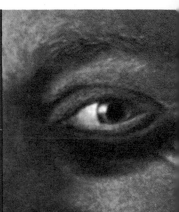

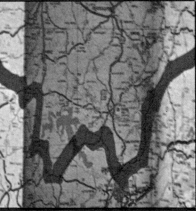

RAILROADS—Control of a main line railroad has been given to a computer which runs all switches and signals automatically. Another railroad uses a computer to keep track of its 36,000 boxcars so that empty ones can be immediately located for use. (Reported in MODERN RAILROADS and THE WALL STREET JOURNAL)

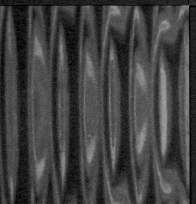

LASERS—Which color a laser emits can be controlled at electronic speeds with a new instrument that can make 125,000 color selections per second. Estimates are that the device will store 100 million bits of data on a square inch of film. (Reported in STEEL magazine)

SIMULATION — In research involving space vehicles, computers have simulated actual conditions of space travel in order to test components and avoid costly trial and error. Mathematical simulation of manufacturing processes has also saved millions of dollars prior to actual operation. (Reported by E. I. Dupont de Nemours & Co.)

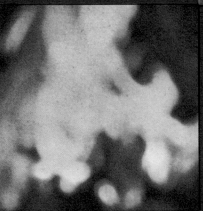

RESERVATIONS—It takes only a few millionths of a second for a computer to tell an airline reservation clerk if a seat is available on any of their flights at any airport in the country. If no space is available, the computer suggests alternate flights with seats available. (Reported on the Earl Nightingale radio program)

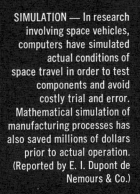

BIDS — In a large corporation's heavy apparatus division where sales are only on a bid basis, a computer has been programed to propose bids for the company on the likelihood of what competitive bids will be. The computer's bids have been "amazingly accurate," according to one executive. (Reported in BUSINESS WEEK)

BRAIN WAVES—Following successful research in performing activities (such as transmitting Morse code and turning on an electric light switch) by amplifying brain waves, experts predict that man (including paralyzed patients) may someday do work through computers by merely thinking about it. (Reported in THE FINANCIAL POST)

"It is my considered opinion, from long experience, that our customers will continue to be reluctant to use information systems—however well devised—so long as one feature of our present intellectual and engineering climate prevails. This feature— and its prevalence is all too commonplace in many companies—is that for many people it is more painful and troublesome to have information than for them not to have it."

Zator Technical Bulletin 136   CALVIN N. MOOERS

CHEMICALS—With the aid of computer prepared punch cards, a chemical company is mixing and preparing for shipping 100 formulations involving 200 different ingredients in varying proportions, all from a central automated control panel. (Reported in CHEMICAL PROCESSING magazine)

MAIL—An electronic optical scanner that reads machine-printed addresses and sorts mail 15 times faster than the best postal clerk is expected to help speed delivery of the 72 billion pieces of mail going through our postal system annually. (Reported in TIME)

DESIGN — Computers which turn complex mathematical formulas into three-dimensional drawings on a screen are greatly aiding designers. The drawing can then be enlarged in detail, changed in perspective, or altered by a designer using a "light pen." (Reported in THE IRON AGE)

LIBRARIES—Use of computers to store and instantly locate millions of pieces of information is well-known. The computer can also store graphic materials—maps, charts, blueprints, photos, etc., and on command reproduce, enlarge and project this material. (Reported in NEWS FRONT magazine)

COUNSELING — Computers are now assimilating data on students' past school records to recommend course programs that the student can handle. This process will also predict which students are likely to encounter academic problems in their present courses. (Reported in NEWSWEEK)

TELEPHONES—Electronic switching has enabled telephone companies to offer such new services as having calls automatically transferred to any number at which you can be reached, automatic dialing of frequently-called numbers, and notifying a caller when a busy line becomes free. (Reported by U. S. I. S.)

SPEECH—An electronic "voice" can now emit human speech without having sounds pre-recorded on tape. An analog computer "translates" a digital computer's "thoughts" into speech impulses. The "translator" has 17 sections that duplicate functions of human vocal organs. (Reported in SAN FRANCISCO CHRONICLE)

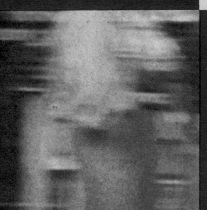

RAPID TRANSIT— A computer run passenger-carrying rapid transit system has been developed. With only a dispatcher at a central panel to monitor the system, the railed cars will travel at great speeds and stop to discharge and accept passengers, all without need for human control. (Reported by WABCO/Union Switch & Signal.)

the trouble with the tin woodman

". . . My tin body contained no heart, and without a heart no one can love . . ."

L. FRANK BAUM
"The Tin Woodman of Oz"

SIMPLICITY LOST

"If a man uses machines, he carries on all the affairs of life like a machine; whoever carries on his affairs like a machine gets a machine-like heart; and when anyone has a machine-like heart in his breast, he loses true simplicity."

TED SILVEY
"Is Artificial Intelligence
Superior to Natural Intelligence?"

ASK A FOOLISH QUESTION . . .

"Professor Elting E. Morrison of MIT says that earlier machines developed by man—engines and generators—set clear limits as to how much misuse they would tolerate before resisting.
" 'Overloaded, abused, they stopped work, stalled, broke down, blew up; and there was the end of it. Thus they set clear limits to men's ineptitudes.
" 'For the computer, I believe, the limits are not so obvious. Used in ignorance or stupidity, asked a foolish question, it does not collapse, it goes on to answer the fool according to his folly. And the questioner, being a fool, will go on to act on the reply.' "

U.S. News & World Report
February 24, 1964

□ That's it—over there on the bureau where you left it last night—your electronic alter-ego. It is no bigger than a pack of cigarettes, yet it has stored in it everything you have ever experienced. Ask it a question, and if it doesn't have the answer, it will plug into some system that does; a Federal central information service, a state service, a municipal one. When you die, you will pass this complete experience on to your children, just as, in helping to create them, you passed on your genetic structure. Their heritage will not be money (it will have disappeared), nor property (who can really *own* anything?), nor sets of cliches and platitudes, but the heritage of a life lived; the experience of a unique organism moving through an environment. Experience is all that we can ever *own;* it is the only thing that can be passed on. Let *you*—through the little black box—be their heritage.

"A whole range of new possibilities is being opened up by the development of extremely small computers, using microcircuitry," says Sir Leon Bagrit in *The Age of Automation.*

"The enormous reduction in size that has taken place during recent years can be illustrated, perhaps, by saying that whereas the computer of 1950 needed a large room to contain it, the 1964 model is down to the dimensions of a suitcase: by 1974, the normal computer will be no bigger than a half carton of cigarettes. . . . It is now possible to envisage personal computers small enough to be taken around in one's car, or even in one's pocket. They could be plugged into a national computer grid, to provide individual enquirers with almost unlimited information."

Your children may not have to take 12 years to get ready to enter college; nor have spent all that time learning things that could be easily found in any branch library. They will have been taught processes; and how to use the little black box, and if they use it rightly, they will ask it what happened on the field of Hastings in 1066; or what the logarithm of 228 is; or how 3 degrees Kelvin translates in Fahrenheit or Centigrade. They will be given a little black box, and the two of them will go to school together; and they may enter what is now considered college at the age of seven — which appears to be the last year that a child really can structure his neural "imprints." Perhaps they will not have to spend —as many of us have—the years after college trying to unlearn what they "learned" there.

And in the work that they do, other variations of the little black box will be their constant companion.

"For example," says John Diebold in "The New World Coming," *Saturday Review,* July 23, 1966, "the newest computer systems may appear as input/output units in individual desks; small television-like screens with keyboards and copying devices. When you ask a question, you see the answer almost simultaneously on the screen. If you want a copy of the answer, you can make it immediately. The heart of the system is a switching center rather like the telephone system. Computers, storage elements of many varieties, and many other devices used as part of the system are accessible as you need them, connected through the switching center to the terminal unit of your fingertips.

"Thousands of people may use such systems at the same time, and each need know no more about the operation of the system than the average person knows about the telephone. In the next decade the typical computer system is going to be of this kind."

The entire structure of our business and economic life will be vastly changed with the spread of computer use. But still there appears in our times to be little understanding of the revolution that is occurring; there still seems to be a tendency to think of the computer as "what the boys in the back room will have;" a gadget that may be fun to play with, but "business is business."

"For example," John Diebold says, "today's business organization structure is a legacy of the first industrial revolution in which specialization of labor was followed by mechanization around specialties. We are now in possession of a technology which allows us to build information systems which transcend the compartmentalized structure of business organization. Much of the difficulty we have been experiencing in putting these new tools to work in recent years results from the fact that it clashes with our fundamental organization system. This is a problem that is not yet recognized by many of the organizations experiencing it."

The portents are everywhere. An editorial entitled, "The Quiet Revolution" in *American Metal Market,* says: "The computer revolution now completely surrounds us. Automation in seemingly only a few years has come on with such a rush, it's as though we live in the eye of an electronic hurricane. Life seems to be as serene as ever, but the endless array of computer consoles means it's becoming entirely different."

In another editorial, this time in *33* Magazine, February, 1965, under the title "Our Chum, the Computer," it is said: "The belief once held that the computer was the *deux ex machina* which would resolve all the knotty problems lying around us with a few clickity clicks of its mechanical brain is no longer with us. . . . Many in management do not have a full appreciation of the role a computer can play in bringing about better operating efficiencies and a better finished product. This lack of awareness too often is the result of irresolution in learning what's going on. Hedged about by such terms as linear programming, nanoseconds, digital, priority interrupt, and trend logging, some men have a tendency to regard computerization as some branch of black magic—with incantations known only to the initiate."

Black magic or white, the cybernetic revolution raises grave ques-

STRANGE NEW WORLD

"The 660-2 (using software for multiply and divide) with 4K of 2-usec-cycle core, sells for $56K as compared to $52.5K for a 4K, 8-usec 910. The 660-5 with 4K of 5-usec core, costs $46K vs. $75.5K for a 4K, 8-usec 920. The company, which also makes telemetry and signal conditioning gear, will also offer a 12-bit, 10-usec core 650, and a hybrid circuit 680."

Business & Science
August, 1965

STATUS SYMBOL

"Sometimes, experts suggest, computers are bought by companies for reasons of prestige—as status symbols. Twinkling lights, spinning tape wheels, chrome cabinets are said to have a mesmerizing effect on some managers."

"Is the Computer Running Wild?"
U.S. News & World Report
February 24, 1964

PHOTOGRAPHY BY BOB FRASER
FIGURE BY MASAMI MIYAMOTO

HEART TROUBLE

"I don't know enough," replied the Scarecrow cheerfully. "My head is stuffed with straw, you know, and that is why I am going to Oz to ask him for some brains."

"Oh, I see," said the Tin Woodman. "But, after all, brains are not the best things in the world."

"Have you any?" inquired the Scarecrow.

"No, my head is quite empty," answered the Woodman, "but once I had brains, and a heart also; so, having tried them both, I should much rather have a heart."

L. FRANK BAUM
"The Wizard of Oz"

tions for men who are now holding middle management positions in business, finance, government and education.

"There is every reason to believe," comments Donald N. Michael in *Cybernation: The Silent Conquest*, "that within the next two decades machines will be available outside the laboratory that will do a credible job of original thinking, certainly as good thinking as that expected of most middle-level people who are supposed to 'use their minds.' There is no basis for knowing where this process will stop . . ."

So what happens to the man in a middle-management job the morning he walks into his office and discovers he has been replaced by a machine? He'll either go up — or get out — because at any lower stage of economic activity, his efforts no longer have any value. We assume he will go up.

In "Will Computers Win Out by Default?" in *Iron Age*, April 15, 1965, the editors say: "There's a growing awareness that the advent of the computer means more work for the manager, not less. It should expand the manager's responsibility, rather than shrink it. The quality of judgment, which the computer can't supply, will be even more urgently needed."

And yet, glancing around rather furtively, one finds little going on to prepare middle management for the computer world. If middle management is to upgrade itself and use these new tools for the benefit of the stockholders who own the company, it is going to have to understand its business and its markets so well that it can program computers to build mathematical models of them for it, and then to test alternatives to discover which one will yield the highest profit, or the greatest production efficiency, or the deepest market penetration. Who's learning to do that?

Gordon S. Brown and Donald P. Campbell, writing on "Control Systems" in *Automatic Control*, describe the new kind of middle management man:

"A systems engineer," they say, "cannot be trained by simply adding together the old specialties. What is wanted is not a jack-of-all-trades but a master of a new trade, and this will require a new synthesis of studies. It will call for advanced work in the fields of mathematics, physics, chemistry, measurements, communications, electronics, servomechanisms, energy conversion, thermodynamics and computational techniques.

"The control engineer will need to know the mathematics of differential equations, functions of a complex variable, statistics and nonlinear techniques, and to have a thorough grounding in modern physics and chemistry. He will also need to be familiar with computational aids, such as differential analyzers and computers."

JUST KEEP IT GOING

"*. . . as cybernation advances, new and profound problems will arise for our society and its values. Cybernation presages changes in the social system so vast and so different from those with which we have traditionally wrestled that it will challenge to their roots our current perceptions about the viability of our way of life.*

"*If our democratic system has a chance to survive at all, we shall need far more understanding of the consequences of cybernation. Even the job of simply preserving a going society will take a level of planning far exceeding any of our previous experiences with centralized control.*"

DONALD N. MICHAEL
"Cybernation: The Silent Conquest"

LET'S NOT

Brockway McMillan, Under Secretary of the Air Force, is one who warns against over-reliance on "electronic brains" in defense. "Let's not try to design things," he cautions, "that we don't fully understand."

DECISION OF THE BOARD

"*An ambitious company president established a team of experts to help him install a total management system. He hired an industrial psychologist to figure out how he made complex decisions; he had a business systems specialist work out exactly what operating data was needed to make these decisions and how they were implemented throughout the company; and he commissioned an operations-research expert to simulate the president's decision-making process.*

"*Finally, when all the bugs were worked out of this flawless new system, the board of directors fired the president; obviously, he was no longer needed.*"

HERBERT E. KLEIN
Dun's Review & Modern Industry
September—1964

OF MORONS AND HEROES

"Man is one of the best general-purpose computers available and if one designs for man as a moron, one ends up with a system that requires a genius to maintain it. Thus we are not suggesting that we take man out of the system, but we are suggesting that he be properly employed in terms of both his abilities and limitations. Some designers have required that he be a hero as well as a genius."

E. LLEWELLYN THOMAS
"Human Factors in Design"
from *Design and Planning*

It may sound as if what is being described is a technician. He is not; he is the new "universal man." Our educational systems have not been organized to produce such men since the Renaissance, and there were precious few of them then. We are not talking about a man who can program a machine — we are talking about a man who uses the most advanced intellectual tools of his time to analyze his business, political, or social environment so profoundly that it *can* be programed.

We have concentrated on "middle management" so far because, although we hesitate to use the abominable cliche, it represents "the power structure" in our society. "Top" management may make the ultimate decisions, but the decisions are based on the information, analysis, and recommendation of middle management. And this is true whether we are talking about business or finance or politics or social or educational systems (as if, in the end, there were really any difference). If middle management does not learn the disciplines that will enable it to make effective use of the new technology, it will in any event compete against those who have: "The economist Strumilin, in a statement to the Soviet Academy of Science," reports Sir Leon Bagrit, "said that 'if capitalism can be characterized as a classical period of the mechanization of work, communism will be seen to be bringing about a new era of total automation in production.' "

As earlier mentioned, we have lost worlds before; it may be we have found a new way to do it. Somewhere between the stock market reports in the morning and the country club in the afternoon, we failed to attend the lecture on differential analyzers — and that is where the action is.

Which brings us to a final point, with all too little space to discuss it. The theory, design, and operation of computers is based upon the extension of a single process of the human mind: mathematics. But we do not, as individual human beings, lead daily lives that are essentially rational or logical. We swim immersed in a world of highly personal, emotional, religious, and largely subconscious reactions. If we overlook that fact; if we build a world that is modeled primarily on additive, analogous and feedback principles, we may very well construct a world in which humanity is lost, and individualism is lost, except to the extent it can be codified into "1" or "0" and processed by a machine.

And so, after this long discourse, we sit here in our Sopwith Camel at the landing field, waiting to fly another "Dawn Patrol" against the hated Red Baron. The mechanic who was supposed to wind up our propellor overslept and as we await his technological approach, we turn the whiskers on our crystal set and pick up a voice. It says, "It's A-OK up here. All systems green and go. Roger and out." The voice comes from an astronaut 400 miles above the earth, traveling at 17,000 mph.

Man, we'll be lucky to make it to the end of the runway! □

THE LEISURE MASSES

CHAPTER DIVIDER:
"COMPOSITION WITH SEVEN FIGURES AND A HEAD (THE FOREST)"
BY ALBERTO GIACOMETTI
OWNED BY THE READER'S DIGEST ASSOCIATION
PHOTOGRAPHY BY HERBERT MATTER

IT HAS BEEN a long-time pleasure of mankind to build castles in the sand. In some respects, human societies are much like sand castles; they are built up out of innumerable small particles whose most important attribute is that they cling to each other. Strange forces beyond their ken shape them into complicated and sometimes grotesque configurations. □ The castle stands most bravely there, but it is only sand. When the inevitable tide comes in, the waves will nibble at the foundations, and ultimately the structure will be swept away, to become another castle on another day. Only the fun of it is left and the love that went into its making. □ It may be that we should consider our own ephemeral society like that, too; a social structure where the work is only incidental but where the fun and the love that went into its making still linger as our shared and common heritage. □ Perhaps we already are beginning to view our society that way. If not, perhaps we should.

PHOTOGRAPHY BY BOB FRASER. CONSTRUCTION BY MASAMI MIYAMOTO

THE 12 o'clock of life

THE SINGLE TRUTH

*"One must work, if not from taste,
then at least from despair. For, to reduce
everything to a single truth:
work is less boring than pleasure."*

J. PIEPER
"Leisure, the Basis of Culture"

THE INVISIBLE MAN

*"Whether one is rich or poor, the
chance of escaping work today is slim.
The pressures toward it are too
great, the lack of comprehension of not
working is too complete. One is not
appalled or indignant on learning
that another doesn't work; one simply
does not understand, doesn't know
where next to turn for conversation,
cannot size up the ostensibly
human object standing there."*

SEBASTIAN De GRAZIA
"Of Time, Work and Leisure"

☐ Few maps you are likely to see will show it, but there is a little village in South America called Chinchero, high in the Andes. If it's any help (and it won't be) it is a few miles from Cuzco, ancient capital of the Inca empire; it is at an altitude of 10,000 feet, and it is in southern Peru.

We learn about this little place, Chinchero, from Allan R. Holmberg, writing on "Cultural Differences and the Concept of Time," in the book edited by Robert S. Kleemeier, *Aging and Leisure*.

"As expressed by the inhabitants of this folk village, according to Dr. Oscar Nunez del Prado, the human organism has in its constitution a given number of ounces of earth. The quantity, although fixed for the individual, varies from person to person. Some have more, others less. The existence of strong and weak people, in fact, is explained on the basis that some people have more earth in their constitution than others.

"Life is maintained and endures in Chinchero in accordance with the conservation of an individual's distribution of earth. Nevertheless, the vitality of an individual diminishes as he walks and climbs through life, which is exactly what he does in the Andes. With every step he takes, he leaves behind little particles of his earth supply, and when this supply is finally used up, death follows.

"It is the belief of these people that human existence unfolds vigorously until the middle year or, as they say, 'the twelve o'clock of life.' . . . Fatigue is great in the old man because the path which he walked, labored, and climbed has eaten his life away."

It is our thesis here that the concept of earth of the Chinchero villagers is somewhat equivalent to our concept of the human use of time. We seem to believe that each human being has just so many units of time (like ounces of earth) at his disposal. When it is used up, he "dies." How each individual decides to use up his particles becomes the basis of many of our moral and social judgments; judgments that may have little or no validity in the world in which we find ourselves today.

We rush in here, where angels fear to tread, because we feel that our society is rapidly approaching an era—perhaps in ten years, perhaps in twenty—when the age-old distinctions between "work" and "play," between "free time" and "leisure," will no longer be very relevant.

There have been times in our past when it seemed possible to draw meaningful distinctions between these activities, but as we move ever deeper into the mechanized, automated and cybernated age, it becomes more difficult for us to define what we are "doing," or what others "ought to do." Like that strangely disturbing surrealist painting, "The Persistence of Time," our private and social clocks have dissolved into the anomalous topology of an old egg broken into a frying pan.

Most of us seem to feel that we know what "work" is—it is what we do, and seldom what anyone else is doing. This is both a personal and social judgment, and we make it all the time, for ourselves and for others. We make it when we say, "He never did a day's work in his life." We make it when we say, "Everyone who is able to, ought to work," or when we say, "These people would be all right if they could only find work." Most importantly, we tend to equate work and income, as if they were directly and proportionately related. Even the most superficial examination of this relationship, historically or currently, would appear to show that it has little if any validity. Yet we are embarking on great social programs in which this relationship seems to be taken for granted.

In earlier times, this inadequacy might not have been particularly important, but now it becomes so. We are going to have to ask ourselves how we evaluate the human use of time when we consider—and vote on—such issues as social welfare programs, the guaranteed annual wage, the shortened work-week, the guaranteed annual income, the war on poverty, and dozens of other considerations that already ride the headlines of our daily newspapers. We cannot delay much longer coming to some sort of personal judgment concerning the kinds of mores, institutions and systems of law we will have to invent, develop and implement, in a society where "work" may become a privilege for a relatively few persons; in an "abundant" or an "affluent" society in which *not* "working" will be not only socially acceptable, but highly desirable, as a way of using human time.

We have, of course, a feeling that time for us is very much like time for everyone else. Even the shallowest moment's reflection should convince us that this cannot possibly be true. The American view of time is shared by few other cultures in the world, which does not mean that it is better or worse, but only that it is not shared.

"As to the use of time as such," says Robert J. Smith in his essay on "Cultural Differences and the Concept of Time," everyone who has had cross cultural experience is well aware that time may be handled in various ways. . . .The Americans are, of course, notorious for their orientation to clock-like scheduling, while the Japanese are not. But it is a standing joke that in Japan only the trains are on time, whereas in the United States only the trains are never on time. One need not look for consistency in practice, but it can be pointed out that in the United States the trains are *supposed* to be on time."

Even within our own culture, we find that the evaluation of the human use of time varies between age groups, occupations, educational backgrounds and races.

Let us see if there is some way we can look, with relative objectivity, into the question of why people should "work" at all . . . □

HOIST BY ONE'S OWN PETARD

"*We penalize the weak for the achievement of the strong. Could we ever imagine the technologically unemployed being paid their full salaries and even getting productivity increases while unemployed? No; laymen and economists, we do not yet see clearly the enormous entrapment of man in the consequences of his own ingenuity. We still think of rewarding the producer; in a word, leaving the hunting animal with his catch. We squirm in the presence of utopia as though it were a painful retirement.*"

MENO LOVENSTEIN
"Guaranteed Income and Traditional Economics"

SONNETS FROM THE JAPANESE

"*The older adult is not, then, a prisoner of time, nor does he feel that it is running out on him. He makes no effort to appear younger than he is. The minutes, hours, and days simply pass, filled up with a variety of activities which are performed as the need to do them arises. Time does not drag and it does not threaten; it is there to be used but it does not stretch emptily before the older person. He works at what he can do or he is of service to those whom he can help, and when he dies he can hope that his family will say of him that his last years were no more burden to himself than to others.*"

ROBERT J. SMITH
"Cultural Differences and the Concept of Time"

THE days of our years

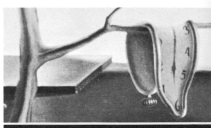

□ In the "Lost and Found" column of a newspaper of the early 19th Century, one might have read the following: "LOST, yesterday, somewhere between sunrise and sunset, two golden hours, each set with sixty diamond minutes. No reward is offered, for they are gone forever." It would have been signed, *Horace Mann*.

There are some rather interesting things to consider about this. Perhaps the most provocative is the implicit assumption that time can be "lost." It is not immediately clear how this can happen; the organism in its environment is already doing everything that an organism is supposed to do; it persists in time, it interacts with its stimuli. What Mr. Mann meant was, of course, that there were two hours during the day when he felt he should have been doing something else. His personal evaluation that he should have been doing something "more valuable" is the product of the culture in which he found himself.

The whole expression reflects what Benjamin Franklin, in his *Advice to a Young Tradesman*, (1786) said so memorably: "Remember that time is money." Both are the reflections of concepts prevalent in the early part of the industrial revolution; both equate the "proper" use of time with the acquisition of material goods (gold, diamonds, money).

Even today, when we should know better, we have a tendency to consider that "work" is somehow more valuable than play or sleep or day-dreaming. Such a concept haunts us, makes us miserable with guilt.

Also implicit in 18th and 19th century philosophy were the assumptions that the human experience of time is a measurable quality, and that we know how it should best be employed. We didn't, of course, know any such thing—nor do we now.

Think about the days you spend, and how they are divided. "What were you doing?" is the most frequent way of asking the question. It might be more meaningful to ask, "What was happening to you?" Young children are usually perplexed by the question "What did you do today?" because they do not "do" things to the world; the world happens to them. It is only later, when they "wise up," that they come up with a description of some purposeful activity, whether real or not. As adults they are almost incapable of admitting they are "doing nothing."

In a purely hypothetical way it is possible to break down the hours of our days and the days of our years into four generally acceptable patterns of activity: work, subsistence, "free time" and leisure. In our society the last category is usually only socially acceptable when performed by the very rich—or the very sick.

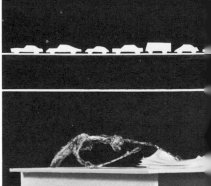

On the adjoining page, we attempt to show how an average person's lifetime in our society may have been spent: "work," as defined, plays a very small part in it. □

JUST A MATTER OF TIME: — We have a tendency, in our society, to assign numbers to everything, as if in giving them a quantitative value we somehow understand them better. Actually, life as we experience it is not a quantified thing, but a continuous spectrum of overlapping experience. Nonetheless, we try to quantify it, and that is what we have done here. We assume an average lifespan of 70 years, or approximately 25,550 days, (613,200 hours) and we have tried to break those hours down into wholly fictitious categories, which we have called subsistence, free, commuting and work time. Actually, many of these activities may take place at the same "time" and are largely matters of what name we—and our contemporaries —choose to give them. Nevertheless, the exercise, though specious, gives us one way to consider how we spend our lives, and how little importance "work" (as defined) is in the lifetime of most human beings.

"To every thing there is a season, and a time to every purpose under the heaven . . . A time to laugh and a time to weep . . ." ECCLESIASTES, III, 1

SUBSISTENCE— 45.8% (Figured at 11 hours per day, sleeping and eating—281,050 hours in 70 years).

This is the time we use up just to stay alive. It includes sleeping, preparing meals and eating them, dressing and undressing, and performing necessary biological functions. These activities are not matters of choice but of necessity. They are very much the same for all living humans, regardless of their culture, geographical area, political system or ideology; and pretty much the same for the rich and the poor. Subsistence time may be considered the constant on which the human use of time is based, and there is no reason to believe that it will change in any important way in the future.

BORN FREE: ". . . I would rather sit on a pumpkin and have it all to myself than to be crowded on a velvet cushion. I would rather ride on earth in an ox cart, than go to heaven in the fancy car of an excursion train . . . The very simplicity and nakedness of man's life in the primitive ages imply this advantage, at least, that they left him still but a sojourner in nature. When he was refreshed with food and sleep, he contemplated his journey again. He dwelt, as it were, in a tent in this world, and as either threading the valleys, or crossing the plains, or climbing the mountaintops. But lo! men have become the tools of their tools. The man who independently plucked the fruits when he was hungry has become a farmer; and he who stood under a tree for shelter, a housekeeper. We now no longer camp as for a night, but have settled down on earth and forgotten Heaven. We have adopted Christianity merely as an improved method of **agri**-culture. We have built for this world a family mansion, and for the next a family tomb. . . . The cart before the horse is neither beautiful nor useful. Before we can adorn our houses with beautiful objects the walls must be stripped and our lives must be stripped, and beautiful housekeeping and beautiful living be laid for a foundation: now, a taste for the beautiful is most cultivated out of doors . . ." HENRY DAVID THOREAU, from "Walden, or Life in the Woods," (1854).

"A Jug of Wine, a Loaf of Bread —and Thou Beside me singing in the Wilderness— Oh, Wilderness were Paradise enow!" OMAR KHAYYAM (1070-1123)

FREE-TIME—34.8% (The remainder after subtracting subsistence, commuting and work— 212,590 hours).

Here time is figured negatively by deducting subsistence, work and commuting time from the work year. It is customarily referred to as "leisure time," but it is anything but leisure. We use it up shopping, calling on friends or relatives, reading, watching TV, going to church or the theater, etc. As free-time increases because of shorter working hours, the new increment of time is largely used for chores around the house, repairs, remodeling or gardening. In our times, free-time is anything but free.

AND WHILE I'M THERE: ". . . This would be a good day to put in a new light in the window in the woodshed and also there is one broken in the shop and one in the henhouse, so the sensible thing would be to do them all at once, as long as I have the putty worked up and the glass cutter out. I ought to hook up the stove in the shop today, and get it ready for winter use. And I ought to run up the road and see Bert and find out why he hasn't delivered the cord of slabwood he said he was going to bring to me. At any rate, I ought to make a place in the cellar for it today, which will mean cleaning house down there a little and neatening up, and finding a better place to keep my flats and fillers for the egg cases. Incidentally, I ought to collect eggs right now, so there won't be any breakage in the nests. It just occurred to me that if I'm going to the mill today I ought to measure the truck and figure out what I shall need in the way of hardwood boards to build a set of sideboards and a headboard and tailboard for my stakes . . . One thing I ought to do today is to take a small Stillson wrench and go down cellar and tighten the packing nut on the water pump so it won't leak. I could do that when I am down there making a place for the slabwood . . ." E. B. WHITE, "One Man's Meat," HARPER & BROTHERS, New York, 1938.

"The world is too much with us, late and soon, Getting and spending, we lay waste our powers: Little we see in nature that is ours." WILLIAM WORDSWORTH

COMMUTING— 3.8% (Figured at 2 hrs. per workday for 49 years— 23,912 hrs.)

This is the time used up in getting from home to the job and back again, including finding a parking space and getting the car serviced; or waiting at train and bus stops.

"See the people come and go, Between the houses row on row." ANON.

WORK— 15.6% (Assuming a person is "fully employed" from age 16 to 65— 95,648 hours).

There is no generally satisfactory definition for "work," but most often it seems to mean an activity undertaken for some purpose beyond the pleasure of the individual himself and usually for pay. It mostly consists of performing certain repetitive actions at some prescribed place for a prescribed number of hours on certain days.

"Work is the curse of the drinking classes." TRADITIONAL

work: THE MYTH THAT BECAME A MONSTER

APPOINTMENT IN SAMARA

*"The ideal of the Sannyasin
(fourth stage of the Hindu Asrama
system) is expressed by Manu:
'He should not wish to die
Nor hope to live,
But wait the time appointed
As a servant awaits his wages.' "*

WILLIAM L. ROWE
"Cultural Differences and
the Concept of Time"

AND THE TIME WAS HEAVY

*"Primitive man, bound to work by iron
necessity, uses most of his time
searching for food, preparing food, and
preparing shelter and clothing.
In the time remaining he attends to
his children and relates himself
to other members of his group and
to the supernatural. If it is easy because
of favorable climate and soil and
water to make a living, he spends more
time in the non-work pursuits.*
*"Man as a member of a complex
modern society discovers the problem
of using time. We might say that
a measure of civilization is the
degree that men perceive the use of
time to be a problem."*

ROBERT S. KLEEMEIER
"The Nature and Values of
Meaningful Free-Time Activity"

A MATTER OF ADDITION

*"It is a very fundamental human need,
for instance, to work for some
reward and to judge and enjoy our
success in proportion to the magnitude
of the compensations we can
accumulate. They may be dollars or
any other possession. They may
even be fellow human beings who
become our slaves—because
of our dollars or medals or other
possessions. They may be good deeds
for which God will repay us.
But one thing is certain: they must
be additive. How else could we
count our gains? How else could we
know whether or not we have
accomplished enough to be satisfied?"*

HANS SELYE
"The Stress of Life"

☐ "It seems that there were two patriotic Americans who met on the street one day," recounts R. L. Cunningham in *The Redefinition of Work.*

"What's this I hear about you?" demanded one, "That you say you do not believe in the Monroe Doctrine?"

The reply was instant and indignant: "It's a lie. I never said I didn't believe in the Monroe Doctrine. I do believe in it. It's the palladium of our liberties. I would die for the Monroe Doctrine. All I said was that I don't know what it *means!*"

When it comes to considering the meaning of work in our society, we are much like the patriotic gentleman; we are quite willing to die for the right of other people to work, but we don't really know just what it is that we mean when we talk about work.

It's no good looking it up in the dictionary; the best of them all, The Oxford, gives nine pages of small type to the way in which English speaking people have used the word; it has become, to that extent, virtually meaningless in modern times. Actually, what appears to have happened is that somewhere along the way, in our society at least, we have confused work and income, so that the two somehow became related in our minds. When people say, "We want work," they usually mean they want income. The two are seldom related in any proportional sense, yet when we think they are we try to build a social structure that assumes work will somehow solve our problems, when what we really mean is that income will solve our problems, or at least some of them.

How did all this come about? Where and when did we begin to feel that work—in and for itself—as a human activity, was somehow valuable?

There's a long, long trail awinding when one tries to follow the concept of work back to its origins, but there does appear to be some agreement about some aspects of it. Almost any culture you dig into does not like it. The Paradises and Golden Ages of our ancient pasts were primarily places where one did not have to work. And most of the concepts of heaven in our various religions have as their chief characteristic the fact that one does not have to work in them.

It is doubtful that ancient man had any concept of "work" at all, and such primitive societies as still exist frequently have no vocabulary that distinguishes between "work" and "free time."

"In many low-energy societies," says Fred Cottrell in *The Sources of Free-Time*, "the concepts of work time and free time hardly exist. A man does what is expected of him, which we westerners may refer to as the performance of ritual or ceremony, domestic duties, production, military service, etc. What is expected may also include the occupation of time in conversation, sleep, recreation, singing and dancing, or what-not.

"A man in such a culture may feel as constrained by necessity to do

PHOTO BY WILLIAM JACKSON © 1966

AND THIS BE PROGRESS?

"Taken as a whole, then, the idea of progress involves three principles: first, the belief that history follows a continuous, necessary and orderly course; second, the belief that this course is the effect of a regularly operating causal law; and, third, the belief that the course of change has brought and will continue to bring improvement in the condition of mankind. The idea is modern and stems from the seventeenth century ..."

GEORGE HILDEBRAND
"The Idea of Progress"

one as the other. It is only when we classify his time into categories meaningful to us that work becomes defined. But if we say that he is working only when he is gaining sustenance, then many 'primitive' men had far more work-free time than we have."

As the world moved out of what we now consider primitivism and into more organized social structure, there grew up the myth of some "Golden Age" which was, perhaps, founded on some lingering memory of the good old days when the concept of work did not exist. All the ancient voices, whose thin dry sounds have come down their thousands of years to become the conscience of us all, considered work at best a necessary evil. "In the Socrates of *Xenophon,* work is an expedient," writes Sebastian de Grazia in his definitive book, *Of Time, Work and Leisure,* "in Virgil's *Georgics* it is a necessity and a mock heroism. In Hesiod's *Works and Days* it is a necessity, too, and, worse yet, a curse.

"To the authors of the Bible also, work is necessary because of a divine curse. Through Adam's fall the world became a workhouse. Paradise was where there was no toil. This is the feeling about work one encounters in most of history's years."

The legend of the ancient earthly paradise, where one did not have to work, is preserved in the amber of Lucretius' words. "Earth first," he says, "spontaneously of herself produced for mortals goodly corn crops and joyous vineyards; of herself gave sweet fruits and glad pastures, which nowadays scarce attain any size even when furthered by our labor; we exhaust the oxen and the strength of the husbandmen; we wear out our iron, scarcely fed, after all, by the tilled fields."

When that great classifier and assigner of categories, Aristotle, took a look at work, he could assign it no very high value, except as a way to achieve leisure, or to *not* work. "Nature," he wrote, "requires that we should be able, not only to work well, but to use leisure well. Leisure is the first principle of all action and so leisure is better than work and is its end. As play, and with it rest, are for the sake of work, so work, in turn, is for the sake of leisure."

The legend of a golden age without work was still a lively one even as late as Rousseau, who described it in this way: "The produce of the earth furnished man with all he needed, and instinct told him how to use it, so that singing and dancing, the true offspring of love and leisure, became the amusement, or rather the occupation, of men and women assembled together with nothing else to do."

One may question the logic of the last part of that statement, but there is little doubt that Rousseau did not feel kindly toward work.

Going back a bit, it was the practical-minded Romans who began, a little, to believe there was virtue in work beyond mere sustenance.

"In the morning when thou risest unwilling," the emperor Marcus Aurelius tells himself, "let this thought be present—I am rising to the work of a human being. Why, then, am I dissatisfied if I am going to do the things for which I exist and for which I was brought into the world?" But, of course, the only "work" that Marcus had to do was to tell others what to do—not such a bad day to get out of bed for.

The early Christians did not look upon work as beneficial so much as a penance. There was no work in the Garden of Eden. But when Adam sinned, the Lord God said unto him, "Cursed is the ground for thy sake; in toil shalt thou eat of it all the days of thy life. . . . In the sweat of thy face, shalt thou eat bread, till thou return to the ground."

The idea then that work, to be called work, must be something that we do not want to do, or that is at least unpleasant, was imprinted quite early in our western culture. "That work should be painful belongs to its very essence," says the chapter on Labor in the *Syntopicon*. "Otherwise it would not serve as a penalty or penance. But in the Christian view, labor also contributes to such happiness as man can enjoy on earth. The distinction between temporal and eternal happiness is a distinction between a life of work on earth and the activity of contemplation in Heaven. This does not mean the elimination of leisure and enjoyment from earthly life, but it does make labor their antecedent and indispensable condition.

"In all these conceptions of a better life," continues the *Syntopicon*, "labor is eliminated or reduced. The implication seems to be that the labor required for the maintenance of all historic societies is an affliction, a drudgery, a crushing burden which deforms the lives of many, if not all. The pains of toil do not belong to human life by any necessity of human labor, but rather through the accident of external circumstances which might be other than they are. . . . Man might have realized his nature more surely and richly if, like the lilies of the field, he neither toiled nor spun.

"The contrary view would maintain that work is not a curse but a blessing, filling man's hours usefully, turning to service energies which would otherwise be wasted or misspent in idleness or mischief. . . . It is even suggested that useful occupations save men from a boredom they fear more than the pain of labor, as evidenced by the variety of amusements and diversions they invent or frantically pursue to occupy themselves when work is finished. The satisfactions of labor are as peculiarly human as its burdens. Not merely to keep alive, but to keep his self respect, man is obliged to work."

Thus, at least three ways of viewing work are easily discernible. In primitive, survivalist societies, work is the condition of life, but it is not

THE CRUCIAL QUESTION

"The European-American society which discovered the Protestant Ethic turned work and play into opposites, something that could not have been understood by the Medieval craftsman. The 19th-Century inner-directed man felt that he should work in order to 'make a living.' Then, paradoxically, he succeeded in making such a good living that he produced an economy of abundance in which his grandson is no longer able to work all his life, but must spend some of his years in retirement, although he still believes that work is a good thing in itself, and he is suspicious of play.

"Thus we are now faced with the fundamental question—Can men be happy in any other way than in work?"

ROBERT J. HAVIGHURST
"The Nature and Values of Meaningful Free-Time Activity"

SEANCE ON A LATE AFTERNOON

How, indeed, do Americans spend their free time—when they're not working or sleeping or commuting? As earlier indicated, this is the major portion of the time of our lives, yet very few studies of the use of free time have been published. Just for kicks, we asked a family we know to keep a diary of a few hours after work one day. The family consists of the mother (Polly), the father (Bill), and two teenage children, (Eric) the boy, and (Kristi) the girl. What is interesting here is that within the context, each evaluated what the other was doing a little differently, and only the boy considered what he was doing as "work." But all, except father himself, of course, considered that father was sleeping when he was, ostensibly, watching television.

We make these judgments about what we are doing, and what others in our vicinity are doing, at every waking moment of every day. Out of these judgments and evaluations come our feelings about who is working and who is not. It is perhaps worth noting that none of the activities recorded appear any place in the Gross National Product; yet they are typical of what most people in our society are doing most of the time.

When we consider that, for most of us, the next twenty years will offer more free time than we have ever had before, it seems important that we should begin to give it at least as much serious consideration as we do the few hours most of us work each day.

4 p.m.

POLLY

"Baking cookies, lying on the couch while they bake. Bill is lying on the bed watching 49'er Highlights, but I really think he is asleep. Eric is in his room with the radio on and supposed to be doing homework. Kristi is out with Tom."

BILL

"I'm watching TV—Polly is resting on the living room couch. Eric is reading in his room and Kristi is out. Everyone is having free time."

ERIC

"I'm doing my homework. I have the radio on and father has the TV on—he is probably asleep and mother is reading in the living room. They both are having free time and I'm working. Kristi is out."

5:30 to 7:30

POLLY

"Bill wakes up and comes into the living room and reads. Eric still the same. Kristi comes home and helps me with dinner."

BILL

"Carve meat and eat dinner. Have coffee and turn on radio to quiet music. Listen to Polly and Kristi discuss school. Eric is in his room and Kristi going back and forth between kitchen and her room."

ERIC

"Feed dog and wait for dinner to be served. Father carves meat and mother serves rest of dinner. Eat. Talk to mother and father while they finish their coffee. Discuss football game. Go to my room to watch TV. Reading my homework during dull moments of program. Father reading and Kristi helping mother."

KRISTI

"Came home (at 5:30) and helped mother with dinner. Eric feeds Schupo (above-mentioned dog) and we eat. I go out to return a borrowed dress. Tom is coming over at 8:00 and must decide what to wear—don't want to wear same outfit I did last time. Father is eating candy, reading and listening to radio. Eric is in his room—he has either TV or radio on and is probably reading at the same time, the way he usually does. Mother is sitting at the dining room table doing some writing. She helps me decide what to wear and I go get ready."

thought of particularly as work. Then there is work as a curse, something we would all avoid if we could. And finally, work as the normal outlet for man's energies, because play is not enough. There is one more main-line idea in our Western culture concerning work—it claims that work in and for itself is of intrinsic value.

This idea may have had its first concrete expression in the Sixth Century when St. Benedict at his monastery at Monte Cassino posted rules for the monks. "Idleness is the enemy of the soul," begins Rule XLVIII. "And therefore, at fixed times, the brothers ought to be occupied in manual labor, and, again at fixed times, in sacred reading."

For the first time not only work as such, but work for a stipulated time, became integral to western thought. In later years we were to confuse the two, so that "putting in the time" became more important than the work. But what was new here at the beginning, with the monks of Monte Cassino, was that work was good for the soul. This was the myth that has become a monster in our times; it drives even the rich to maintain the illusion that they are working, and those who do not work into an incessant apologia for being alive.

"Today, the American without a job is a misfit," comments Sebastian de Grazia. "To hold a job means to have status, to belong in the way of life. Between the ages of twenty-five and fifty-five, that is, after school age and before retirement age, nearly 95 per cent of all males work and about 35 percent of all females. Various studies have portrayed the unemployed man as confused, panicky, prone to suicide, mayhem and revolt. Totalitarian regimes seem to know what unemployment can mean; they never permit it."

The "work" monster gained a certain substance from the idea that the progress of a society or a culture is something like the natural progress of the life of a man; as he grows older and works harder, he accumulates more wisdom and more material things.

"Augustine was therefore able to insist," says George Hildebrand in *The Idea of Progress*, "that mankind could well be regarded as a single man, whose earthly experience constituted a gradual advance through education, effecting a slow transition from ignorance to knowledge and finally to faith. . . . In the 17th Century this analogy became fundamental to the formulation of the modern idea of progress . . .

"Progress came to be looked upon as the normal tendency in human affairs, the gradual and inevitable development of the human race."

It is probably no accident that the idea of social progress and the sanctity of work as a means to achieve it grew into a now virtually unex-amined ethic at the same time that the Industrial Revolution began to need more "workers." This kind of work was not like the work that had

NOTHIN' DOIN'

"Work occupies fewer hours in the lives of everyone; what work there is grows less like work every year . . . Compared to the day's work that confronts most of mankind every morning, most U.S. citizens are not engaged in work at all."

GERARD PIEL
"The End of Toil"
Nation—1961

MATTER OF DEFINITION

*"There goes the happy moron,
He doesn't give a dam';
I wish I were a moron,
My God! Perhaps I am."*
"When they've got two weeks' vacation they hurry to vacation ground they swim and they fish but that's what I do all year 'round."

NIALL BRENNAN
"The Making of a Moron"

TO AFFORD TO DARE

"When the accumulation of wealth is no longer of high social importance, there will be great changes in the code of morals. We shall be able to rid ourselves of many of the pseudo-moral principles which have hag-ridden us for two hundred years, by which we have exalted some of the most distasteful of human qualities into the position of the highest values. We shall be able to afford to dare to assess the money-motive at its true value . . ."

J. M. KEYNES
"Essays in Persuasion'"—1932

GOOD QUESTION

"More frequently than not, an executive who gets along easily with others, who does not fight too hard for his position, who is willing to see the point of view of the other fellow, especially if the other fellow is his superior, gains a reputation of being constructive and cooperative. And that he is.
"The question remains, what else is he?"

ELI GINZBERG
"The Study of Human Resources"
in "The Pluralistic Economy"

NO CONTAINER FOR TIME

"In the last ten years we have wasted 25,000,000 man-years of potential economic production because of mass unemployment. An hour of human labor is the most perishable economic value in the world. A ton of steel can be made in 1961 and put in a warehouse. If it is properly oiled and kept covered, it can be consumed in 1964 . . . But an hour of human labor cannot be stored . . .
"We have poured down the economic drain $600 billion in our potential gross national product which we could have created if we had had full employment and full production and an adequate rate of economic growth during the past ten years."

WALTER P. REUTHER
"First Things First"

gone on before; it was specially oriented in space (in the factory or foundry) and structured in time (the necessity for the worker to be in a certain place, at certain times, performing certain prescribed activities).

The dangers of this concept of work were seen long ago by Adam Smith, who pointed out, "In the progress of the division of labor, the employment of the far greater part of those who live by labor . . . comes to be confined to a very few simple operations, frequently one or two. . . . The man whose life is spent performing a few simple operations . . . has no occasion to exert his understanding or to exercise his invention. . . . He naturally loses, therefore, the habit of such exertion, and generally becomes as stupid and ignorant as it is possible for a human creature to become."

Later thinkers have come up with slightly different interpretations of what is "wrong" with "work." Niall Brennan, in *The Making of a Moron* finds a somewhat different reason: "The unpleasantness of a job has nothing to do with whether it is repetitive or not. It depends solely on how many of the parts of man are used and how well they are being used. Acting is monotonous in the literal sense of the word; but few occupations use the whole man so intensely. . . . If only a part of a man is being used, the salvation of his sanity depends on what he himself does with the unwanted parts.

"But if ostensibly the whole man is bought by the employer, and only a part is used, or parts wrongly used, and the worker himself is denied right use of his own parts, then his sanity, in the sense of the fullness of his personality, is in danger. Either the unwanted parts atrophy for sheer lack of use, or they are mutilated by misuse, and he ceases to be a whole man."

This same view of industrial labor—which is the symbol of what most of us mean by work—is reflected in Alexander Heron's, *Why Men Work*. He says, "There are few jobs in the industrial world which are inherently interesting; there are reports that even wine samplers, selectors of beautiful models, and private detectives become bored with their tasks."

Again, it gets back to the partial use of the whole man: work in our society may be dull or worrisome or unpleasant, not because it is work, but because so much of the human being is left out of it. Artists of all persuasions, including, of course, mathematicians and physicists, seldom really think of what they do as work (though they may, out of convention, call it that) because so much of them is used up in the process of what they are doing. It is the paper shufflers and the ditch diggers, if, indeed, there are any of the latter left, that find work boring.

We must not, however, believe that any single view of the industrial worker is wholly valid. There are many people to whom work is simply hours to be gotten through, in order to receive sustenance. They accept it as a part of their role in life, unquestioned and unexamined. "There are," says Eli Ginzberg in *The Study of Human Resources,* "further defects in an approach which sees the typical worker as an automaton, frustrated from the time he starts work until the quitting whistle blows. Most men have a realistic opinion of their strengths and weaknesses . . . they know how hard their fathers had to work to support their families, so if their own lot is easier, they are likely to be reconciled to it. . . . But they are not industrial slaves, as Marx called them, nor are they company serfs, forced to do what the employer wants . . ."

Even so, the idea that one should show up at a certain place at a certain time and perform some prescribed activity for a certain number of hours, whether the activity is meaningful or not, remains today what we usually think of as work. We have constructed a society in which participation in this activity almost becomes the goal of life itself.

We need at this point to make a little more precise definition of the two kinds of work. "Object-oriented" work is activity directed toward transforming some natural resource into some object useful to man's needs or wants. Ore transformed into metal, chemicals into plastics, petroleum into gasoline and lubricating oils, water, solar radiation and carbon dioxide into food—these are "object-oriented" types of work. At most levels, this kind of work uses only a small part of a man's total ability and consists of relatively simple, repetitive actions, performed over a prescribed period of time.

"People-oriented" work is directed toward service to others; providing transportation, distributing goods, teaching, social welfare work, government service, providing entertainment or recreation for others. This, too, is repetitive action. But it involves much more of the person who is doing it, and it is constantly refreshed by the new human contacts that occur during the working period.

It is the "object-oriented" work in our society that is being replaced by mechanization, automation and cybernation. In the years ahead, it is the "people-oriented" type of work that is likely to increase. "The Work of the world remains to be done," says Gerard Piel. And the work of the world for the next twenty years would appear to be more and more that which has to do with people rather than objects. Let the machines produce objects; let people become more concerned with people.

The modern work syllogism seems to run something like this: it is natural for a society to "progress," and at the base of progress is the use of human energy in the form of work. Therefore the more people in our society who work, the more will we progress. People who do not contribute to progress by working should not share equally in its fruits

OLD RUSSIAN SAYING

"Work does not make one rich, but round-shouldered."

TIME IS MONEY

"In the automated future, the term 'leisure' will be increasingly inadequate to express the revolution in time itself that is taking place, a revolution in which time is no longer a by-product of the machine, but a basic form of wealth."

PHYLLIS DAIGNAULT
"New Markets in Time"
Sales Management—June 18, 1965

THE JOB IS THE MEDIA

"What we call 'jobs' represent a relatively recent pattern of work. When a man is using all his faculties we think he is at leisure, or at play. The artist doesn't have a job because he uses all his powers at once. Were he to pause to work out his income tax, he would be using only a few of his powers. That would be a 'job.' A mother doesn't have a 'job' because she has to do forty jobs at once. So with a top executive or surgeon . . ."

MARSHALL McLUHAN
"Guaranteed Income in the Electric Age"

THE QUESTION

"Men who do not need to work in order to satisfy their wants for anything money can buy are still driven, induced, or inspired to work—and work hard. Other men, and all of us in general, who must work because we need the money and things that money can buy, are not working steadily, not working effectively, not working happily or willingly.
"We do not know today the fundamental reasons why men work or why men do not work. The old answers do not fit the question today."

ALEXANDER HERON
"Why Men Work"

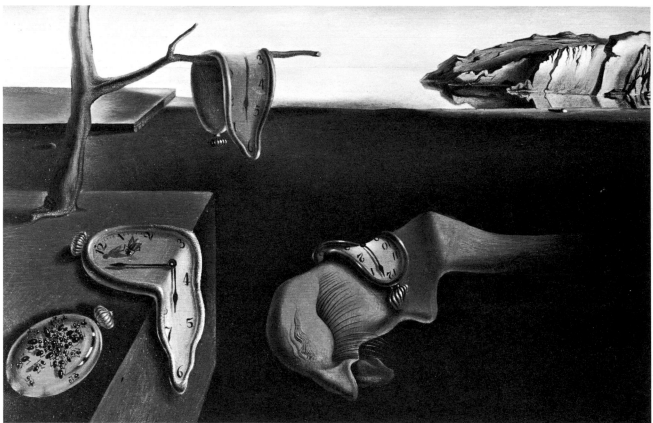

DETAIL FROM "THE PERSISTENCE OF MEMORY" BY SALVADOR DALI, PERMANENT COLLECTION THE MUSEUM OF MODERN ART, NEW YORK

SOMETHING FOR EVERYONE

"It is a new leisure on the one hand, that de Tocqueville had told us would come with the mass, democratic society; a time of ease, low taste, vulgarization. But it is leisure, on the other hand, that foretells a heaven on earth, that supplants the Christian concept of the Devil and the Flesh with the Judaic concept of the good, earthly life of optimistic outlook and a unity of Spirit and Flesh. It is a leisure permitting of the best and the worst in man.

"It is a leisure in which all men may find their wants met—the loafer and the doer, the scholar and the sportsman, the Las Vegas gambler and the suburban gardener, the numismatist and the Saturday night astronomer, the hot-rod fanatic and the Lucy Ball fan, and the Presley, Proust and Puccini audiences."

MAX KAPLAN
"Leisure in America"

with those who do work.

This is a sociological imprint we have inherited from another time and place, namely, the Industrial Revolution of the 18th and 19th Centuries; we continue to act as if our world was the same as then—when, in fact, it is quite different.

"In the United States we produced, in the year 1850, 440 horsepower hours of energy per person in the population," says Fred Cottrell in *The Sources of Free Time.* "In 1900, the figure soared to 1,030, and during 1950, 4,470 horsepower hours were produced. In 1958, about 5,100 was the output. The sources of energy were of course altered. In 1850, human beings produced 13 per cent of the energy used, animals 52 per cent, and inanimate sources 35 per cent. In 1950 humans produced less than one per cent, as did animals, and 98 per cent was derived from inanimate sources."

As Cottrell points out elsewhere, "A new order of predictable choice —a new hierarchy of values may thus emerge out of a changed flow."

We are beginning to see the consequences of that changed energy flow, and with it the demand for new ways of looking at work and the role it plays in our society. What has happened and is happening is that the necessity for individual human labor as a means toward progress has begun to change over to the management of inanimate energy sources. This new type of "work" precludes the active participation of large segments of our society because the effect of each individual's labor is magnified many times by the inanimate energy he controls.

It is quite possible that much of our current educational system is engaged in preparing young people for "jobs" that simply will not exist in our society by the time these students come into the marketplace. It is equally possible that a goodly segment of the "jobs" being performed in our economy today are simply atavisms of 19th Century concepts of work which have little economic, social, or even personal value today, and will have even less value in the future as our developing technology changes the nature of the use of human energy.

Even today, with most of our technological advances yet to be felt, in the United States only 38 percent of the population is "employed," in the Bureau of Labor Statistics' definition of the word, and during their working years, from 16 to 65, they spend less than 23 per cent of their total time engaged in work, even if "fully employed" for all those years.

Of those now fully employed, most are in occupations likely to shrink under the onslaught of an automated technology. "This is still," says Ben J. Wattenberg in his monumental study of the 1960 census, *This U.S.A.*, "predominantly a non-white-collar nation—a nation of makers. Most people do not go to work in a business suit or an office dress. Most (56% in 1964) work in factories and garages, drive trucks, dig ditches, cut hair, clean houses and grow food. . . . But it is equally important to realize this; there are more and more Americans concerned with jobs traditionally associated with the paper-shuffling world of words, figures and abstract thought normally associated with the phrase 'white collar.' The enormous growth of the white-collar occupations has lured many into believing that it has become the majority way of life in America. It has not. Not yet!"

Not yet. But perhaps sooner than most of us want to think. What happens when, as some have predicted, two per cent of the American population is employed in producing the necessities of life, and 98 per cent is not? How, indeed, can we hope to live meaningful lives in an "economy of abundance?" The tragedy is not, as some seem to believe, that this way of life may come about well within our lifetimes; the tragedy is that, knowing this, we are doing little or nothing to prepare ourselves or the younger generation to cope with it. When and where will we begin to chip away at the antiquated work ethic and come up with new systems and institutions in which leisure, and not work, is the desirable and socially acceptable goal of man?

One scans the horizon of two decades ahead and sees the almost inevitable collision of two great forces — exploding population and exploding technology — and one of the results of that collision will almost certainly be a society in which some other ethic than the sanctity of work will have to be found. □

A STEP BEYOND

"Man also steps beyond the chain of ends and means that binds the world of work, in love, or when he takes a step towards the frontier of existence, deeply moved by some existential experience, for this, too, sends a shock through the world of relationships, whatever the occasion may be ". . .

J. PIEPER
"The Philosophical Act"
from "Leisure, the Basis of Culture"

NOT TOUGH ENOUGH FOR WHAT?

"The danger is not that we won't toughen up or work harder. The danger is that the idea of leisure will be mistaken or dropped. If it is mistaken for free time, it will be thought of as the opposite of work, as unproductive, and even as weakening us for the forthcoming struggle with whomever it is we shall end up struggling with."

SEBASTIAN DeGRAZIA
"Of Time, Work and Leisure"

LEISURE:

old ROCkiN' CHAIR'S QOT ME

CONFORMITY OR CREATIVITY?

*"The historian Arthur Schlesinger, Jr.
asks of the new age, 'Will it be an epoch
when the American people, seeking
mass distractions and mass surcease
through mass media, will continue
to grow more and more indistinguishable
from one another? Or will it be
an epoch when people use leisure
creatively to develop their own
infinitely diverse individualities?'"*

MAX KAPLAN
"Leisure in America"

BUT NOBODY'S TRYING TO

*"The leisure problem is fundamental.
Having to decide what we shall do with
our leisure is inevitably forcing us
to re-examine the purpose of human
existence, and to ask what fulfillment
really means . . . this involves a
comprehensive survey of human
possibilities and methods of realizing
them; it also implies a survey of
the obstacles to their realization."*

JULIAN HUXLEY
"The Future of Man"

TOPSY-TURVY WORLD

*"In his well-known study of capitalism,
Max Weber quotes the saying that
'one does not work to live; one lives to
work,' which nowadays no one has
much difficulty in understanding; it
expresses the current opinion.
We even find some difficulty in grasping
that it reverses the order of things
and stands them on their head.*

*"But what ought we to say to the opposite
view that 'we work in order to have
leisure?' We should not hestitate to say
that here indeed 'the world of
topsy-turvydom,' the world that had
been stood on its head, has been
clearly expressed. To those who live
in a world of nothing but work, in what
we might call the world of 'total
work,' it presumably sounds immoral,
as though directed at the very
foundations of human society."*

J. PIEPER
"Leisure, the Basis of Culture"

□ "We hold these truths to be self-evident, that all men are created equal, that they are endowed by their Creator with certain inalienable Rights, that among these are Life, Liberty and the pursuit of Happiness."

The men who wrote the Declaration of Independence, and those among them who later framed the American Constitution, did not, anywhere in either document, include the word "work" in the sense of human labor. The first Ten Amendments to the Constitution, adopted in 1791, do not include it either.

Yet the UNESCO Universal Declaration of Human Rights, which nearly all of the nations on earth have signed, clearly states that "Everyone has the right to work." (It also proclaims that everyone has the right to leisure).

The exclusion of the right to work in one, and the inclusion of it in the other, some 175 years apart, is one measure of what has happened to us all in the less than two centuries between the two documents.

The men who wrote the Declaration of Independence were, for the most part, cultured men. Their culture derived from classic Greece and from the early days of Christianity; in both, the goal of human society was to create an environment in which men could enjoy leisure; the "pursuit of Happiness" was not, in their lexicon, the idle chase after ephemeral pleasures, but the attainment, through study and contemplation, of such divinity as mere mortals could aspire to.

Then, too, the men who phrased The Declaration wrote within the context of a world not too different from that of the ancient Greeks or the early Christians; a world in which everyone who could, worked, because men and their domesticated animals supplied most of the energy transfers that could create a civilization out of a wilderness. Of course everyone worked; only the very young, the very old, the very rich, and the very sick did not contribute to the grand enterprise; survival required no less. Work meant the labor of men and animals; the colonial society did not as yet have the steam engine, nor the combustion engine, nor electricity in a useful form nor, of course, the human use of atomic energy.

But nearly two centuries have passed, two incredible centuries, in which "work" has become more and more the management of inanimate energy, and in which the use of human energy has become of less and less importance, and therefore all the more desired for that. Hence, "the right to work" became a part of the Human Bill of Rights, because the opportunities to find work had become less and less, just as the "pursuit of happiness" had special value in an era when few people could find time away from their jobs to pursue it. Just the same, "leisure" is assumed to be a basic right of human beings, both in the Declaration

PHOTO BY WILLIAM JACKSON © 1966

of Independence and in the Declaration of Human Rights.

So far, we have spoken of leisure as if we are all agreed upon what is meant by the term, but it is unlikely that we are. Despite what advertising copywriters tell us, leisure is not, in its "real" sense, recreation; it is not simply time off from the job; it is not idleness. The phrases, "leisure homes, leisure clothes, leisure everything" have to do with the use of free time — those hours we do not happen to be on the job.

Leisure, both in the classical sense, and in the one we are using here, is an *activity*—the active pursuit of truth, an understanding of ourselves as living beings, of the societies we have constructed, and of the physical world in which we find ourselves. Leisure, in its truest sense, is an act of aesthetic, psychological, religious and philosophic contemplation: a category of activity almost entirely missing from American life today.

"If we could judge which of the leisure activities measure up to creative values, we must be directly concerned with the model of the Good Life. This is precisely a model we no longer have," says Max Kaplan in *Leisure in America*. "The church model of the selfless, cooperative man? The rural American of Li'l-Abnerian honesty and naiveté? The medieval model of Man on Horseback? The Adam Smith-Herbert Hoover model of the faithful little capitalist, saving for a rainy day? If these are dated and scarcely pertinent to the hydrogen-bomb age, we hardly have a new model . . . The fact is that this very diversity of values, the destruction of the monolithic, authoritarian dogmas, should be a cause of rejoicing, a fruition of liberal humanistic struggle of the last thousand years. Uprootedness is freedom-giving, and freedom brings with it the task of finding new values, new relationships of man to man or man to God; and, assuming that aesthetic values, like all others, are a part of the culture stream, even a new aesthetic philosophy must be sought."

We have, in our society at the present time, almost no concept of training people (other than the children of the wealthy) for a life of leisure. We do not know even whether people can accept leisure as a way of life. Yet perhaps they can. Says Dr. Hans Selye in *The Stress of Life*, "No sensitive person can look at the sky on a cloudless night without asking himself where the stars come from, where they go, and what keeps the universe in order. The same questions arise when we look at the internal universe within the human body, or even just at that pair of sensitive and searching human eyes which constantly strives to bridge the gap between two universes."

We are on the threshold of a time when leisure is at last possible for most people in our society, and we are doing almost nothing to prepare them for this new dimension of human life. □

DETAIL FROM "THE BEANERY" BY EDWARD KIENHOLZ USED BY PERMISSION OF THE OWNER, BURT KLEINER, LOS ANGELES

BEHOLD, THIS DREAMER

"*The most acquisitive person is so busy reinvesting that he never learns to cash in. 'Realistic people' who pursue 'practical aims' are rarely as realistic or practical, in the long run of life, as the dreamers who pursue their dreams.*"

HANS SELYE
"The Stress of Life"

WE'VE NEVER LEARNED

"*In our time even the aged and retired rarely wish to lead a life of contemplation. This may have to do with the fact that they have never been taught contemplation. Contemplation, which is neither just thinking nor reminiscing, is actually a very special type of mental activity that in our culture is hardly known and little practiced.*
"*The deeper reason for people's disinclination toward leading a contemplative existence lies, however, in the fact that action ranks so high in the value system of our culture that contemplation, like all other forms of passive participation, is apt to be little appreciated. People who are not active are made to feel useless, indeed, even worthless.*"

CHARLOTTE BUHLER
"Meaningful Living in the Mature Years"

THE POVERTY OF AFFLUENCE OR THE MANY SPLENDORED THINGAMOBOB

AFFLUENT OR ABUNDANT?

"Let me first clear up my terminology. I shall talk about the affluent *or* provident *society when I think of the present American economy. By an* abundant *economy or society, I shall indicate the society of the near future expected and discussed by many writers in which automation, computerization and cybernation will have shifted practically the entire task of production to machines . . ."*

WALTER A. WEISSKOPF
"The Great Transformation"
American Scholar—Spring, 1966

THE TYRANNY OF GOODS

"One has only to look at the ads showing the American consumer in his leisure time to see this; he is surrounded by a multitude of goods and gadgets which subject him to the burden of their consumption. Even today, before we have reached a completely automated abundance, we are enslaved by the tyranny of goods, which direct the use of our leisure. The producers and advertisers are not only luring us into buying a multitude of goods; they also dictate to us in this way how to use our leisure. Freedom from necessity would also require freedom from consumption of certain types of goods.

"The more there will be produced, the more goods will be turned out by robots, the greater will be the time-and-energy consuming burden of consumption, and the more will our freedom be restricted. The time and energy used in the consumption of goods and gadgets will be taken away from the time and energy available for the satisfaction of non-economic needs.

"Not enough time and energy will then be available for love and friendship, for the enjoyment of nature, the contemplation of beauty and truth, for artistic expression and non-purposive behavior."

WALTER A. WEISSKOPF
"Brief on the Economics and Psychology of Abundance"

☐ "The advent of abundance is not yet comprehended in the theory and practice of our economy," says Gerard Piel (in *The Bulletin of the Atomic Scientists;* June, 1963). "In truth, one must confess the opposite: our abundance is dodged, minimized, and concealed as well as squandered, burned and shut down. We resolutely pretend that we can go on managing the production and distribution of abundance through agencies created for the management of scarcity. Yet we are already in transition from the economy of scarcity to the economy of abundance."

The enormity of this thought has not yet penetrated the thinking processes of most Americans; nearly all of our institutions — business, industrial, governmental, religious, educational — were created during periods when there was never quite enough of anything to go around. That we have crossed—or shortly will cross—the Great Divide between scarcity and abundance has not yet, to any appreciable extent, affected most of our society.

"Is it possible," asks Walter A. Weisskopf (in *Brief on the Economics and Pyschology of Abundance*), "to visualize at least dimly on the horizon a civilization in which 'playful' artistic and contemplative pursuits satisfy the higher needs of people; games and circuses all sorts of lower needs, fishing and sheer loafing the lowest needs; and where necessities and means of survival are of little importance because they are produced routinely by cybernetically controlled robots?"

It is not only possible, we almost have within our grasp today the means for such a society. The question is no longer whether we can produce enough for all, but whether having produced it we are willing to share it with all. We have vast educational systems devoted to showing us how to produce things, but very little in the way of telling us how we could share them. Nor much, either, in the way we should spend our individual lives if our most ingenious energy transfer systems become, as it appears they will, almost completely automated.

In an "economy of abundance," or "the affluent society," call it what you will, the nature of "work" will have changed profoundly — almost certainly within our lifetimes.

"Automation is information," says Marshall McLuhan (in *Understanding Media*), "and it not only ends jobs in the world of work, it ends subjects in the world of learning. It does not end the world of learning. The future of work consists of *learning* a living (rather than *earning* a living) in the automation age . . . As the age of information demands the simultaneous use of all our faculties, we discover that we are most at leisure when we are most intensely involved, very much as with the artists in all ages."

Certainly there is no concensus among the thinking men of our times about the possible individual and social consequences of "the affluent society." There are serious questions raised.

Back to Weisskopf: "Automated abundance is supposed to change all this because it will relieve man of the burden of work. But as long as we are primed to work towards the production of goods and as long as we maintain an attitude that only the result counts, we may break down under the burden of leisure and abundance. If, as stated above, abundance is our ideal and work the only legitimate way of passing one's time, the accomplishment of abundance can only lead to . . . disintegration, boredom and nihilism."

Getting off this futuristic tennis court for a moment, we might listen to Walter P. Reuther (in *First Things First*), "I think that pretty soon we are going to have to make a very important decision as to whether our society wants to use the resources of technology to provide more and more gadgets and to raise the level of material comforts even higher, or whether we want to make it possible for each person to have more leisure so that more resources, more time, more attention, can be directed toward the non-material values and actions of the human family. It may be that we will arrive at the necessity for such a decision long before we are prepared for it. The real tragedy in America may be that we will satisfy all our material needs and then find leisure time on our hands before the average person is in any way educated to know how to use it."

There is another question that must be asked—"Can we, with our backgrounds and orientation, ever really have an economy and a society that provides 'enough' for all?"

Fred Cottrell (in his essay, *The Sources of Free Time*), suggests, "There is another dimension here which is perhaps of greater significance still. This is the changing values of the American people. We are no longer content to rest when we have achieved the level of living which had to satisfy our forebears . . . What are now necessities are as binding on us as were their necessities on them. Among the goods now necessary are things and services whose production uses up time, reducing that left to be used at our discretion. Few of us wish idly to watch the sunset, to walk in the cool of the evening, to lie in the noonday sun each day and every day . . ."

The sunset, the cool of the evening, to lie in the noonday sun—these are experiences that we had in childhood, lost, tried—often too late—to regain in our declining years. Something has happened to us between the ages of 16 and 60; something rather frightening.

"It is a pity that nowadays most people are so anxiously bent on being practical, to get ahead in life, that they no longer find time to

DON'T NEED OR WANT THEM

"Reflect for a moment how many people actually want to own an automobile, take home a 'handy six-bottle carrying case' of soft drinks, or have a drawer full of shirts they can call their own? In the final analysis, not many . . . People in a busy, rapidly moving, affluent society increasingly realize they are not interested in things per se, but rather in their use in a convenient and worry-free manner."

FERDINAND F. MAUSER
Professor of Marketing
Wayne State University

WHAT? WHAT?

"If our human 'what?' is to be restricted chiefly to flabby mushroom-pale dwellers in high-rise apartments whose leisure, at the end of the working day, or with full guaranteed-income freedom, is to be filled with TV time killers like Peyton Place, *the calorie demand on our soils ... will have one dimension, as will the need to maintain wildlife and its habitat ...*

"Without trying to forecast the kinds of people America will have over the next few decades, I hope for something better than those TV watchers mentioned above, and I am proposing that not only an abundance of food and water (for a variety of uses and enjoyments) but also a varied, interesting and beautiful countryside can contribute to the richness and happiness of living."

WILLIAM VOGT
"Conservation and the
Guaranteed Income"

WELL, WHY NOT?

"Retraining has some meaning in that it may well raise the total level of skills and to the extent that knowledge is never entirely wasted, this is useful. But it would be better if we could create a system under which the industrial jobs would be available on an area-wide basis, say, instead of on a one-plant basis, and thus create mobility between jobs. For example, in a city like Chicago, a man might work one week in a packing house, another week in a steel mill, and another week in an automobile plant ... This would make for diversity of skills, and as long as the mobility was kept within a particular geographical area there would be no problem of families having to work."

RALPH HALSTEIN
"Jobs, Machines and People"

make sure where they really want to go," says Dr. Hans Selye (in *The Stress of Life*). "After awhile, the prosperous businessman, the efficient administrator, the up-and-coming lawyer begin to get that lost feeling of aimlessly drifting from day to day—toward retirement."

Would it be possible that in "the age of affluence" some of this great loss of experience could be avoided? Well, in the first place, we have to ask ourselves whether an "age of affluence" really is upon us, or at least "dimly seen on the horizon."

Ours cannot, yet, really be called an "age of affluence" or even an "abundant economy" when something like 30 million of our population, at least one out of seven people in this country, exist at levels that the others consider to be in "poverty." It can scarcely be called an "abundant economy" in which the water and air are increasingly polluted; where the package costs more than the food that is in it, where vistas that were once a beauty to the eye are gobbled up to make tracts of houses that will scarcely outlive the first mortgage, much less the second; where getting from one place to another by almost any means of transportation becomes more and more dangerous. It is not an "age of affluence" when children are neglected and elderly people are consigned to a human scrap-heap; where the ability to add is more important than the ability to feel.

We do not have either an "age of affluence" or an "economy of abundance," but we do appear to have the means now to create one. The "Great Society" is not with us yet; the rather frightening — and perhaps tremendously exciting — prospect is that we could create one if we really wanted to. If we really want to, then it appears we must consider how our days are spent, and how all of us could perhaps spend them more meaningfully than in making a fast buck or preparing for some dim and lustreless life in a "leisure city," playing shuffle-board and bridge.

"Life can be lived in a meaningful or meaningless way," says Dr. Charlotte Buhler (in *Aging and Leisure*). "Time can be spent meaningfully or not. To use it meaningfully is to spend it in a way which contributes to the fulfillment of life, which may be considered as an experience of completion, a hoped-for satisfaction, toward which we have directed our lives. Fulfillment can be experienced in different forms and at different times. All through life, people experience smaller or larger fulfillments, in consequence of events or accomplishments which seem to answer needs or hopes, desires or expectations ...."

It is perhaps of passing interest that man has named two major areas on the moon, "The Sea of Tranquility" and "The Sea of Serenity." He has few such names for places on earth. □

PHOTO BY WILLIAM JACKSON © 1966

THE FUN LAB

"In London we are going to create a university of the streets—not a 'gracious park' but a foretaste of the pleasures of 1984. It will be a laboratory of pleasure providing room for many kinds of action . . .
"In the music area we shall have, by day, instruments available, free instructions, recordings for anyone, classical, folk, jazz and pop disc libraries; by night jam sessions, jazz festivals, poetry and dancing—every sort of popular dancing, formal or spontaneous . . ."

JOAN LITTLEWOOD "The World in 1984"

WHERE THE
WHANGDOODLE SINGS

THOREAU THOUGHT SO, TOO

"There used to be a kind of person in America who openly proclaimed his aversion to work. The type, though not already gone from sight, seems to be going fast. He is, or was, called the hobo. He seems even to have had some intellectual justifications for his way of life. Though the justification never reached a high level, it was undeniably based on the ancient idea that if one has not wealth, he might yet avoid work by cutting down his requirements for life . . ."

SEBASTIAN DE GRAZIA
"Of Time, Work and Leisure"

THE BIG ROCK CANDY MOUNTAINS

*"I'm headed for a land that's far away
Beside the crystal fountains.
I'll see you all this coming fall
In the Big Rock Candy Mountains.*

*In the Big Rock Candy Mountains,
There's a land that's fair and bright,
Where the handouts grow on bushes
And you sleep out every night,
Where the boxcars all are empty
And the sun shines all the day—
Oh, the birds and the bees and the
cigaret trees,
The rock-and-rye springs where the
whang-doodle sings,
In the Big Rock Candy Mountains."*

JAILHOUSE SONG—
Traditional

YEH, MAN, YEH!

*"Oh, why don't I work like the other
men do?
How can I work when the skies
are so blue?
Hallelujah, I'm a bum!
Hallelujah, bum again,
Hallelujah! Bum a handout,
Revive me again.
Why don't you work, like the other
men do?
How'm I gonna work, when there's
not work to do?"*

HOBO SONG—
Traditional

☐ The proper study of Man may *not* be Mankind, after all, but instead the study of Utopia, for here we find a reflection in the mirror of the future of all our legends of Paradises Lost; here in Utopia we at last can truly explore "the countries of the mind."

"In sum, we cannot ignore our Utopias. They exist in the same way that north and south exist; if we are not familiar with their classical statements, we at least know them as they spring to life each day in our own minds," says Lewis Mumford in *The Story of Utopias*. "We can never reach the points of the compass; and so no doubt will never live in Utopia; but without the magnetic needle we should not be able to travel at all . . ."

Our Utopias are the needles that point in the direction we should like our society to go: the republican society of the Founding Fathers, with its promise of "life, liberty, and the pursuit of happiness," was a Utopia — something to be achieved; so was the dream of a classless society of workers as envisioned by Marx and Engels; so too is the "Great Society" of our contemporary, mid-1960's government. The clash between ideologies today in our world is not between things as they are, but between things as we would like them to be; the War, in short, cold or hot, of the Utopias.

Nearly every Utopia we can think of was born as a criticism of the existing order of things. In America, Utopia has taken at least two easily identifiable forms: in the one we shall build a Great Society in which there are no poor and in which everyone who is able to work can find employment. The Utopia is "work-for-all," and to that end we are committed to educational and job-training programs, even as we enter an era in which, more and more, machines will do the work. Our Utopian ideal is the natural reflection of the ills of a job-and-work-oriented society, where it becomes harder and harder to find productive jobs for the millions of newcomers into the labor market each year.

Yet the Great Depression spawned a quite different Utopia. In a time when jobs were very hard to find, the expression of Utopia was not a place where everyone could find work, but "The Big Rock Candy Mountains," where "they boiled in oil the inventor of toil." It was the dream of a workless society.

As we try to grope our way toward the end of the century, we find our Utopian compass pointing in opposite directions.

"What can be done? What should be done?" asks Eli Ginzberg (in *The Pluralistic Economy*). "Some argue that the United States confronts no special problem with respect to employment and that therefore nothing needs to be done beyond following policies that will insure a continuing growth of the economy in general. Others contend that we are on the verge of the new world in which the productivity of the new machines will make almost all of us redundant. All that needs to be done is to guarantee an income to each individual and family so that they will be able to purchase the goods that the new automated machines will gush forth."

Thus, the two Utopias confront each other every day in the newspapers, in the legislative halls, in the board rooms of corporate enterprises; yet we bring to this confrontation only ancient, outworn beliefs and traditions.

Continues Ginzberg, "No statesman, conservative or liberal, can reach a determination about the desirability of a suggested policy or program unless he can fit it into his concept of the operation of the economy. It is therefore surprising that the concept of the American economy commonly held by businessmen, politicians and academicians today is largely the same as that which has dominated the scene since the emergence of this nation as a major industrial power toward the end of the nineteenth century . . . But this concept does not square fully with the facts, neither with the reality of yesteryear, nor with the conditions that prevail today."

Again, Meno Lovenstein (writing on *Guaranteed Income and Traditional Economics*); "But for all the talk about markets and gross national product and the federal debt not many possess the attitude and training needed for a disciplined analysis of economic activity. The result is that most popular economic notions are superficial and distorted. They cannot be used to describe the economy as it is, much less as it may be."

Into this welter of confusion there has recently been introduced the concept of a "guaranteed annual income." This is not to be confused with the guaranteed annual wage, which is an instrument intended to smooth out seasonal variations in income in some types of work. The guaranteed annual income is exactly that; it is not related to work but to the subsistence needs of the individual. The concept has a long and honorable lineage in American history. We decided at the outset that the purpose of our society was to provide an environment in which each individual could enjoy "life, liberty, and the pursuit of happiness." We added (something virtually new at the time) that every individual was entitled to an education as a basic right. Later on we decided that young children should not be forced to work. Later on we decided that elderly people should not be forced to work, either. Later still, we decided that every individual should enjoy, as a basic right, adequate medical care. Now what is suggested is that individuals should also enjoy, as a basic right, an income that is at least consistent with our standards of a decent, if not affluent, life.

THE IRONY OF LEISURE

"Ironically, the people with the most free time are often the ones least equipped to handle it. A survey reported in McCall's recently showed the new leisure bringing more chaos than comfort to the lives of many union members on a 30-hour week. Those who were not moonlighting were often turning to beer, long naps, and moping around the house.

"The other side of the paradox is that the people who could most profitably use more time to pursue a wide spectrum of interests — the more highly educated, cultured and interested members of top management, for example — will be the least likely to get it."

PHYLLIS DAIGNAULT
"New Markets in Time"
Sales Management—June 18, 1965

WE COULD BE ANYTHING

"The difference of natural talents in different men is, in reality, much less than we are aware of . . . The difference between the most dissimilar characters, between a philosopher and a common street porter, for example, seems to arise not so much from nature, as from habit, custom, and education. When they came into the world, and for the first six or eight years of their existence, they were perhaps very much alike, and neither their parents nor play fellows could perceive any remarkable difference."

ADAM SMITH
"The Wealth of Nations"

THE UNEXPLORED WORLD WITHIN

"Everyone is equipped by nature to receive and assimilate sensory experiences. Everyone is sensitive to tones and colours, has sure touch and space reactions, etc. This means that by nature everyone is able to participate in all the pleasures of sensory experiences, that any healthy man can also become a musician, painter, sculptor, architect, just as when he speaks he is a 'speaker.' "

MOHOLY-NAGY
"The New Vision"—New York, 1939

Rather naturally, this proposal has generated a noticeable lack of enthusiasm among those who would have to pay for such a plan in the form of taxation on the income they derive from work or investments. In addition to the reduction of their own income to provide income for others, there seems to be an instinctive reaction that this would somehow destroy the incentive to work and the free enterprise system.

"The guaranteed-income proposal," says Robert Theobald in partial answer (in *The Background to the Guaranteed-Income Concept*), "is based on the fundamental American belief in the right and the ability of the individual to decide what he wishes and ought to do. This is surely the basic meaning of the phrase 'private enterprise:' that the individual should have the right to obtain enough resources to do what he believes to be important. In the past, the individual could go into business for himself and thus obtain resources. Today all the evidence shows that neither the self-employed business nor the small company can compete with the large corporation. The ideal of private enterprise can, therefore, be preserved only if the guaranteed income is introduced."

Extending this thought, Eric Fromm (writing on *The Psychological Effect of Guaranteed Income*), says, "Guaranteed income would not only establish a principle deeply rooted in Western religious and humanist tradition; man has the right to live, regardless! This right to live, to have food, shelter, medical care, education, etc., is an intrinsic human right that cannot be restricted by any condition, not even the one that he must be socially 'useful.'

"The shift from a psychology of scarcity to that of abundance is one of the most important steps in human development. A psychology of scarcity produces anxiety, envy, egotism . . . A psychology of abundance produces initiative, faith in life, solidarity. The fact is that most men are still geared psychologically to the economic facts of scarcity, when the industrial world is in the process of entering a new era of economic abundance. But because of this psychological lag, many people cannot even understand new ideas as presented in the concept of a guaranteed income, because traditional ideas are usually determined by feelings that originated in previous forms of social existence."

Nevertheless, the concept of a society in which work is voluntary and at least subsistence income is guaranteed appears to be one of the great issues that we will have to decide upon in the next twenty years.

It is quite possible that the guaranteed annual income will not be approached in any broad, sweeping piece of legislation, but more cautiously through extensions of existing programs. As *The Wall Street Journal* put it in an article "Antipoverty Tack" (Sept. 15, 1966): "Out of the question for the considerable future are the so-called negative

HEADED THAT WAY

"One of the basic principles of progressive taxation is that persons whose incomes are less than an agreed minimum should not be taxed at all. From this it is only a step to the guaranteed-income principle. Those who have no income, or those whose incomes are below the taxable minimum, would receive their guaranteed income in the form of tax deductions, just as everybody, rich or poor, now receives tax deductions for dependents.

"Indeed, the time will never come when everybody is richer than everybody else . . ."

C. E. AYRES
"Conservation and the Guaranteed Income"

ANOTHER WAY TO DO IT

"Employment on a part-time basis is no new idea. It has particular merit or the least drawback, when the periods not spent at work are devoted to additional general education or to retraining for new or wider skills. Two persons sharing one job has long been a feature of the educational system at Antioch College; one studying while the other is working, then vice-versa."

BENJAMIN GRAHAM
"The Flexible Work-Year:
An Answer to Unemployment"

GESUNDHEIT!

Discussion about work and wages, organization and industry, which is sc rife at present ought, it seems to me, to start with the study of a law which would have as its basis a theory of rest."

P. T. PROUDHON
"Die Sonntagsfeier, aus dem Gesichtspunkt des offentlichen Gesundheitwesens, der Moral, der Familier—und burgerlichen Ver haltnisse betrachtet." (Kassel, 1850)

FIGURE BY MIKE ANDERSON. PHOTOGRAPH BY JAN MAR

WILDERNESS ENOW'

"One of the oldest rules of political science holds that men come together to keep alive; they stay together to live a good life. In this country men have refused to budge from the first stage; they have acted as if there were a wilderness yet to conquer, some great work yet to do, that keeps them from the second stage. What is this great work? The frontier ended with the twentieth century, and the wilderness long before."

SEBASTIAN De GRAZIA
"Of Time, Work and Leisure"

SET MY PEOPLE FREE

"Of course not all, nor the majority, have those scientific, artistic, literary or scholarly interests which make leisure the one thing valuable to their possessors. Many look upon the last half of life chiefly as a period for enjoyment of other sorts; for travel, for social relaxation in the company of their life-time friends; a time for cultivation of all manner of personal idiosyncrasies and special tastes, and the pursuit of every imaginable form of recreation; in a word a time for the leisurely and unperturbed appreciation of the good things of the world which they have helped to create."

EDWARD BELLAMY
"Looking Backward: 2000-1887"

income tax and other novel, dramatic and costly 'income maintenance' schemes for direct government cash payments to all families whose incomes fall below certain 'poverty levels.'. . . Instead, there will be a series of smaller moves . . . Year by year, the theory goes, benefits under these and other programs would be increased, and more and more poor folk would be given some sort of help. A few years hence, it's figured, almost every needy family would actually be getting enough government help to rise out of poverty."

There immediately arises, of course, the question, "What would it all cost?" Nobody really knows; estimates run all the way from $2.5 billion a year to $33 billion.

Says Edward Schwartz (professor, University of Chicago), "About $11 billion a year would bring all poor families up to the $3,000 income level we have taken to be the minimum for a decent life. . . .The burden — one-fifth of the annual defense budget, less than two per cent of the Gross National Product—would certainly not be intolerable."

We do not, of course, have any way to say with accuracy what these poor people already cost the economy; in welfare, in lack of purchasing power, in vice control, and in the loss of their participation in the mainstream of an otherwise energetic and affluent society. These studies are yet to be made in any definitive way, but it is possible that we already are spending more to keep them in poverty than to get them out of it.

Along with the guaranteed income concept, another that will seriously be considered in the next twenty years is payment to students for attending school. "We must recognize," says Robert Theobald (in *Cybernation, Immediate Threat and Future Promise*) "that the student is already 'working' as least as relevantly as the man in the factory. The time has come when we must introduce the concept of a student salary, starting possibly at 14, and increasing with age, payable to all students attending high school or university . . ." One cannot help but wonder how many drop-outs there would be if a student were paid to attend school, instead of, as now so frequently happens, he were out looking for a non-existent job.

Be that as it may, the challenge of the next twenty years is clear; how do we learn to think about things differently than we do now?

"The question is," says Walter Weisskopf, "how can we, products and children of our time, molded by the existing institutions, values and attitudes, transcend them? This is possible because we are human beings endowed with a certain degree of freedom which enables us to transcend to some extent conditions, ideas and ideals."

It would be a premise of our next Utopia that we do, indeed, transcend them. □

WE HAVE COME A LONG WAY TOGETHER, you and I, since first we set out upon this strange, uncertain pilgrimage. We picked our way through the Slough of Despond and found that the bogs and quagmires were but figments of our imagination; we have visited the City of Despair and found it walled in only by its own fantasies of Space and Time; we have confronted the Lions of Automata and discovered them to be ephemera, the mirror image of our own minds; we have traversed the Valley of Paradise and eaten of its strange fruit, Leisure. Now, we have but a little further to go and our Pilgrimage will be at an end. We must cross the Delectable Mountains. They may seem far away, shimmering there; but that is an accident of our eyesight. They really are right here under our feet, if we will but look. Like the Chinese journey of a thousand miles, we shall approach them one step at a time. Shall we go? Now?

DETAIL FROM "TWO SAGES AND AN ATTENDANT UNDER A SPREADING PLUM TREE," 12TH-13TH CENTURY PAINTING BY MA YUAN. COURTESY THE MUSEUM OF FINE ARTS, BOSTON

CHAPTER DIVIDER: "BUST OF DIEGO" BY ALBERTO GIACOMETTI, OWNED BY THE READERS DIGEST ASSN. PHOTOGRAPHY BY HERBERT MATTER, NEW YORK

4

Walking Abroad Without Keepers

'PHANTASTIC'

"A century ago Thomas Carlyle stated that the 'fine arts' had got into 'an insane condition and walk abroad without keepers, nobody suspecting their bad state, and do phantastic tricks.' Art no longer plays 'phantastic tricks.' It tells the truth, and often the whole truth. But in nearly every other sphere the means have outgrown man and 'walk abroad without keepers'."

SIEGFRIED GIEDION
"Mechanization Takes Command"

NO PHILOSOPHY, NO BREAD

"There is an old saying that philosophy bakes no bread. It is perhaps equally true that no bread would ever have been baked without philosophy. For the act of baking implies a decision on the philosophical issue of whether life is worthwhile at all. Bakers may not have often asked themselves the question in so many words. But philosophy traditionally has been nothing less than the attempt to ask and answer, in a formal and disciplined way, the great questions of life that ordinary men put to themselves in reflective moments."

TIME, January 7, 1966

NEVER ON SUNDAY

"The word philosophy means the love of wisdom. And the love of wisdom, I suppose, is like any other sort of love—the professionals are the ones who know least about it."

ABRAHAM KAPLAN

☐ "In the wilds of Afghanistan, the big car of an American tourist broke down and refused to start," recounts Peter Drucker in *Landmarks of Tomorrow*. "No one could figure out what was the matter; even the factory representative who was flown in gave up. The tourist was ready to abandon the car and go home when someone remembered that an old blacksmith who lived beyond the mountains some fifty miles away had, in his youth, tinkered with engines.

"In his despair, the tourist sent for him. Three days later, the old man appeared on a mule. He took one look at the car and asked for a hammer. He gently tapped one spot on the engine twice, and said, 'Start her up.' and the engine purred as smoothly as if it had just left the test stand.

" 'What do I owe you?' the grateful tourist asked.

" 'A hundred dollars.'

" 'What, a hundred dollars for two taps with the hammer?'

" 'Well, I can itemize it for you,' the old man said: 'For two taps with the hammer—ten cents; for having known *where*—99 dollars and 90 cents.' "

A part of the tragedy of our times is that we are willing to pay for action but not for thought.

Already we know, or have in sight the possibility of knowing, how to solve most of the major problems that seem to surround us on every side like a pack of hungry wolves. But we do not apply this knowledge. We cower in the shelter of our primitive sleds, and from time to time throw a baby out to appease the wolves. Perhaps we could do better.

"We are confronted with a great scrap heap of words and misused symbols and next to it an immense storehouse bursting with new discoveries, inventions and potentialities, all promising a better life," comments Siegfried Giedion in *Mechanization Takes Command*. He goes on to say, "Never has mankind possessed so many instruments . . . But the promises of a better life have not been kept. All we have to show so far is a rather disquieting inability to organize the world, or even to organize ourselves. Future generations will perhaps designate this period as one of mechanized barbarism, the most repulsive barbarism of all."

This barbarism, mechanized or not, is repulsive not in the light of what has gone before, but in the light of what we now know. If we find our own civilization a failure in some respects, it is not because it is not incomparably better than our past, but because it is incomparably less than our future. Like the donkey who starved to death between two bales of hay, unable to make up his mind which one to eat, we are poised in our times between the reverence of the past and the acceptance of the future we see glittering there before us.

"From the dawn of human history," said Alfred North Whitehead in *Science and the Modern World,* "mankind has always been losing its religious faith, has always suffered from the malignant use of material power, has always suffered from the infertility of its best intellectual types, has always witnessed the periodical decadence of art.

"And yet, mankind has progressed. Even if you take a tiny oasis of peculiar excellence, the type of modern man who would have most chance of happiness in ancient Greece at its best period is probably (as now) an average professional heavyweight boxer, and not an average Greek scholar from Oxford or Germany. Indeed, the main use of the Oxford scholar would have been his capability to write an ode in glorification of the boxer.

"Nothing does more harm in unnerving men for their duties in the present than the attention devoted to the points of excellence in the past as compared with the average failure of the present day."

And, of course, that *is* one of our problems. When we do compare the slums of a major modern city to the glory that was Greece and the grandeur that was Rome, we not only compare apples and transistors, but our yearning for the past obscures the reality of today and the promise inherent in our tomorrow. We are still blind to what appears to be a fact; that something most extraordinary is happening to us. We close our eyes and lament our blindness. What is unforeseeable in the foreseeable future, is that we will open them. And yet, what is to be seen is reasonably clear.

"We do not walk upon an alien earth. Something in the universe corresponds to human intelligence. But we do not have to put it outside the universe and give it separate existence, whether we call it God or the creative principle," says the biologist, N. J. Berrill. "Suffice it to say that, in man's interior evolution, change is evident . . ."

"Yes," says Philip R. Harris in *The Changing Man* "with the intensification of consciousness, man is becoming more aware of the forces of evolution and can decide to cooperate and influence them . . . Man is becoming sensitive to man, and in turn, to the whole of creation and its very source . . . He is experimenting more and more with going out of the individual self to the service of others in the human group."

And it is of this that we will speak in the following pages; how it is that by turning inward to ourselves, we will see the outer world we have ourselves created; and how, by turning to each other, we will find the worlds within ourselves. Should we fail to do this, and soon, then Jacques Ellul's grim conclusion, "When the edifice of the technical society is completed, the stains of human passion will be lost amid the chromium gleam," may, alas, be all too prophetic. □

IT'S UP TO US

"In the past, men could shrug their shoulders in the face of most of the evils of life because they were powerless to prevent them . . . Now there is no one to blame but ourselves. Nothing is any longer inevitable. Since everything can be accomplished, everything must be deliberately chosen. It is in human power for the first time to achieve a level of human welfare exceeding our wildest imaginings or to commit race suicide, slowly or rapidly. The choice rests only with us."

JEROME D. FRANK
"Galloping Technology;
A New Social Disease"

NOWHERE ENGRAVED ON HIGH

"There is no system of philosophy to spin out. There are no ethical truths; there are just clarifications of particular ethical problems. Take advantage of these clarifications and work out your own existence. You are mistaken to think that anyone ever had the answers. There are no answers. Be brave and face up to it."

DONALD KALISH
Philosopher, U.C.L.A.

DEW LINE

"I think of art, at its most significant, as a DEW line, a Distant Early Warning system that can always be relied on to tell the old culture what is beginning to happen to it."

MARSHALL McLUHAN
"Understanding Media"

THE GlobAL iMPERATIVE

FAIT ACCOMPLI

"Man is born with the capacity to react with a variety of emotions (has within him the lion and the rabbit), and his early childhood experiences largely determine in which of these ways he will react under stress. Stated in another way, the evolutional process of man's emotional development is completed in the bosom of the family."

DANIEL H. FUNKENSTEIN
from "Frontiers of
Psychological Research"

☐ On an estate near Vienna, not too many years ago, the Austrian zoologist, Konrad Lorenz, performed an experiment that may turn out to be one of the great contributions to peace in our times. Being a zoologist, he did it with goslings.

He took a clutch of eggs from a goose, divided the eggs into two groups, and had one group hatched by the mother and the other in an incubator. The goslings hatched by the goose immediately followed their mother about the estate. But the goslings hatched in the incubator did not see their mother. The first living thing they saw was Lorenz. Then they followed him about the estate!

Since that time, the experiment has been performed with other kinds of geese, with ducks, with guinea pigs, with sheep, turkeys, pheasants, quail and chickens. The consistency of results has led to the theory of "imprinting," the hypothesis that early experiences in the life of animals determine their later social behavior. We have no reason to believe that the mechanism operates differently with human beings. If it does operate the same way, perhaps we can account for the fact that our "rational" society is, in essence, an irrational one, and that much adult behavior can be explained on the basis of incidents in infancy. (Freud said the same thing, of course, but explained it somewhat differently.)

"Students of behavior generally agree," says Dr. Eckhard H. Hess in his essay, *'Imprinting' in Animals,* "that the early experiences of animals (including man) have a profound effect on their adult behavior . . . Thus the problem of the investigator is not so much to find out whether early experience determines adult behavior, but rather to discover *how* it determines adult behavior."

There appears to be, over the last two decades, sufficient evidence that, "as the twig is bent, so is the tree inclined." Let us go further and see what pertinence, if any, this theory may have for the next twenty years.

It seems pretty generally agreed that the family unit is the "cell" of the social organism, whether the social organism is a tribe, a community, a nation or a world. We do not know very much about the family cell— not nearly as much as we do about the biological cell—but we can probably agree that it consists of a mother, a father, and children. We may characterize the family unit as a small factory in which the parents provide the genetic structure (the "raw materials"), and the processing (which is imprinting), and the child is the "product" whose neural responses are as fixed as those in a printed electronic circuit. Essentially, what one gets is a world of earlier-imprinted children imprinting new children; a childish world based on childish experience.

What kind of imprints? In our society, at least, ideas concerning time

PHOTO BY ROBERT A. ISAACS

THE RITES OF SPRING

"In a paper called 'The Spring Rivalry of Birds,' published in the Irish Naturalist *in 1903, C. B. Moffat observed that property-holding birds sing not so much to impress the female, nor even to express the sheer joy of being rich, so much as to scare the appropriate daylights out of anybody with designs on their property . . .*

"Moffat suggested that the male's bright coloration exists for the same reason. 'Have we not here some ground afforded us for suspecting that the bright plumage may have been originally evoked as war paint? In other words, as a sort of warning coloration to rival males, rather than attractive coloration to dazzle the female?'"

ROBERT ARDREY
"The Territorial Imperative"

PRIVATE PROPERTY: KEEP OUT!

The first studies of animal behavior that indicated that much of it is based on the concept of property and the defense of it, were made by observing birds. Later on it was discovered that, in defense of their territorial rights, howler monkeys howled, gorillas beat their chests, the usually placid moor hen flew into rages and attacked any intruder, and even lowly fish turned bright colors and erected their fins to defend the particular pile of pebbles they considered their own.

But, usually no actual combat occurs; most of the territorial defense among animals consists of display; bright plumage, ruffs of feathers or manes of hair; loud noises, and strutting performances. Any similarity between these acts and the policy of deterrence in the human world, with its martial displays and loud noises by politicians, surely cannot be wholly coincidental.

REWARD AND PUNISHMENT

"Our present tentative conclusion is that emotional and motivational mechanisms can indeed be localized in the brain; that certain portions of the brain are sensitive to each of the basic drives. Strong electrical stimulation of these areas seems to be even more satisfying than the usual rewards of food, etc. This finding contradicts the long-held theory that strong excitation in the brain means punishment. In some areas of the brain it means reward."

JAMES OLDS
"Pleasure Centers in the Brain"

*FOLDED, SPINDLED
AND MUTILATED*

"It is a commonplace of psychiatry that the most severe and disabling psychic injuries in patients are always found to have been inflicted in infancy or early childhood. Parents do not inflict these grievous injuries wittingly; the damage often results from rigid 'moral' principles of child-rearing or by inadvertence. The consequent defects of character and personality are what the psychiatrist later has to deal with in attempting to restore his patient's usefulness and zest."

HOWARD S. LIDDELL
"Conditioning and Emotions"

A FAMILY AFFAIR

"Clinical experience with human beings indicates that people who have been deprived of affection in infancy may have difficulty forming affectional ties in later life. From preliminary experiments with our monkeys we have found that their affectional responses develop, or fail to develop, according to a similar pattern."

HARRY F. HARLOW
"Love in Infant Monkeys"

(as something broken into segments, instead of flowing); of space (as something circumscribed by boundaries, instead of horizons); of the identity of words and events ("that *is* a cow" instead of, "the collection of experiences you are having is called, in our language, 'cow' "); a whole panoply of "either-or" syndromes—right and wrong, good and bad, black and white, etc.; concepts of property (that a human being can "own" something, and that the more he owns, the more important he is); ideas about life and death that have little or nothing to do with the real world, since both concepts are meaningless; fear (and not respect) for authority.

Here, too, in the early years of life and within the family environment are imprinted nearly all of the basic ideas a person is likely to have on race, sex, nationality, morals, ethics and religion.

It is through the grid of these imprint systems that the growing human organism filters nearly all of its subsequent experiences. The net result is what we call "human nature," a frozen network that, as "everyone knows," cannot be changed. It stubbornly relates each new experience to the "go—no-go" system of its infantile imprints.

One does not have to accept all of this in order to believe that it may help to explain why—in societies made up of repetitive childish imprints—social institutions change so slowly, or why there is great resistance to new ideas, whether in art, science, economics, sociology, or religions; nor why communities of people with childish imprints frequently act like children.

The question rather naturally arises whether there are any ways to change the "imprints." And it does appear that there are. Nearly every human we know of who has profoundly affected the way we live has somehow broken through his infantile imprints. Historically we know of a number of ways; most of them related to some traumatic incident; some vast, new experience that shatters the ancient imprints and forces them into new combinations. Nearly all of our great art and music came about that way; so did most of our scientific advances.

What kind of traumatic incidents? Well, among them, severe emotional disturbance, such as the loss of a loved one; failure to "succeed" in a world of conformity; the collapse of economic or political systems; changes in body chemistry through the introduction of drugs or alcohol; a religious experience so powerful it breaks earlier imprints; or intensive study (as with savants of both the Western and Eastern worlds). In all of these methods the effect is to bring about new levels of understanding that change the infantile imprint.

Up to this point, we seem to have neglected the genetic heritage and to have said in effect that what is "wrong" with our society is that behavioral imprints are passed on from parents to children in infantile form. Naturally, you cannot build a printed circuit unless you have something to build it from, and in animals and humans this appears to be the germ plasm pool of the species as passed on by the individual parents. Enough has been popularized in recent years concerning genetic mechanisms for us to bypass them here. Much remains to be discovered, but the basic theory of genetic processing seems to be well established.

There is one part of genetic theory that needs some amplification, if only because it is rather new, and because it relates to the most important part of our human enigma, namely, the concept of nationalism and the imperative of world peace.

It is best described in a book called *The Territorial Imperative*, by Robert Ardrey. Briefly, the thesis here is that out of our study of animals, we come up with the concept that the possession and holding of a territory, however small, imparts something of strength to the holder; that out of these observations we may consider that many of the things man does that seem inexplicable or irrational come from this quite primitive relationship between the organism and the property it occupies.

As Ardrey says, "That man's territorial nature is inherent and of evolutionary origin is scarcely a new thought, it is only an ignored one. . . . Yet it would seem to me a thought we can ignore no longer. As our populations expand, as a world-wide movement from countryside to city embraces all peoples, as problems of broken homes and juvenile delinquency, of mass education and delayed independence of the young rise about us, as David Riesman's phrase 'the lonely crowd' comes more and more aptly to describe mankind, have we not the right to ask: Is what we are witnessing, in essence, not the first consequence of the deterritorializing of man?"

We shall discuss this concept more fully later but in effect Ardrey is saying that it is the sense of proprietorship that provides both animals and men with their personal sense of security (this is *my* place); their sense of stimulation (don't you dare come here); the excitement of border conflicts, and with the sense of identity—as Ardrey describes it, "identification with a unique fragment of something larger and more permanent than the animal itself; a place, whether social or geographic, that is his and his alone."

And so, if we take imprinting and the territorial imperative, just two legacies from the virtually new science of ethology, we may begin to understand a little of what has happened to us, how we might change it, and whether we want to or not. It is, of course, unforeseeable that we shall do any of these things: the imprints are too strong.

But it seems kind of worth thinking about. □

NOT IF, BUT HOW

"Three statements are usually made about the effects of early experience. The first is that early habits are very persistent and may prevent the formation of new ones. This, of course, refers not only to the study of experimental animals but also the rearing of children. The second statement is that early perceptions deeply affect all future learning. This concept leads to the difficult question whether basic perceptions—the way we have of seeing the world around us—are inherited or acquired. The third statement is simply that early social contacts determine adult social behavior. This, of course, is imprinting."

ECKHARD H. HESS
"Imprinting in Animals"

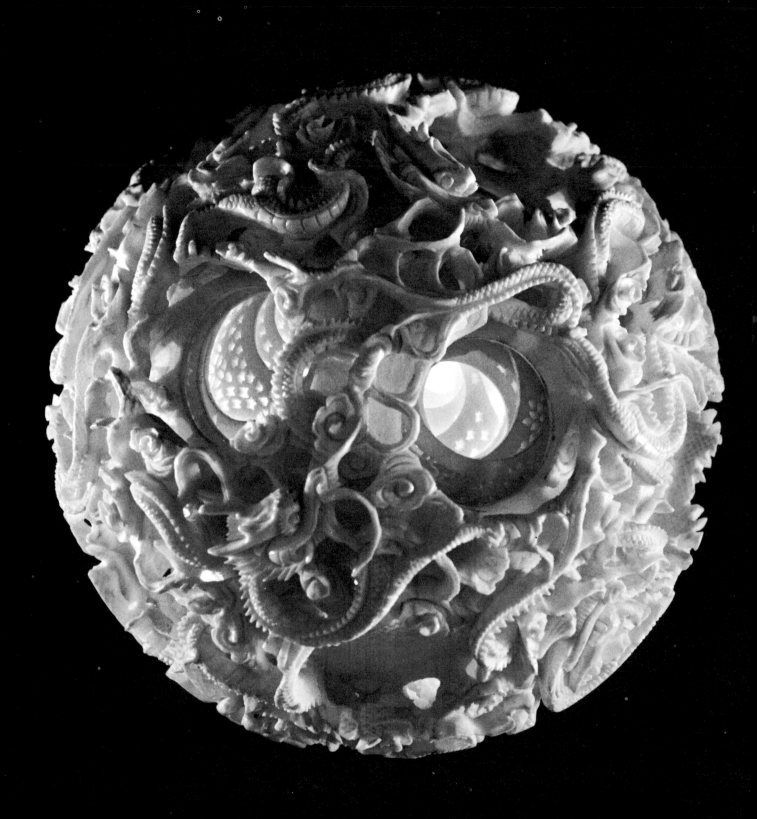

worlds within worlds

☐ Along about half a millennium ago, say the 14th Century, in Canton, China, some inspired artisan introduced the carving of concentric spheres from a single piece of ivory. Today, when a Westerner first sees one of these, he is most likely to ask, "How did they get the little spheres inside each other?"

And the answer that anyone of Eastern persuasion would give is, "The little spheres were always inside the larger ones, but it took the skill and vision of a master artist to set them free."

One might consider that the individual human being—and the social institutions that are a reflection of him, as in some crazy fun house mirror—are much like the carved spheres; worlds within worlds that can only be given freedom, combined with an integral, frictionless relationship to each other, through patience and understanding and the application of consummate skill.

For one who aspires to be a student of "allness," there may be much to be learned about ourselves in the contemplation of these carvings. Consider, first, that the raw material was only a piece of ivory; a lump of stuff. That it contained worlds within worlds was only in the mind of the artist. With infinite patience and excruciating skill he began to free the hidden worlds, just as a master sculptor once set free the Winged Victory from a block of marble.

To form the little spheres within spheres, the craftsman first shaped the lump into a ball, then delicately cut circular holes, each to the same depth, in the outer sphere. With a very sharp, curved blade he undercut the remaining lacework of the outer surface, setting the interior ball free. Working through the outer holes, he repeated the process to free another sphere, and so on until he reached the core of the ball.

Often it took a man's whole lifetime, but the end result was a model of the internal and external world of man. The process and the time it took was not much different from the time and process that goes into the craftsmanship of a great painter or musician; into the building of a mathematical theory; into the study of the lives of ants or birds or the formation of crystals; or into the teaching of a religious revelation by a messiah.

Let us now consider whether the concentric spheres can serve as an instrument for a better understanding of ourselves and the many worlds within worlds in which we live, and whether this contemplation gives us anything at all relevant to "foreseeing the unforeseeable" within our next twenty years.

Always, one comes back to the beginning, and the beginning is a vision; a vision that sees in the amorphous lump of man or man's society some configuration as yet unexpressed. We know, historically, the

PHOTOGRAPHY BY BOB FRASER

CATCH A FALLING STAR

"Thus the individual learns to cope with more and more difficult problems. At the highest stage in this progression, the intelligent human adult selects from innumerable, previously acquired learning sets the raw material for thinking. His many years of education in school and outside have been devoted to building up these complex learning sets, and he comes to manipulate them with such ease that he and his observers may easily lose sight of their origin and development."

HARRY F. & MARGARET HARLOW
"Learning to Think"

DIAGNOSIS

"Any behavior is a complex event that is the result of several forces, both internal and external; these forces are continually interacting with one another and are often extremely small and transitory."

From Introduction, "Frontiers of Psychological Research"

OF HUMAN BONDAGE

"Geographically, economically, and politically as well, every country of the world has now become a mere part of our planet. Nowadays, anything happening in any corner of the earth affects sooner or later the entire international society in which our nations grow. Human solidarity, until recently a vague moral inspiration, has become actual interdependence."

LUIS QUINTANILLA
Former President, O.A.S.

BANG BANG

"A Russian revolutionary once suggested that everyone over 25 should be shot. His proposal was not adopted, but he might feel reasonably comfortable in the U.S. today. Nearly half of all Americans are now 25 or under, and the rest of the population, while not yet in danger of being liquidated, appears rather nervous and definitely on the defensive."

"On Not Losing One's
Cool About the Young,"
TIME, December 24, 1965

EVERYTHING'S RELATIVE

"Science has proved that there exists no ethical principle which is, even theoretically, acknowledged by all human societies. Hence ethical values are nothing but functions of the societies in which they originate. The question of what is morally good or morally evil has no meaning except in reference to the moral value system of a given society. There are therefore, no 'absolute' criteria by which the value system of a given society can be judged objectively. It may, of course, be judged on the basis of the value system of another society. But there is no possibility of deciding 'objectively' which of the two value systems is morally better. If the two societies clash, one can only wait to see which of the two will prevail."

KURT VON FRITZ
"Relativism and Absolute Value"

names of some of these visionaries, to whom man was more than a beast with an oversized brain (in that respect not much different from the fiddler crab with his oversized claw). They saw something hidden beneath the surface and they carved holes to penetrate a little deeper—the first step in a fantastic voyage to the inner world. Through these holes, others carved still deeper and brought to light new worlds of consciousness and understanding. It has been the work of ten thousand years; it is by no means completed yet.

Implementing the vision (itself inexplicable after all these thousands of years) was the cutting tool—the neuropsychological imprints in the human organism; not the brain alone, mind you, but a razor's edge of awareness that constituted the whole organism and its reaction to stimuli both from without and within.

It is of more than passing interest that we have as yet but little understanding of that razor's edge—the interface between the neural system and the stimuli of environment. It seems to have something to do with ion exchanges, and triggering mechanisms at the synapses, subtle changes in complicated chemical compounds, reversals of polarities, minute changes in electrical fields—something to do with quite a bit, but what to do with everything we still do not know.

It is quite possible that the next great age of science will be dedicated not to the study of the "outer" world of nature, nor to the "inner" world of the psyche, but to an exhaustive examination of those processes that take place at the interface between the biological/neural imprints and the stimuli that constantly bombard them.

This new science—we might call it "the third science"—may come up with a working field theory of a man/world "hyphenation," just as our contemporary physics has expressed the equivalence of mass and energy and space/time and as psychology has come up with the mind/-body concept. We are beginning to move into the world of hyphens; holes that may lead us to other spheres. We may find, in this third science we have postulated, that there is no meaningful distinction between the world and man, except as thinking makes it so. (This is, interestingly enough, the philosophic basis of Eastern religions which find, in the eternality of man through successive reincarnations, considerable kinship with the theory in modern physics of the conservation of energy.)

We would say that the development of this "third science" is a foreseeable unforeseeable; that it will ultimately come to pass appears to have high probability; that it will come to pass in the next two decades seems to have a low probability. We can but wait and see.

As we go on contemplating these little carved spheres, we might

PHOTO BY BOB FRASER. CONSTRUCTION BY MASAMI MIYAMOTO

THE CROSS OF IRON

". . . a life of perpetual fear and tension;
a burden of arms draining the wealth
and the labor of all peoples; a wasting
of strength that defies the American
system or the Soviet system or any
system to achieve true abundance and
happiness for the people of this earth . . .

Every gun that is made, every warship
launched, every rocket fired signifies, in
the final sense, a theft from those
who hunger and are not fed, those who
are cold and are not clothed.

This world in arms is not spending
money alone.
It is spending the sweat of its laborers,
the genius of its scientists, the hopes
of its children.

THE COST OF ONE MODERN HEAVY BOMBER
IS THIS: a brick school in more than 30 cities.
It is two electric power plants, each
serving a town of 60,000 population.

It is two fine, fully equipped hospitals.

It is some 50 miles of concrete highway.

WE PAY FOR A SINGLE FIGHTER PLANE WITH
A HALF MILLION BUSHELS OF WHEAT.

WE PAY FOR A SINGLE DESTROYER WITH NEW
HOMES THAT COULD HAVE HOUSED MORE
THAN 8,000 PEOPLE . . .

This is not a way of life at all,
in any true sense. Under the cloud of
threatening war, it is humanity,
hanging from a cross of iron."

IS THERE NO OTHER WAY THE
WORLD MAY LIVE?
General Eisenhower, *New York Times,*
April 17, 1953

NEVERMORE

"Let us be clear that at least one course will not be open to us. We will not be able to afford, because it will be unworkable, a society whose 'cultural' divisions run as deep, and whose cultural discrepancies rise as high, as do the present discrepancies and divisions in wealth and income."

JOHN R. SEELEY
"Time's Future in Our Time"

THE GLOBAL PRESCRIPTION

"But let us consider the Secretary-General of the United Nations as the super-apothecary of the world, to whom everyone comes with a prescription for peace. It seems to me that our super-apothecary must reply: the prescription for peace is compounded of elements drawn from all over the face of the globe. There is an herb that grows on some unclimbed summit of some great mountain; there is another that may be found in the swamps of impenetrable jungles in tropical areas; there is a third that blooms in the desert, perhaps when it rains once in ten years or even once in a millennium; and all of these, and others, must be gathered and brewed before we can succeed in finding the prescription for the panacea that the impatient ask for now."

PHILIP C. JESSUP
Judge, International Court of Justice

THE MAGNIFICENT ACTIVITY

" 'Every living thing is a world performance.' This is the heart of it— a realization that illuminates not only botany but every human life and action. All the markets of the world are flowing with goods and services miraculously produced by the continuous interplay of sun and earth, air and water, and the inexhaustible imagination and energy of man. Wherever you touch an object made or conveyed by man, you are touched by all the men and women and children in the world who have reached their hands to make this possible for you. For one who is conscious, daily use is daily communion."

ARTHUR P. MOOR
"You Cannot Pick a Dandelion,"
from *The Freeman*, April 1964

speculate that *if* there is a "third science" it may give rise to a "third philosophy," some system of thought that stands outside of, but encompasses, the two primary philosophies under which we have labored for thousands of years. These would be, of course, the Platonic world of innate ideas through which we decipher the flickering shadows on our cavern wall; and the Aristotelian world where a thing either is or it isn't, and we can tell whether it is or it isn't just by looking at it. What this third philosophy may be, we do not know, except that, if we can perceive the Platonic/Aristotelian dualism then, rather obviously, we must stand philosophically on some third sphere that enables us to see the other two.

Howard Gossage has given us a good parable to describe this sphere-outside-of-sphere situation. To paraphrase it, one can imagine an ant living in an anthill until he gets outside of it and looks back. He does not know that the anthill is inside a greenhouse until he crawls outside the door and looks at it from the world outside. In much the same way, perhaps the "third philosophy" is about to cross the threshold and give us the wider perspective one gets from being outside other systems.

Assuming a "third science," which we characterized as unforeseeable, giving rise to a "third philosophy," doubly unforeseeable, we might as well compound the error by suggesting a "third politics," arising from the improbabilities of the first two systems. Let us examine, for a moment, the deficiencies of current politics to see if they offer any clue as to what the new politics might be.

You may recall that somewhat earlier we described "imprinting" as a process wherein our major responses to our environment are "built in," quite early in life, and suggested that all subsequent experience is filtered through—and our responses conditioned by—these infantile imprints. We might now consider whether the imprint thesis may not apply to human societies as well as individual human beings.

If this be so, then at any given stage in our socio-political development, we are acting out roles conditioned by the infancy of the society—tribe, community, nation, ideology. These imprints were formed most usually under stress—through revolution, war, riots, or the collapse of religious, philosophic or economic systems. The imprints hardened into institutions, and all of our subsequent political and social judgments have been filtered through the mesh of this institutionalized society, until some traumatic incident breaks the institutionalized imprint and begins to develop new and—hopefully—more intelligent or socially sympathetic imprints.

One of the imprints through which we now operate is that the world is engaged in a struggle between "communism" and "capitalism," and a large part of our economic and political energies are poured into supporting this image, which was imprinted in the traumatic experiences we had in Europe and Asia immediately following World War II. The confrontation, however, is not really between these two ideologies (which are at root the same, communism being the heresy of capitalism, in much the same sense that Protestantism is the heresy of Catholicism) but between the means by which the needs of the individual's desire for freedom can be balanced with the need for authority if we are to have an orderly world. Our argument is about the means to achieve an end, not about the end. Our own Constitution established a system whereby authority could be set up, but the authority was circumscribed by its responsibility to uphold the Bill of Rights. All political systems are engaged in the search for a workable balance between individual freedom and collective security.

The belief in our ideological imprint burdens us (as well as our adversaries) with a war-oriented economy at the expense of the educational, cultural, economic and social advances we could make that would end the necessity for a war economy. Until we break this imprint, we are not likely to go too far in the next twenty years. We can foresee, with reasonable clarity, that there are at least two traumatic incidents that could break the imprint. The first is the not quite so unthinkable hydrogen war, and the second is that we will have either a mass psychological trauma that will create a new way of looking at things, such as the mass use of psychedelic chemicals, or through the emergence of a new religion. We shall examine both possibilities later on.

Another political imprint with which we have to struggle, at least in our part of the world, is that "democracy" or the "democratic process" is the ultimate and necessary condition for a free society. Let us say that the framers of the Constitution were not trying to set up a democracy but a representative republic, which is quite something else. Mere plurality rule has never guaranteed individual freedom and government by law; one has only to recollect the excesses of the French and the Russian revolutions to recognize that.

The concept that a democracy can be made to work assumes several things that do not appear to be true; among them, that man is a rational being and given "all the facts" will react "rationally" in his own best interest as well as that of his neighbors; that the conditions of communication within a society are sufficiently good so that all members of a democracy will have access to the sort of facts upon which they can base an intelligent decision; that a plurality or consensus is automatically right, etc. Indeed, had mankind accepted plurality as the determining factor in society, we would still be living on a flat earth around which

HEREDITARY GOTHIC

"*The pursuit of peace resembles the building of a great cathedral. It is the work of generations. In concept it requires a master architect; in execution, the labors of many. The pursuit of peace requires time, but we must use time as a tool and not as a couch. We must be prepared to profit from the vision of peace left by great men who came our way.*"

HUBERT H. HUMPHREY
Vice-President of the United States

GENTLEMEN,
START YOUR ENGINES

"*There lies before us, if we choose, continual progress in happiness, knowledge, and wisdom. Shall we, instead, choose death, because we cannot forget our quarrels? We appeal, as human beings to human beings. Remember your humanity, and forget the rest. If you can do so, the way lies open to a new Paradise; if you cannot, there lies before you the risk of universal death.*"

The Russell-Einstein Appeal
July 9, 1955

BUT WAITING IS PAINFUL

"*In the last resort peace must be built in the hearts of men. For this purpose dialogue at various levels is necessary and would prove an effective instrument. People around the globe are not only organized politically, but also ideologically and religiously. Channels of dialogues must be opened and pursued at all these levels.*"

MUHAMMED ZAFRULLA KHAN
Judge, International Court of Justice

MANIFESTO
FOR A MOVEMENT IN A MINOR

(From "Time's Future in Our Time," a paper for the Minister's Conference on Recreation, Toronto, November 1966 By John R. Seeley of the Center for the Study of Democratic Institutions.)

■ If we had looked for that trace, that first, faint, foreshadowing, twenty years ago, of what the new society might be like, we should perhaps have looked toward San Francisco and Venice and North Beach — to "The Beatniks." There, then, visibly, audibly, sensibly, in joy and grief, ecstasy and agony, wail and laughter, mad motions and quiet contemplation, orgy and debate, what was to be was being sought and seized and shaped, with leadings and misleadings, tremolo and blatancy, false start and brave beginning. There, then, in the quiet womb of time, reposed and stirred that whose spiritual issue and descent today is what is being variously called The New Generation, The New Youth, The New Left, The Movement . . .

What is it that I see in the range of the young, in what might best be loosely termed, "The Movement," that makes me suggest that the seed of the transition society is there highly visible and palpitating?—

Disavowing work as intrinsically and inherently valuable—and particularly the glorification of work to avoid coping with the problems of aggression . . .

Withdrawal from the idolatry of self and those merely projected and extended selves—my family, my city, my class, or race or religion or nation—in favor of something more than tolerance . . .

The abandonment of overdrawn distinctions, particularly dualisms like good-evil, masculine-feminine, right-wrong, in favor of a sense of the spectrum of similarities that underlies experience . . .

A heightened appreciation for goods that are good only in the giving (such as folk song singing or the playing and reproducing of music) as against the standard goods that are mere counters in a game, based on heightened envy . . .

Refusal to accept combative and competitive approaches in nearly all of their forms . . .

An enormously enhanced and increased valuation of love in all its extended and various manifestations, its range of aims and objects . . .

A foreswearing of the furious enjoyments of fanaticism; the food and fuel of most previous movements . . .

Discarding rules as the tools of principal reliance, preferring, instead, a unique and personal response to a situation that is viewed in its own uniqueness and novelty . . .

■ Do you see, as I see, faintly but sufficiently clearly, the foreshadowing both of the end of what is and the beginning of what is to be? On one side, one may see in them the emergence of a transitional character between that necessitated now and that which will be apt for the era of abundance. One can see in their society, I think, the seeds of the transitional society . . . They are engaged in bringing rapidly to an end the most dramatic instances of that which even now makes us utterly morally incredible, and what would, under plenty, bring us to an end altogether. ■

the sun revolved daily; human illness would be caused by devils and demons, and kings would rule by "Divine Right." In short, it would be a Medieval world upheld by consensus.

There does appear to be the need for some sort of consentive, participative method of organizing society that lies somewhere between mob rule and representative government. What this system may be we would not hazard a guess, but the need for it is obvious.

The really great confrontation in our present world, and one not too likely to change in the next two decades, is between those who have and those who do not. This is true within any society we know of, and it applies to nations as well as individuals. In a technological milieu in which we can—if we desire—produce all of the physical things that anyone in the world needs (not wants, *needs*), this confrontation becomes a sort of make-believe imagery, because we still act on an imprint that goes back to a much earlier time: "The poor we shall always have with us." We will have the poor just so long as we consider it to our interest to keep them that way.

The real have-nots are not only the poor, but the disenfranchised elements of our technological society; those too young to be allowed a voice in our government or economic system (though old enough to fight)—young people generally, who will shortly outnumber all the rest; those too old to participate in any meaningful way in the society they helped to build; those too ill to participate in anything but self-survival; those too ignorant (because our education system never managed to get through to them) to find useful places in society; those who are in jails or concentration camps or urban slums or dirt-poor rural areas who cannot participate because they have never been given the incentive nor the means to do so. Even in our society this applies to the majority of the people; it applies to an even larger majority elsewhere.

It has been suggested that a "World Parliament of Man" be called for some time in the next few years. It would give a forum for the expression of discontent of the disenfranchised of the world—whether disenfranchised by age, sex, disability, nonconformity, poverty, race, religion, nationality or ideology. The Parliament would be the natural outcome of "the New Politics" as generated by "the Movement," as opposed to the "Old Politics" and "the Estabishment."

Whether such a Parliament of Man shall come to be, and whether, if it does, anything of consequence will come of it, is one of the unforeseeables of our next twenty years. But perhaps—and only perhaps—here lies the beginning of the "third politics," perhaps here may be created a participative system that transcends nations and ideologies and says only "Ecce Homo!" ☐

UNFAMILIAR WORLD

"What then is a tick's world like? Von Uxkell has described it as consisting of a whiff of butyric acid, an ability to sense warmth (the infra-red end of the spectrum), the touch of fur and the taste of blood. Since ticks are known to have gone without food for as long as 18 years we can assume that their sense of time passing is also very different from our own. But this is such an unfamiliar world and so far away from ours and none of us suppose that we are likely to be asked to cooperate in designing a tickery, a home for ticks."

DR. H. F. OSMOND
"Worlds Apart"

THE FANTASTIC VOYAGE

☐ "Which is better," Aldous Huxley once asked, "to have Fun with Fungi or to have Idiocy with Ideology?"

The "Fun with Fungi" he referred to, of course, was the recent expansion in the use of psychedelic drugs, some of which are based on chemicals found in fungi, and the "Idiocy of Ideology" refers to what you read on the front page of your newspaper every day.

His question brings sharply into focus something we have discussed earlier, namely the theory that some of the irrationalities of our modern day actions result from infantile imprints, either in the individual or in the social organism, that are as difficult to change as the imprinted circuits of a transistor radio.

One way to disrupt the circuitry of the radio is to smash it with a hammer; this is the method still preferred by our society. Another way to change the circuits is to get inside the radio, trace out the circuitry, and then see if other connections are possible.

What we would like to consider here—among the little collection of unforeseeables we have piled up beside us on this turbulent beach— is that LSD, or its equivalents, may offer sensitive tools for the exploration of human awareness and the changing of early imprints that today separate man from man and man from the world he inhabits.

Says *Progressive Architecture* (in "LSD: A Design Tool?" August, 1966); "The social and cultural implications of the psychedelic drugs have been widely commented upon. It is easy to speculate that 20th Century Man, living in an age of scientific revolution that has overthrown in the span of a few decades the social and moral assumptions of several centuries; an age where the theologians themselves are forced into anguished debates as to the very existence of God, and where the new technology is rapidly dehumanizing man—in such a context the appeal of drugs that promise man a supposed ability to transcend the routine senses and environment are obvious. Whether these more mystical claims to self-discovery have any legitimate scientific base remains the job of steady, sober scientific study in the years ahead."

It does appear that little is known about the psychedelic chemicals (although they have been used by various peoples since the dawn of history) and that much remains to be found out. What is surprising is that we know so much about how to blow people to pieces—as a result of steady, sober, scientific thought—and so little about how to make whole men out of them.

"The pharmacology of LSD is not yet fully understood," understates *Time*, June 17, 1966. "The tracing of injected radioactive LSD shows that only an infinitesimal amount ever reaches the brain—and that is gone before the effect begins to be felt. It is generally thought, therefore, that

TRIP INTO TRUTH

"LSD has two major effects. For one thing, it tends to shatter and dissolve the usual web of associations and habit patterns. A telephone, for instance, is suddenly nothing but a black plastic object of a certain shape—how outrageous and funny to see someone pick it up and talk to it as though it were a person. The boundaries that normally separate things from each other, or from oneself, may be dissolved also. This may cause the impression that one's limbs and torso are liquefying and flowing away (horror!); or that one is in such close rapport with others in the room that one can read their thoughts (love!); or that the barriers of logic have disappeared to reveal a tremendous insight, for instance, that death and life are the same (truth!)."

TIME, June 17, 1966

INCREDIBLE EXPLORATION

"The exploration of the interior of the human brain will be as dangerous as that of the Antarctic continent or the depths of the oceans, and far more rewarding."

DR. J. B. S. HALDANE
London Symposium, 1962

PAINTING BY ROBERT ALEXANDER

HERE AND NOW

*"Psychotropic drugs in new and varied
forms will doubtless be used . . . to
enhance and diversify experience. The
social problems of addiction, and
even of their medical use on a growing
scale as 'tranquilizers' will have
to be faced long before 1984."*

LORD BRAIN
"Knowing Our Minds Better"

IT'S WHAT'S HAPPENING

*"Philosophers, theologians, psychologists
—what doctors call 'lay people'—
want to use drugs like LSD because in
fact they already have used them,
and continue to experience the results:
radically new and different insights
into the workings of the mind; striking
sensory experiences that often enough
have persisted in the form of a new
outlook on people and society; a fresh
and absorbing interest in symbolic
and religious matters; in many instances
an asserted loss of one or another
'problem,' fear, or psychiatric symptom;
finally, the possession of an unshakable
calm and a defiantly unyielding
joy that are conspicuously absent in
the rest of us."*

ROBERT COLES
"The Case for LSD,"
Book Week, July 24, 1966

LSD does not act directly but triggers an unknown series of metabolic processes." Here, again, we come up against that mysterious interface between the psychoneural system and its internal and external stimuli, and it appears that LSD, or drugs like it, may be tools that will enable us to find out more.

However, the use of "consciousness-expanding" chemicals still appears to bother a society that readily accepts the use of alcohol, sleeping pills, tranquilizers, depressants, stimulants and pain-killing drugs—all of them chemicals that affect the central nervous system.

"The fog of notoriety that swirls around the 'hallucinogenic' drugs," says *Business Week* (June 25, 1966), "was penetrated last week by a few shafts of clear scientific light. When the six day 'LSD Conference' was over, an imposing roster of medical opinion was found to credit the hallucinogens with a solid list of potential medical and psychiatric benefits to match their oft-trumpeted dangers to the unwary . . . No evidence has been shown that LSD is particularly toxic or addictive . . ."

"In fact," comments *Newsweek* (May 9, 1966), ". . . there is no known lethal dose of LSD. The only known victim of LSD was an elephant at the Oklahoma zoo, given an unintentional overdose."

Now the point here, if indeed there is one, is that the "consciousness expanding" drugs may offer a way out of some of the problems that plague our current society. As Chicago psychiatrist Dr. Marvin Ziporyn has said, "LSD is, if you like, a psychiatric X-ray. With LSD you have no greater vision of the universe than you did before. It no more expands your consciousness than an X-ray expands your lungs when you see them on the screen. All you do is get a better look."

All you do is get a better look. Getting any kind of look at ourselves and our relationships to each other and the world in which we live is uncommon enough. A *new* look? What more could we ask?

Perhaps the most exciting prospect of all is suggested by *Progressive Architecture* (August, 1966), which says, "Another interesting aspect of the psychedelics is what several research psychologists have termed the similarity between the effects created by these chemicals and the sort of consciousness identified with creativity . . . A rather far removed speculation is the fascinating possibility that in future years the psychedelic drugs may make accessible to the average man the levels of consciousness and perception previously restricted to the artist."

It may be a bit premature to suggest that the world's leaders—political, scientific and economic—be allowed to take a psychedelic "trip" as one of the ways for preparing for the strange new world that confronts us in the next twenty years. But, on the other hand, what do we have to lose? Only elephants. □

THE AGE OF MIRACLES

☐ "If you do not think about the future, you cannot have one," wrote John Galsworthy in 1928. Today the statement has an ominous ring of truth, for the great danger of our time is that if we do not have a future, it will be because we have not thought enough about it.

But given the choice, most of us would probably take for granted that we will have one, and the question then becomes, "Just *what* are we to think about the future?"

We have a checkered career to draw on. History has shown that sometimes even the experts have bet against a forest growing where just a tree once stood. In 1835, for instance, a noted French philosopher declared that man would never know anything of the chemical structure of heavenly bodies. Invention of the spectroscope negated his belief. At the end of World War II, one of the world's most prominent scientists argued against U.S. research into the development of an intercontinental ballistic missile, saying that such a thing "will not be done for a very long time." By 1957, the USSR had its first ICBM. Britain's Astronomer Royal stated flatly that "space travel is utter bilge." That was in 1956, a year before the first sputnik.

There is, in fact, a whole inventory of things we rely on today that were completely unanticipated before their appearance, including x-rays, lasers, relativity, nuclear energy, photography, transistors, radio and television. Unforeseen breakthroughs in our scientific knowledge were needed to make them possible. Science fiction author Arthur C. Clarke offers the explanation that, "Anything that is theoretically possible will be achieved in practice, if it is desired greatly enough."

Perhaps because we have been caught unaware too often and the stakes are too high now, or simply because it had to happen in the course of man's search for knowledge, there has lately sprung up a specific interest in the very mechanism of foreseeing the future. One study, conducted by Theodore J. Gordon and Dr. Olaf Helmer under the auspices of the RAND Corporation in California, used a systematic approach called the "Delphi technique" in questioning 82 experts in various fields about the long-range future. The respondents were sent a sequence of questionnaires, each one based on results of the last one, and each man therefore had the opportunity to change his views as information and the views of other respondents were given to him.

The result of this study is a book, *Social Technology*, published by Basic Books, Inc., that probably comes as close as it is possible to come to outlining the more distant future. On the following four pages are some of the things felt by the experts surveyed to be "unforeseeable" within the next 20 years. Most of them, it seems, need only to be "desired greatly enough." ☐

UNIMAGINABLE

"Scientists tend to agree that some of the most exciting future developments will come out of insights and discoveries yet to be made, with implications we cannot now foresee or imagine. So we live in an era where not only anything that we can imagine seems possible, but where the possibilities range beyond what we can imagine. In such an era it is hard to tell physics from metaphysics, to distinguish the mad scientists from the real ones, to judge what is a true possibility and what is sheer rot. But there is no resolving this kind of uncertainty. Even the scientists cannot give us sure guidance of what is really going to happen."

ALBERT ROSENFELD
"Will Man Direct His Own Evolution?"

SUPERMARKET

"Only 10 or 15 years hence, it could be possible for a housewife to walk into a new kind of commissary, look down a row of packets not unlike flower-seed packages, and pick her baby by label. Each packet would contain a frozen one-day-old embryo, and the label would tell the shopper what color of hair and eyes to expect as well as the probable size and I.Q. of the child. It would also offer assurance of freedom from genetic defects. After making her selection, the lady would take the packet to her doctor and have the embryo implanted in herself, where it would grow for nine months, like any baby of her own." / DR. E. S. E. HAFEZ, Biologist, Washington State University

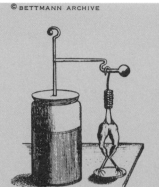

© BETTMANN ARCHIVE

© BETTMANN ARCHIVE

GENETIC MANIPULATION:
The ability to control the formation of new beings may be one of the most basic developments of the future. Recent discoveries about the nucleonic acids, the basic building blocks of life, have led to the belief that man may some day be able to treat genes in such a way that desired characteristics can be realized. With "human prescriptions" we could develop nearly any type of man desired—super-intelligent, highly talented, better able to survive in severe climates, in rarified atmospheres of other planets, or underwater, etc. Other research indicates that "tissue culture" reproduction may also become possible. This would allow a man to have cells from his own body placed in storage so that a complete replica of himself could be grown from these cells after his death. (Reported in LIFE)

NUCLEAR ELECTRIC POWER:
Practical nuclear power sources for every nation on earth are well within our technical capability in this century, provided the "unforeseeable" element of political and financial support is exerted. To answer the staggering future energy needs of the world, nuclear power is the most efficient source known for electric power, and could be developed in either of two systems: small, self-contained reactors could serve individual buildings and complexes, or vast distribution systems could be set up to draw from huge multi-megawatt nuclear plants. Nuclear fusion, still a relatively undeveloped field, could provide vast energy sources without the side effect of radiation, but a great deal of research is necessary to make this practical. (Reported in PROGRESSIVE ARCHITECTURE)

ADVENTURES IN MAGNETISM:
Research into magnetism and superconducting magnets, made possible by new high energy power sources, may one day result in surprising new uses for magnetic force. One possibility is a wheelless railroad in which the cars, powered by strong magnetic forces, would be suspended in the force field between opposing magnets. Frictionless bearings are another potentiality. At least one company is doing research on an engine with no moving parts, powered by a magnetic fluid that turns heat directly into electricity, and another is using huge magnets to push metal into shaped dies, permitting forming jobs previously thought impossible. Superconducting magnets may some day be used to confine superhot plasmas, to protect astronauts from cosmic radiation, and to increase resolution in electron microscopes so that atomic arrangements may be actually "seen." (Reported in STEEL magazine)

LASER TECHNOLOGY:
An "unforeseeable" of the recent past, lasers may one day see uses we cannot imagine. Laser technology is still in its infancy, yet vast research efforts are underway. Lasers are creating an exciting new field called holography, in which light waves from an object can be recorded on film and later reproduced in mid-air as a three-dimensional "photograph." Most laser research, however, is going into the eventual development of a long-range communications system, using light waves. Many obstacles need to be overcome first, but the laser's unique properties, including highly directional, coherent, monochromatic light and its extremely wide frequency range, make this use particularly promising. Lasers may one day provide us with instant interplanetary television. (Reported in SCIENTIFIC AMERICAN and SAN FRANCISCO EXAMINER)

METHUSELAH REVISITED

"Today, throughout the Western world and especially in America, man's attitude toward the mystery of death is making a break with human tradition. Medically, death seems to be constantly receding, and some scientists think seriously about an almost indefinite life span for man . . ."

"On Death as a Constant Companion," TIME, November 12, 1965

COMMUNICATION WITH OTHER SPECIES: Recent studies at Port Elizabeth Aquarium in South Africa indicate that communication in modified English can be established with dolphins. A vocabulary of several hundred sounds has been set up by recording dolphin language electronically. English words have also been converted into electronic sounds that dolphins can hear and "understand."

The process used is an electronic translation of tone into intensity variation, the media used by dolphins. It is said that dolphins brains react 16 times faster than humans but that their memory level is lower. Similar studies on other higher primates indicate that man may one day be able for the first time to communicate in an abstract way with the other species of life on this planet. (Reported by ASSOCIATED PRESS)

INCREASED LIFESPAN: Many scientists now believe that resistance to disease, which declines in advancing years, allowing the onset of fatal infection and illness, is partially a function of heredity and therefore probably amenable to control by man. Hereditary material in the cells may, through damage or simple degeneration of effectiveness, gradually stop directing these cells to repair or rebuild themselves. Recent understanding about the nucleotides that govern life itself may eventually lead to our ability to intervene genetically and augment or introduce any protective function in the body, perhaps adding 50 years or more to expected lifespans. (Reported in NEWS FRONT)

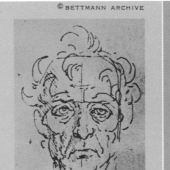

© BETTMANN ARCHIVE

EXTRASENSORY PERCEPTION: The brain's capacity for sending and receiving signals through means other than the known senses has been indicated in a number of experiments. In one, totally deaf subjects experienced pure tone hearing, speech hearing and music hearing when low frequency RF energy was beamed at them. Particularly gifted deaf subjects have even experienced thought transfer over distances approaching 200 miles, though the carrier system, its modulation and the brain channel used are unknown. In another experiment, a doctor successfully transmitted Morse code by controlled brain waves alone. The phenomenon, capable of activating a computer, demonstrated the "sending" ability of the brain. ESP, the subject of extensive research, is unlikely to become a controlled science in this century, but its potential is remarkable. (Reported in MISSILES AND ROCKETS and THE FINANCIAL POST)

CONTACT WITH EXTRATERRESTRIALS: Evidence is mounting that intelligent life exists on other planets, and both Darwinian and probability theory suggest this as a fact in literally thousands of places within the universe. A recommendation has been made to construct a 6 mile diameter radio telescope system that could provide detailed pictures of radio emissions from nearby galaxies, and might also locate intelligent life within 10 light years from earth. Although we do not know when, how or in what language or code communication with such beings might take place, experts believe that such a transaction will be made possible through the use of computers. Codes are being devised that might serve as an easily translatable language. (Reported in SCIENTIFIC AMERICAN and MISSILES AND ROCKETS)

QUORUM FORUM

"Within the next decade or two the human species will
establish communications with another species: non-human, alien, possibly
extraterrestrial, more probably marine . . ."

DR. JOHN C. LILY
Director, Communications Research Institute

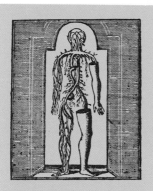

REGENERATION OF BODY PARTS: In addition to the great advances likely to be made in the field of artificial organs for the human body, a new study is emerging—the stimulation of natural regrowth of body parts that have been damaged or removed. A recently-developed mathematical formula may provide the key, and is based on the theory that as an organ grows it releases growth inhibitors into the bloodstream, so that at the right time, the organ is inhibited from further growth. If the organ is removed by damage or surgery, the process might be restarted. In experiments, a rat's kidney compensated for the removal of its other kidney by increasing in size. The study may eventually result in some means of stimulating the regenerative process for new kidneys or livers, and may even be a means of restraining the growth of a cancer. (Reported by University of California, Berkeley)

© BETTMANN ARCHIVE

HUMAN ROBOTS: The day when a household robot assumes everyday chores for housewives may not occur in the next twenty years, but such an electro-mechanical helper will probably exist eventually. Up to now, robots have been built which can perform many worthwhile activities, including some that are impossible for a human being. But the ability to cope with the unforeseen and do anything of its own accord is still outside practical robot capability. An electronic circuit that imitates two neurons, the cells of the human brain, has been built, and has enabled a robot to deal with some unexpected situations, but the neuron structure was bulky. The brain has billions of neurons, meaning an incredible miniaturization job will be necessary before truly "human" robots are developed. (Reported in NEWS FRONT)

MAN-MACHINE SYMBIOSIS: Humanizing machines and mechanizing humans are cross trends that are sure to occur in the future, but the extent to which man and machine will be united is uncertain. Computers exist which can learn, remember, see, seek goals, reason, walk, sing on key, talk, be irritable, play games, grasp, adapt to an environment and even design improvements in themselves. While artificial organs made possible by miniature electronic components are being used in the human body, man-like computers may one day contain plasma circulating through a viscera-like envelope, allowing them to be self-healing. Direct mind-machine communication is also being explored for the transfer of thoughts instead of words. (Reported in STEEL and SCIENCE NEWS)

© BETTMANN ARCHIVE

DIRECT EDUCATION OF BRAIN CELLS: Experiments indicate that certain chemicals in the brain will, when implanted in another brain, transfer knowledge. Untrained rats have suddenly performed as if taught when injected with chemicals from the brains of trained rats, and scientists believe that memory storage, involving the DNA and RNA molecules, is the same in animals and humans. These chemicals, perhaps in pill form may eventually have highly beneficial uses. Electrical and chemical stimulation of brain cells has also shown remarkable results in calming nervous monkeys, changing basic needs of rats and even stopping a bull in mid-charge. These early efforts may lead to a totally new understanding of the human brain, and new means of correcting mental disorders. (Reported in NEWS FRONT)

SORCERER'S APPRENTICE

"Some years ago the eminent French biologist Jean Rostand even predicted that a man might one day be able to have a culture of his own cells—cells from almost anywhere in his body—stashed away somewhere so that a complete new replica of himself could be grown in case he met with an untimely accident."

ALBERT ROSENFELD, "Will Man Direct His Own Evolution?"

© BETTMANN ARCHIVE

TIME TRAVEL: Albert Einstein's theory of relativity stated that our experience of space and time are inseparable from each other. The space-time continuum theorizes that as matter approaches the speed of light—186,000 miles per second—time (and its effects, such as aging) actually slows down until at the speed of light, it stands still. Today we know a great deal about space but comparatively little about time, yet "time dilation," as physicists call it, is entering into long-range space navigation planning, for as space vehicles achieve greater speeds, they may eventually reach a velocity of 10% of the speed of light, at which this phenomenon is believed to begin taking effect. That a man may one day explore the vast reaches of space in his lifetime, while thousands of years pass on earth, might seem a fanciful concept, but the speeds necessary to demonstrate it may not be unattainable. (Reported in THE NATIONAL OBSERVER)

DIRECT PRODUCTION OF FOOD: Synthetic foods, textured and flavored so as to be indistinguishable from foods we now know, may be used to feed a world population that will have doubled by the end of this century. The vital nutrients for these foods may by then be obtainable economically by direct synthesis, completely bypassing the need for livestock and plants as their source. Research has shown that proteins can be synthesized from such substances as petroleum, coal, and even waste material. Hydrocarbons in these materials nourish protein-producing microorganisms, and the result is a yeast in the form of powder or white flakes that is odorless and tasteless, yet rich in the amino acids vital for nutrition. Direct photosynthesis of sugars also needed for body growth is now in research stages and may attain practical status. (Reported in SCIENTIFIC AMERICAN)

COMPUTERIZED MEDICINE: Introduction of computers into the field of medicine has already had remarkable results, and is likely to cause even more startling future breakthroughs. Computers now store staggering amounts of medical data for instant access by doctors and nurses, they prepare prescriptions, detect mental and physical disorders, aid psychiatrists in therapy work, analyze data from medical examinations and make diagnoses with greater accuracy than doctors. Much of the "unforeseeable" future in the realm of medicine may depend on the use of computers. (Reported in BUSINESS WEEK and THE NEW YORK TIMES)

ANTIGRAVITY: The neutralizing of gravitational force has thus far only been accomplished in specific inertial experiments such as space vehicle "weightlessness," and is otherwise still a theoretical phenomenon. The existence of antigravitational force to cancel the force of gravity would seem to depend upon the existence of antimatter, much as the neutralization of a magnetic force requires the presence of its opposite magnetic polarity. Antimatter might be a mirror image of matter, including reversed electrical and magnetic properties, reversed time and a negative gravitational mass. Scientists have discovered some anti-particles, including anti-protons and anti-deuterons (the anti-nucleus of heavy hydrogen). But experiments are inconclusive, and antigravity remains, a possible breakthrough, if it exists at all. (Reported in SCIENTIFIC AMERICAN and SCIENCE NEWS)

ECCE HOMO HUMANUS

ETERNAL GAMBLE

"But innovation is more than a new method. It is a new view of the universe, as one of risk rather than of chance or of certainty. It is a new view of man's role in the universe; he creates order by taking risks. And this means that innovation, rather than being an assertion of human power, is an acceptance of human responsibility."

PETER DRUCKER
"Landmarks of Tomorrow"

BALANCING ACT

"Our period demands a type of man who can restore the lost equilibrium between inner and outer reality. This equilibrium, never static, but like reality itself, involved in continuous change, is like that of a tightrope dancer who, by small adjustments, keeps a continuous balance between his being and empty space. We need a type of man who can control his own existence by the process of balancing forces often regarded as irreconcilable: man in equipoise."

SIEGFRIED GIEDION
"Mechanization Takes Command"

☐ "There is a story about one of our great atomic physicists," recalls Loren Eiseley in *The Firmament of Time*. "This man, one of the chief architects of the atomic bomb, was out wandering in the woods one day with a friend when he came upon a small turtle. Overcome with pleasurable excitement, he took up the turtle and started home, thinking to surprise his children with it. After a few steps, he paused and surveyed the animal doubtfully.

" 'What's the matter?' asked his friend.

"Without responding, the great scientist slowly retraced his steps as precisely as possible, and gently set the turtle down upon the exact spot from which he had taken him up.

"Then he turned solemnly to his friend. 'It just struck me,' he said, 'that perhaps, for one man, I have tampered enough with the universe.'

"He turned and left the turtle to wander on its way.

"It was not a denial of science. It was final recognition that science is not enough for man. It is not the road back to the waiting Garden, for that road lies through the heart of man. Only when man has recognized this fact will science become what it was for Bacon, something to speak of as 'touching upon Hope.' Only then will man be truly human."

Here, in this simple story, is a parable for our times. Here in capsule form, is the emergence of Homo Humanus, the "human man" out of Homo Sapiens, "the rational man." It perhaps may be a chrysalis that released its butterfly too late; or in the wrong season. Or perhaps it is on schedule and we just don't know what that schedule may be.

The single, stunning, enormous fact of our times is that psycho-social man is undergoing a mutation; he is making the "Great Psychic Leap."

We tend to think of mutations as being biological and of occurring purely in the genetic structure, or process, have it as you will, of germ plasm. This is because the terminology originated with the geneticists. But social organisms undergo mutations too, and that is what we are talking about here.

There may be a new species of man emerging, and he may create a wholly new society, a new science, a new philosophy, a new religion, and a new morality. The mutational force is his own technology; the hard rays of his own making have created within the social organism the necessity for a change of truly universal dimensions. The fact appears to be that with the introduction of "the ultimate weapon," human beings have changed the rules of the game by which they have acted out their roles for tens of thousands of years.

Now the old concepts of territoriality, of property ownership, of nationalism and patriotism—of race and color and creed—that once were the ingredients for survival of this species on this planet, become turned inside out. The global man, the human man, may become the cell of the new society in which the use of the territorial imperative will become an exercise as meaningless as the Crusades. We have long since given up war as a means of spreading religious ideas; we now move into an era in which we may have to give up war as a means of spreading political and economic ideas. And this will take a new kind of man, and a new kind of family unit. Hopefully—for the time grows short—both already are emerging.

You can see the new man, if you look for him. He will most likely be carrying a placard in a picket line; singing hymns in front of a city hall; sharing his pad with people who "talk funny" or have differently colored skins, or "need" a shave and a hair cut; or serving in the Peace Corps.

There are at least two ways the mutation may take effect. There may be a hydrogen war, in which technological man will surely perish. It is our well-known heritage that if a man has a rock in his hand, he will throw it; a club in his hand, he will swing it.

Except there is another way; like the scientist and the turtle.

If there *is* a hydrogen war; if the mutation to Homo Humanus takes place too slowly, then the remnants of mankind—and there would probably be a few hundred million left—would, out of the changes in their genetic structures (99 per cent of which would not be conducive to human survival), create, from the one percent favorable genetic changes, a new kind of man. If there is *not* a hydrogen war, then it will be because we have changed ourselves dramatically, and made the very idea of a hydrogen war (which means any kind of war since they almost inevitably escalate to the use of the largest weapon) preposterous.

Our most important deficiency is that we take ourselves seriously. Homo Humanus, scanning his own actions, can but burst into laughter; the human posture is so ridiculous, it can provoke only that. Can we but learn to laugh at death (a human invention as obsolete as the button-hook) and view ourselves as ripples in a stream that constantly flows —then indeed we shall become the superior beings we consider our-selves to be. It is laughter that shakes the firmament—not tears.

"Let the storms blow through the streets of cities," says Loren Eiseley, "the root is safe, the many-faceted animal of which we are only one flashing and evanescent facet, will not pass with us. When the last seared hand has flung the last grenade, an older version of that hand will be stroking a clinging youngster hidden in its fur, high up under some autumn moon. I will think of beginning again . . . I will think of beginning again, in a different way . . ."

Even if some giant Doomsday bomb explodes the planet, it will be

FAINTLY SERIOUS

". . . if these things are to be done by and with the people, rather than for and to them—then 'tomorrow' means five years at least before private opinion can become public policy. And then? And then, if we are even faintly serious about the altered society we foresee, we must allow time and means for the alteration of men to fit that society. And men are not to be altered like armaments—by scrapping what is no longer apt and 'refitting' what is only in part so. If the changes envisioned are far-reaching, new men must be grown—by men willing and able to undergo the agony of making themselves over so far as they are able, even while they must foster, and subsequently tolerate, what is newer, and hence more alien, yet."

JOHN R. SEELEY
"Time's Future in Our Time"

GUILT BY ASSIMILATION

"We are seeking research methods and a scientific approach that will view man not as a cluster of functions and sub-systems, but as an individual—an experiencing, feeling, acting person. In other words, we believe that mechanistic approaches, so successful in the physical sciences, are not entirely adequate for the study of human beings, and need to be supplemented with a more humanistic approach. By failing to account for man's subjective experiences, the behavioral sciences can fall short of their full potential."

Western Behavioral Sciences Institute

but another Star of Bethlehem to a billion other worlds. On Alpha Centauri, some bi-focaled astromer will remove the exposed plate from his telescope, see the little flash of light on it, and say, "How interesting."

We think too much of these things, too little of ourselves. It is the secret of Eastern religions and philosophies that the universe lives in man. He has made of it many things, and whether he makes a heaven of it, or a hydrogen hell of it, or something in between, will, however it goes, be but a fantasy of his own making.

"Time and death and the space between the stars remain the substance of evolution and of all that we are," comments Robert Ardrey in *African Genesis.* "They rest unseen in a gesture of farewell, in a handshake or a kiss, or a child's goodnight. We read a book or think of friends, or remember our grandmother's little grey house where a trumpet vine softened the kitchen window. We go to bed, or build a pyramid, or accomplish a peak in Darien and stand hushed by the view of an unknown sea. We regret. We learn or love. It is all of a piece, and the moment of our consciousness is the moment of all things."

It is not death we fear, not even for the species. It is pain.

It was Dr. Robert Oppenheimer who said, at the eye-wrenching man-made dawn at Alamagordo, quoting from the *Bhagavad-Gita,* "Suppose a thousand suns should rise together in the sky; such is the splendor of the Shape of the Infinite God," thus bringing together the ancient wisdom of the Hindus and the newer wisdom of the Manhattan Project.

What was not quoted were lines from the Buddhist *Dhammapada,* "If one man conquer in battle a thousand times a thousand men, and if another conquer himself, he is the greatest of conquerors. One's own self conquered is better than all other people conquered; not even a god could change into defeat the victory of a man who has vanquished himself."

At Alamagordo Western man conquered a thousand times a thousand men. In the woods when he set the turtle down, he conquered himself.

"And looking so, across the centuries and the millenia, toward the animal men of the past, one can see a faint light, like a patch of sunlight moving over the dark shadows of the forest floor. It shifts and widens, it winks out, it comes again, but it persists," says Loren Eiseley in *The Firmament of Time.* "It is the human spirit, the human soul, however transient, however faulty men may claim it to be. In its coming man had no part. It merely came, that curious light, and man, the animal, sought to be something no animal had been before. Cruel he might be, vengeful he might be, but there had entered into his nature a curious wistful gentleness and courage . . ."

PHOTO BY WILLIAM JACKSON © 1966

WE THANK WHATEVER GODS MAY BE . . .

Out of the dreaming past, with its legends of steaming seas and gleaming glaciers, mountains that moved and suns that glared, emerges this creature, man—the latest phase in a continuing process that stretches back to the beginning of life. His is the heritage of all that has lived; he still carries the vestiges of snout and fangs and claws of species long since vanished; he is the ancestor of all that is yet to come. Do not regard him lightly—he is you.

BUT THAT WAS LONG AGO
WASN'T IT?

"And the time be gone with its creed
When men were as beasts that bleed,
As sheep or as swine that wallow,
In the shambles of faith and of fear . . ."

ALGERNON CHARLES
SWINBURNE
From poem, "The Last Oracle"

RECIPROCITY

"If the red slayer thinks he slays,
Or if the slain thinks he is slain,
They know not well the subtle ways
I keep and pass, and turn again.

"They reckon ill who leave me out;
When me they fly, I am the wings;
I am the doubter and the doubt,
And I am the hymn the Brahmin sings."

RALPH WALDO EMERSON
"Brahma"

L'ENVOI

"And my youth returns, like the
rains of Spring,
And my sons, like the wild geese flying;
And I lie and hear the meadow-lark sing
And have much content with my dying."

STEPHEN VINCENT BENET
"Ballad of William Sycamore"

Remarked Soren Kierkegaard, "He who fights the future has a dangerous enemy. The future is not; it borrows its strength from the man himself and when it has tricked him out of this, then it appears outside him as the enemy he must meet."

If there are any eyes that see, they are the eyes of youth, and they do not see the future as an enemy, but as a friend; for the young shall inherit the earth. It may be true, as Ralph Gleason has said in *The Great War Between Kids and Society:* "The New Youth is finding its poets on juke boxes and its religion in rock 'n roll, its preachers in night clubs and its philosophers with long hair and guitars. They are bound to come into conflict with authority, just as every religious movement has."

They are not too different from the youth of another time and place who saw the emergence of their future in the streets of Galilee, or while seated before the living Buddha, some six centuries earlier, in the Deer Park at Benares. They saw what older eyes were blind to. Perhaps they—and the artists—see it now.

"Nature *does* make jumps," says Emile Benoit in *Interdependence on a Small Planet,* "they are rare, but when they do occur, a new system emerges and that new system is no longer understandable and predictable by the laws that governed the old one."

Yet out of newness, there emerges the old. We are but products of all that went before.

"Long is the story of our natural world, and we are a page that turns," says Robert Ardrey. "Glory is written on us, for we are kings. But our kingship is a limited sovereignty; we are a part of all things. We stand upon creatures lost in pre-Cambrian slimes. Our genes still reflect their ambitions. We may anticipate species unborn, times beyond prediction, sovereignties beyond Homo Sapiens, and beings that we shall never know. But we shall be a part of them, influencing their destinies as others have influenced ours."

In our youth lies our future, and, as Rousseau advised in *Emile,* in 1762, "Keep your child's mind idle as long as you can." *There* is the world of tomorrow; in the dreaming mind of children.

Should one want a recipe for it, it can be found, strangely enough, in an Hawaiian cookbook, entitled, *A Cook's Tour of Kauai.* It is not credited, and it is called, simply, "Preserved Children." It goes like this:

"Take 1 large field, half a dozen children, 2 or 3 small dogs, a pinch of brook and some pebbles. Mix the children and dogs well together; put them on the field, stirring constantly. Pour the brook over the pebbles, sprinkle the field with flowers, spread over all a deep blue sky and bake in the sun. When brown, set away to cool in a bath tub."

Ecce. Homo Humanus. □

A PARTIAL BIBLIOGRAPHY ▪ *Books are doors, opening on corridors. Open one, and the rest is easy. You just wander down the corridors, opening first this door and then that one. Some of the rooms you find are empty, some contain exotic gardens, some are full of trash, and some open into still other corridors. This is not a bibliography, it is a wandering—down many corridors.*

Certain books were fundamental to the entire study; we returned to them again and again.

Among these was Olaf Helmer and Ted Gordon's *Report on a Long Range Forecasting Study*, published by the Rand Corporation, Santa Monica, California in 1964. It is available in book form under the title *Social Technology*, Basic Books, New York, 1967.

The two-volume paperback, *The World in 1984* edited by Nigel Calder and published by Penguin Books, Baltimore (215 pages each) was useful as an over-all guide.

Understanding Media by Marshall McLuhan, McGraw-Hill, New York, 364 pages, (paperback) underlies much of the thinking in the series.

Other books we found valuable were:

EDWARD BELLAMY. *Looking Backward: 2000-1887.* Dolphin Paperback, Doubleday, New York; Random House, Modern Library, 1951 (276 pp).

HARRISON BROWN, JAMES BONNER, JOHN WEIR. *The Next Hundred Years.* Viking Press, 1961 (193 pp).

VICTOR COHN, *1999—Our Hopeful Future.* The Bobbs Merrill Company, Inc., Indianapolis, 1956 (205 pp, illus.).

OTTO FEINSTEIN, EDITOR. *Two Worlds of Change.* Doubleday & Co., Inc. Anchor Book (pb), 1964 (420 pp).

J. T. FRASER. *The Voices of Time.* George Braziller, 1966. (710 pp).

HEINZ GARTMANN. *Man Unlimited.* Pantheon Books, Inc., 1957 (214 pp).

GEORGE RUSSELL HARRISON. *What Man May Be.* Wm. Morrow & Co., 1956 (278 pp).

ALDOUS HUXLEY. *Brave New World Revisited.* Harper & Brothers, New York, 1958 (147 pp).

PROSPECT FOR AMERICA. *The Rockefeller Panel Reports.* Doubleday & Co., Inc., 1961 (486 pp).

CHAPTER I: THE DYNAMICS OF CHANGE

The two most important sources for this chapter were H. G. Barnett's *Innovation: the Basis of Cultural Change*, McGraw-Hill Paperbacks, New York, 1953 (462 pp) and Eric Hoffer's *The Ordeal of Change*. Harper & Row, Publishers, New York, 1963 (150 pp).

Other sources we found important were:

HENRY ADAMS. *Education of Henry Adams.* Houghton Mifflin, 1918 (519 pp).

SAMUEL BOIS. *Explorations in Awareness.* Harper & Row Publishers, Inc., New York, 1957 (212 pp).

KENNETH BOULDING. *The Image.* University of Michigan Press: Ann Arbor, 1961 (175 pp, paperback).

DENNIS GABOR. *Inventing the Future.* Alfred A. Knopf, 1964 (238 pp).

ERIC HOFFER. *The True Believer.* Harper & Bros., New York, 1951 (176 pp).

OLIVER L. REISER. *Integration of Human Knowledge.* Porter Sargent Publisher, Boston, Mass. (478 pp).

TED F. SILVEY. "Technology and Cultural Lag," *Adult Leadership,* Nov., 1955.

ALVIN TOFFLER. "The Future as a Way of Life," *Horizon,* Summer, 1964.

JOHN WILKINSON. "The Quantitative Society" (pamphlet) published by the Center for the Study of Democratic Institutions, Santa Barbara, Calif., 1964.

CHAPTER II: THE PROMISED LAND

The definitive work here is *Man's Role in Changing the Face of the Earth,* edited by William L. Thomas, Jr. University of Chicago Press, Chicago, 1956 (1193 pp, illustrated). Other important sources were Jonathan Garst's *No Need for Hunger,* Random House, New York, 1963 (182 pp), and *Resources in America's Future,* by Hans Landsberg, et al, Johns Hopkins Press, 1963 (1017 pp).

Among other sources consulted were:

ISAAC ASIMOV. "The World of 1990," *Diners' Club Magazine,* January 1965.

CAPT. J. Y. COUSTEAU WITH JAMES DUGAN. *The Living Sea.* Pocket Books Inc., New York, 1964 (239 pp, illus).

BY THE EDITORS OF FORTUNE. *The Changing American Market.* Hanover House, Garden City, New York, 1955 (304 pp).

EDWARD HALL. *The Silent Language.* Premier Books, Fawcett Publications, Inc., Greenwich, Conn., 1965 (192 pp).

LAURENCE B. HOLLAND (ed). *Who Designs America?* Anchor Books (pb) Original, Doubleday & Company, Inc., New York, 1966 (357 pp).

GYORGY KEPES, EDITOR. *Structure in Art and Science.* George Braziller, Publisher, New York, 1965 (189 pp).

JOSEPH B. MACINNIS. "Living Under the Sea," *Scientific American,* March, 1966.

FAIRFIELD OSBORN. *Our Plundered Planet.* Little Brown & Co., Boston, 1948 (217 pp), also in paperback.

ROGER REVELLE. "The Problem of People," *Harvard Today,* Autumn, 1965.

SUMNER H. SLICHTER. *Economic Growth in The United States.* Collier Books (pb) 1963 (189 pp).

F. G. WALTON SMITH AND HENRY CHAPIN. *The Sun, The Sea and Tomorrow.* Charles Scribner's Sons, New York 1954 (210 pp).

CHAPTER III: TELEMOBILITY: WHEN FAR IS NEAR

No single book covered this general area; nearly all of the material was drawn from contemporary periodicals. Some of the articles are listed below:

WM. A. BUGGE. "Highway Transportation After 1975," *Civil Engineering,* January, 1962.

JOSEPH M. S. COYLE. "Traffic & The Computer," *Traffic Management,* April, 1966.

PHYLLIS DAIGNAULT. "New Markets in Time," *Sales Management,* June 18, 1965.

W. H. FERRY. "Masscomm as Educator," *The American Scholar,* Spring, 1966.

MORRIS J. GELMAN. "The Invisible Shield," *Television,* Dec., 1965.

LAWRENCE HALPRIN. "Motation," *Progressive Achitecture,* July, 1965.

EVAN HERBERT. "Traffic," *International Science & Technology,* May, 1964.

PAUL D. SPREIRIGEN. "The City As a Work of Art," *Saturday Review,* January 8, 1966.

HER MAJESTY'S STATIONERY OFFICE. *Traffic in Towns.* 1963.

CHAPTER IV: AUTOMATION: LIFE WITH A LITTLE BLACK BOX

There is a vast amount of material available on the general subject of computers and their relationship to man. The ones we found most basic were Norbert Wiener's two works, *Cybernetics,* John Wiley & Sons, Inc., New York, 1948 (194 pp) and *The Human Use of Human Beings,* Doubleday & Co., New York, 1954, an Anchor paperback (199 pp). Also of great value was *The Mathematical Theory of Communication* by Claude E. Shannon and Warren Weaver, University of Illinois Press, 1964 (125 pp); John von Neumann, *The Computer and the Brain,* Yale University Press, New Haven, 1958 (82 pp), also in paperback, and *Automatic Control,* a *Scientific American* book, Simon and Schuster, New York, 1955 (149 pp, ill.) also in paperback.

Some of the other sources were:

SIR LEON BAGRIT. *Age of Automation.* Weidenfeld & Nicolson, London, 1965. (86 pp).

JEREMY BERNSTEIN. *The Analytical Engine: Computers Past, Present and Future.* Random House, New York, 1964 (113 pp, paperback).

J. BRONOWSKI, *Science & Human Values*. Harper Torchbooks Science Library, Harper & Brothers, 1956 (94 pp).

GILBERT BURCK AND THE EDITORS OF FORTUNE. *The Computer Age and Its Potential for Management.* Harper & Row, Publishers, New York, 1965 (148 pp, paperback).

JOHN DIEBOLD. *Beyond Automation.* McGraw-Hill, Inc., 1964 (220 pp).

JOHN DIEBOLD. "New World Coming," *Saturday Review*, July 23, 1966.

BUCKMINSTER FULLER. *Nine Chains to the Moon.* J. B. Lippincott Co., 1938.

"Will Computers Win Out by Default?" *Iron Age*, April 15, 1965.

DONALD N. MICHAEL. *Cybernation: The Silent Conquest.* Center for the Study of Democratic Institutions, Santa Barbara, Calif., 1962 (48 pp. pamphlet).

GERARD PIEL. "The Computer as Sorcerer's Apprentice," *Scientific American*, October 28, 1964.

ARNOLD J. TOYNBEE. *A Study of History.* Oxford Univ. Press, London, 1947.

"Is the Computer Running Wild?" *U.S. News & World Report*, Feb. 24, 1964.

W. GREY WALTER. *The Living Brain.* Norton, New York, 1963. (311 pp), also in paperback.

CHAPTER V: THE LEISURE MASSES

There were three works here that were fundamental to our treatment. *This U.S.A.* by Ben J. Wattenberg and Richard M. Scammon, Doubleday & Co., New York, 1965 (520 pp) is a delightful and penetrating study of our country, based on the 1960 census figures. *Of Time, Work and Leisure*, by Sebastian de Grazia, Doubleday & Co., New York, 1964, Anchor paperback (584 pp) is a definitive work and fundamental to any understanding of what is happening to us in these fields. So too is the compendium of essays edited by Robert W. Kleemeier, *Aging and Leisure*, Oxford University Press, New York, 1961 (447 pp).

Other sources we used include:

CHARLES AND MARY BEARD. *Basic History of the United States.* Doubleday, Doran & Co., New York, 1944 (554 pp).

NIALL BRENNAN. *The Making of a Moron.* Sheed & Ward, New York, 1953 (189 pp).

JOHN K. GALBRAITH. *The Affluent Society.* Mentor Book, (pb), 1958 (286 pp).

JOHN K. GALBRAITH. *American Capitalism*, Sentry Edition (pb), Houghton Mifflin Company, 1952, 1956 (208 pp).

ELI GINZBERG. *Human Resources: Wealth of a Nation.* Simon & Schuster, New York, 1958 (183 pp).

ELI GINZBERG, DALE HIESTAND, BEATRICE REUBENS. *The Pluralistic Economy.* McGraw-Hill Book Co., 1965 (228 pp).

ALEXANDER HERON. *Why Men Work.* Stanford Univ. Press, 1948 (197 pp).

MAX KAPLAN. *Leisure in America: a Social Inquiry.* Wiley, 1960, paperback.

J. M. KEYNES. *Essays in Persuasion.* Harcourt, Brace, N.Y., 1932 (376 pp).

LEWIS MUMFORD. *The Story of Utopias.* Compass Books, 1962 (315 pp).

GUNNAR MYRDAL. *Beyond the Welfare State.* Yale (pb), 1960 (287 pp).

Challenge to Affluence, Vintage Book (pb), Random House, 1965 (183 pp).

GERARD PIEL. *Advent of Abundance.* Bulletin of the Atomic Scientists, June, 1963.

GERARD PIEL. "The End of Toil," *Nation*, 1961.

J. PIEPER. *Leisure, the Basis of Culture.* New American Library, 1964 (pb).

DAVID M. POTTER. *People of Plenty.* Phoenix Books (pb), Univ. of Chicago Press, 1958 (217 pp).

W. W. ROSTOW. *The Stages of Economic Growth.* Cambridge University Press, 1960 (178 pp, paperback).

HANS SELYE, M.D. *The Stress of Life.* McGraw-Hill, 1956 (324 pp).

FREDERICK J. TEGGART AND GEORGE H. HILDEBRAND. *The Idea of Progress.* Univ. of California Press, Berkeley and Los Angeles, 1949 (453 pp).

ROBERT THEOBALD, Editor. *The Guaranteed Income.* Doubleday & Co., Inc., 1966 (233 pp).

"Antipoverty Tack," *Wall Street Journal*, September 15, 1966.

WALTER A. WEISSKOPF. "The Great Transformation." *American Scholar*, Spring, 1966.

CHAPTER VI: FORESEEING THE UNFORESEEABLE

The works we found most useful here include *Human Behavior* by Claire Russell and W. M. S. Russell, Little, Brown and Company, Boston, 1961 (533 pp, illustrated), a most important book; Robert Ardrey's *The Territorial Imperative*, Atheneum, New York, 1966 (390 pp) and *Frontiers of Psychological Research*; *Readings from Scientific American*, selected and introduced by Stanley Coopersmith, W. H. Freeman and Company, San Francisco, 1964 (322 pp). Useful sources on the possible emergence of new philosophies and religions based on both Western and Eastern systems are in *Three Ways of Asian Wisdom* by Nancy Wilson Ross, Simon & Schuster, New York, 1966 (222 pp), an excellent introduction, and *Cosmic Humanism* by Dr. Oliver Reiser, Schenkman Publishing Co., Inc., Cambridge, Mass., 1966 (586 pp) is a definitive work in this area.

Other sources used in this chapter are listed below:

PETER F. DRUCKER. *Landmarks of Tomorrow.* Harper & Row, Pub., New York, 1959 (270 pp).

JAMES A. DYAL. *Readings in Psychology: Understanding Human Behavior.* McGraw-Hill Book Company (pb), 1962 (444 pp).

LOREN EISELEY. *The Firmament of Time.* Atheneum, New York, 1960 (182 pp).

LOREN EISELEY. *The Immense Journey.* Random House, New York, 1957 (210 pp).

JOSEPH FLETCHER. *Situation Ethics.* Westminster Press (pb), 1966 (176 pp).

BY THE EDITORS OF FORTUNE WITH THE COLLABORATION OF RUSSELL DAVENPORT. *U.S.A. The Permanent Revolution.* Prentice-Hall (pb), New York, 1951 (267 pp).

THEODORE J. GORDON. *The Future.* St. Martin's Press, 1965 (184 pp).

WILLIAM JAMES. *The Varieties of Religious Experience.* Random House, Inc., New York (526 pp).

EDWARD T. HALL. "The Language of Space," *ATA Journal*, February, 1961.

EDWARD T. HALL. "The Silent Language," *ATA Journal*, February, 1961.

IRVING KRISTOL. "The Troublesome Intellectuals," *The Public Interest*, #2 Winter, 1966.

KONRAD Z. LORENZ. *King Solomon's Ring.* Apollo Editions (pb), Thomas Y. Crowell Company, 1952 (202 pp).

DONALD N. MICHAEL. *The Next Generation.* Random House, 1965 (218 pp.).

CHARLES E. OSGOOD. *An Alternative to War or Surrender.* Illini Books (pb), University of Illinois Press, Urbana, 1962 (183 pp).

SIR GEORGE THOMSON. *The Foreseeable Future.* Cambridge University Press, 1955 (166 pp).

ARNOLD J. TOYNBEE. *Civilization on Trial.* Oxford Univ. Press, 1948 (263 pp).

INDEX

(Roman numerals refer to chapters, Arabic numerals refer to pages within chapters.)

L. DalSanto

L. DalSanto